CONTENTS
Domestic Gas Safety On Site Guide – Part 2

Part 2 Chapters:

14. Central Heating Boilers
15. Carbon Monoxide/Dioxide Atmosphere Sampling
16. Cookers
17. Ducted Air Heaters
18. Gas Fired Space Heater
19. Water Heaters
20. Gas Meters
21. Tumble Dryers
22. Leisure Appliances
23. Emergency Service Provider Engineer and Meter Installer

Glossary and Appendices

CONTENTS
Domestic Gas Safety On Site Guide – Part 2

Part 1 Chapters:

1. Gas Safety Legislation

2. Gas Emergency

3. Combustion and Flue Gas Analysis

4. Ventilation

5. Pipework

6. Tightness Testing and Purging

7. Checking and Setting Regulators

8. Gas Industry Unsafe Situations Procedures

9. Gas Rate & Heat Output

10. Safety Devices & Controls

11. Flueing/Chimney Standards

12. Re-Establishing Gas Supplies

13. Labels and Notices

Glossary and Appendices

Chapter 14
Central Heating Boilers

		Page No.
14.1	Introduction	14.1
14.2	Scope	14.1
14.3	Design Considerations	14.2
14.4	Appliance Types	14.3
	14.4.1 Regular non-condensing boilers (standard boilers)	14.8
	14.4.2 Back boiler units with fire fronts (outset or ILFE)	14.11
	14.4.3 System boilers	14.13
	14.4.4 Combination boilers	14.14
	14.4.5 Condensing boilers	14.16
	14.4.5.1 Condensate removal	14.17
	14.4.5.2 Condensate in-line neutraliser devices	14.26
14.5	Room Types and Location	14.28
	14.5.1 General	14.28
	14.5.2 Boiler compartments	14.28
	14.5.3 Basements	14.29
	14.5.4 Shower rooms/bathrooms	14.29
	14.5.5 Bedrooms	14.29
	14.5.6 Under stairs	14.29
	14.5.7 Airing cupboards	14.30
	14.5.8 Toilets and cloakrooms	14.30
	14.5.9 Roof space installations	14.31
	14.5.10 External installations	14.31

Chapter 14
Central Heating Boilers

		Page No.
14.6	System Protection	14.32
	14.6.1 Open vented systems	14.32
	14.6.2 Sealed systems	14.33
	14.6.3 Frost	14.34
	14.6.4 Corrosion	14.34
14.7	Ventilation	14.35
14.8	Gas Supply	14.35
14.9	Electrical Supply	14.36
	14.9.1. Legislation	14.36
	14.9.1.1. Notification of building work	14.38
	14.9.2 Means of isolation	14.40
	14.9.3 Safe system of work	14.42
	14.9.3.1 Risk assessment	14.42
	14.9.3.2 Safe to touch	14.43
	14.9.3.3. Test instrumentation	14.45
	14.9.3.4 Safe isolation procedure	14.49
	14.9.3.5 Means of locking off	14.51
14.10	Controls	14.52
	14.10.1 Air/gas ratio valve	14.53
	14.10.2 Operating sequence for fan assisted boilers with automatic ignition	14.53

Chapter 14
Central Heating Boilers

	Page No.
14.11 Commissioning and Servicing	14.54
14.11.1 Commissioning procedure	14.54
14.11.2 Servicing procedure	14.56

References in this Chapter

[1] BS 6798: 2014 Specification for selection, installation, inspection, commissioning, servicing and maintenance of gas-fired boilers of reated input not exceeding 70 kW net

[2] BS 5871: Specification for the installation and maintenance of gas fires, convector heaters, fire/back boilers and decorative fuel effect gas appliances –
Part 1: 2005 Gas fires, convector heaters, fire/back boilers and heating stoves (2nd and 3rd family gases)
Part 2: 2005 Inset live fuel effect gas fires of heat input not exceeding 15 kW, and fire/back boilers (2nd and 3rd family gases)
Part 3: 2005 Decorative fuel effect gas appliances of heat input not exceeding 20 kW (2nd and 3rd family gases)
Part 4: 2007 Independent gas-fired flueless fires, convector heaters and heating stoves of nominal heat input not exceeding 6 kW (2nd and 3rd family gases)

[3] BS 6644: 2011 Specification for the installation and maintenance of gas-fired hot water boilers of rated inputs between 70 kW (net) and 1.8 MW (net) (2nd and 3rd family gases).

[4] IGEM/UP/10 Edition 4 +A: 2016 Installation of flued gas appliances in industrial and commercial premises.

[5] BS 7671: 2018 + A1: 2020 Requirements for electrical installations. IET Wiring Regulations Eighteenth Edition

[6] BS 5422: 2009 Method for specifying thermal insulating materials for pipes, tanks, vessels, ductwork and equipment operating within the temperature range -40°C to + 700°C.

[7] BS 5970: 2012 Thermal insulation of pipework, ductwork, associated equipment ad other industrial installations in the temperature range of -100°C to + 870°C. Code of practice.

Chapter 14
Central Heating Boilers

[8] PD 54823: 2016 Code of practice for domestic butane and propane gas-burning installations. Installations in boats, yachts and other vessels.

[9] BS EN ISO 10239: 2014 Small craft. Liquefied petroleum gas (LPG) systems.

[10] IGEM/G/6 Gas supplies to mobile homes

[11] Liquid Gas UK CoP 22: Design, installation and testing of LPG piping systems

[12] BS 1362: 1973 Specification for general purpose fuse links for domestic and similar purposes (primarily for use in plugs).

[13] BS EN 61010-031: 2015 Safety requirements for electrical equipment for measurement, control and laboratory use. Safety requirements for hand-held probe assemblies for electrical measurement and test.

[14] BS EN 61243-3: 2014 Live working. Voltage detectors. Two-pole low voltage type.

14.1 Introduction

The information within this Chapter relates to domestic, Natural and Liquefied Petroleum Gas (LPG) central heating boilers (flue types B and C). They may also apply, in part, to cookers with integral boilers used to provide central heating.

The installation of gas boilers shall be in accordance with the GS(I&U)R and should comply with the guidance of BS 6798[1] and where applicable, BS 5871[2] parts 1 & 2 in the case of back boiler units (BBUs).

NOTE: Any reference to a "boiler" means a wet central heating boiler.

14.2 Scope

BS 6798 specifies the requirements for the selection, installation, inspection, commissioning, servicing, repair and maintenance of both new and previously used gas-fired boilers used for wet central heating and other purposes such as hot water. It applies to appliances burning 1st, 2nd or 3rd family gases designed to operate in condensing or non-condensing mode with a total heat input not exceeding 70 kW net installed in domestic dwellings, or domestic dwellings in commercial premises as either an individual boiler or as a group of boilers.

This standard also applies to cookers with an integral boilers used to provide central heating (cooker boiler), with some clauses also relevant to the installation of pool or spa heaters (the appliance manufacturer will advise on which parts are relevant and any other special installation instruction). For BBUs additional information is contained in BS 5871 parts 1 & 2.

BS 6798 does not apply to individual boilers with a rated input greater than 70 kW net or groups of boilers with individual ratings less than 70 kW net, but with an aggregate heat input in excess of 70 kW net. In these cases BS 6644[3] and IGEM/UP/10[4] applies.

Groups of boilers with an individual heat input less than 70 kW net, but with an aggregate heat input of 70 kW net or less, may be installed to this standard, however specialist advice will be required from the appliance manufacturer with regards to system design, control and installation requirements.

14.3 Design Considerations

The main considerations that would be addressed when selecting a boiler for a given situation can be listed as follows:

Flue type - it is important that the installation of the flue is in accordance with both the manufacturer's requirements and that of BS 5440 part 1 (see Chapter 11). The effects of pluming should be considered as to its nuisance value.

Size - the heat output requirements of the boiler shall be calculated in order to size the boiler. This can be achieved by adding the total heat output of all the heat emitters, making allowance for any hot water requirement and taking account of heat losses through pipework. It is often considered prudent to oversize the boiler to allow for future expansion to the installation should the customer wish to extend the property at a later date.

Location - this is important right from the onset as the location may dictate the type of mounting, i.e. wall mounted, floor standing or inset into a builder's opening for a BBU (it is useful to note that the boiler's efficiency rating is paramount at the design stage with energy conservation in mind). The physical size of the boiler can be influential in its choice with regards to the structural ability of the building, i.e. its weight may determine the requirement of additional structural support. Another factor in the location and subsequent selection of the boiler may be dictated by the flue type and the possible flue termination sites available.

Sealed or open vented - the choice between open vented or sealed heating system will have a bearing on the options available to an installer. It is important that the manufacturer has identified the boiler's suitability in either case, and that the installer is aware of this. It should be noted at this point that the vast majority of installations today are sealed system as the popularity of combination/system boilers increases.

Other considerations should include:

- ○ The suitability of the existing water, gas and electrical supply requirements.
- ○ Location in which the appliance is to be installed.
- ○ Ventilation requirements of the appliance which should be in accordance with the manufacturer's installation instructions and BS 5440: part 2.
- ○ Is drainage available for condensing boilers and system.

- Pressure and/or temperature relief discharge point.
- Domestic hot water demand.
- Location and compatibility of system controls (existing and new).
- Consultation and approval of design by the relevant official bodies such as local building control, water authority, fire authority, etc.

14.4 Appliance Types

New central heating appliances shall be CE marked. Where previously used boilers are to be reinstalled other than in its original location, the appliance must carry either a CE mark or shall conform to the relevant current British Standard.

Where a previously used appliance is being installed, the installer shall ensure that the appliance is in a safe and serviceable condition. Where the appliance does not have a CE mark it should be fitted as per the manufacturer's instruction. Where these instructions are not available a copy shall be obtained from the manufacturer or their agent prior to installation. All appliances must be suitable for the gas type and pressure supplied. If a conversion is required this shall be performed in accordance with the manufacturer's instructions and using an approved conversion kit, ad hoc conversion is not permitted.

All appliances need to have a readable data plate which provides important information in relation to:

- Gas type;
    - G20 is nat. gas @ 20 mbar.
    - G30 is butane @ 29 mbar.
    - G31 is propane @ 37 mbar.
- Intended country of use (GB).
- Supply pressure.
- Operating pressure (burner)

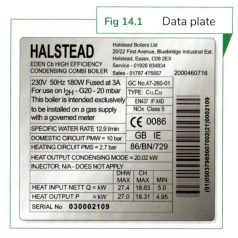

Fig 14.1   Data plate

The appliance serial number (together with the make and model) is required if spare parts have to be ordered. The appliance and part GC number (Gas Council number) may also be required.

Boilers are manufactured as either condensing or non-condensing models and may be wall hung, floor standing or BBUs. Generic types of boiler can be categorised as one of the following:

- **Regular boiler** - normally referred to as "heat only" boilers as they do not have an internal facility to provide domestic hot water. A separate hot water storage system is used for this purpose (vented or unvented). Where the regular boiler incorporates ancillary heating controls and components such as a circulating pump, expansion vessel, pressure relief valve, etc. within their casing they are commonly known as "system" boilers.

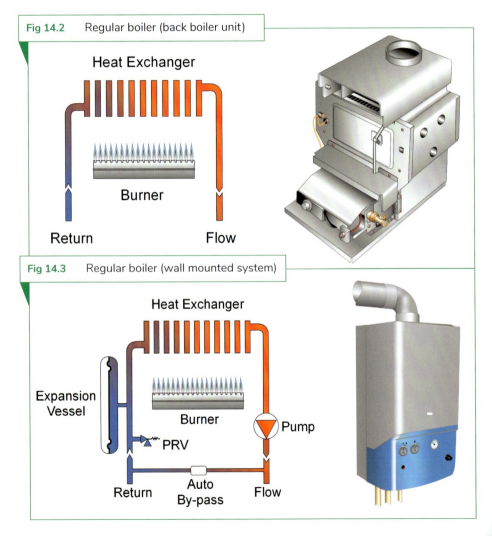

Fig 14.2 Regular boiler (back boiler unit)

Fig 14.3 Regular boiler (wall mounted system)

○ **Combination boiler** - these types of boilers provide both heating and hot water as part of their design. They can be either instantaneous, providing a continuous flow of hot water on demand, or of the storage type which has a small to medium storage facility inbuilt. Once this water reserve is used up the appliance returns to instantaneous mode.

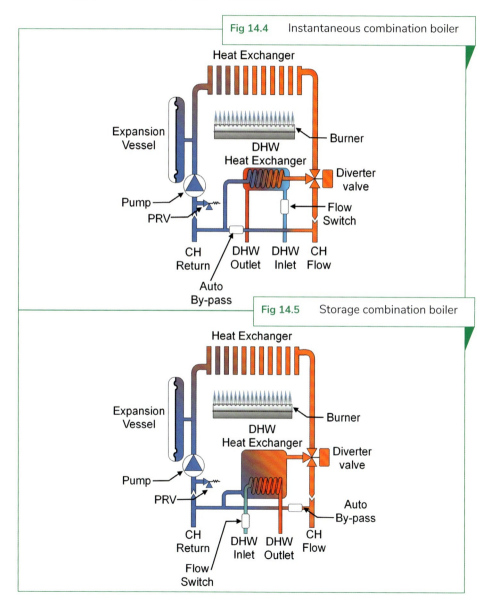

Fig 14.4   Instantaneous combination boiler

Fig 14.5   Storage combination boiler

- **Combined primary storage units (CPSU)** - this type of boiler is a combination boiler with a very large storage facility (greater than 70 litres). The stored water is normally at pressure (unvented) and is used to provide enough hot water at a reasonably high flow rate (fig 14.6). In most instances the stored hot water is for domestic use (i.e. similar to a storage cylinder) however, it may contain central heating water which is used to heat cold water passing through a heat exchanger within the storage vessel; this type of unit is commonly known as a thermal store (fig 14.7). As with most types of combination boiler these units are normally hot water priority.

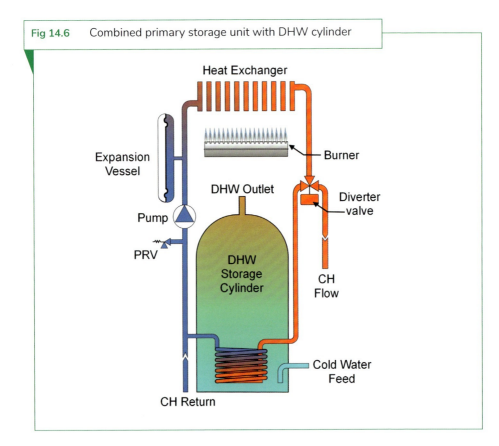

Fig 14.6 Combined primary storage unit with DHW cylinder

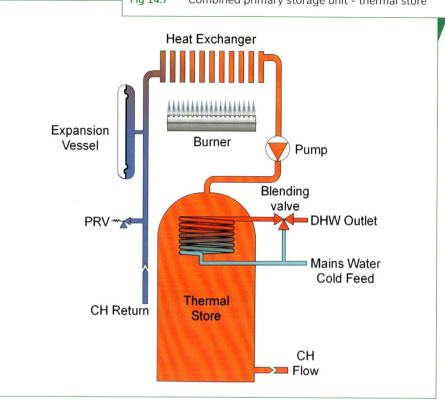

Fig 14.7 Combined primary storage unit - thermal store

○ **Range cooker boiler** - these are cookers which have a boiler inbuilt or attached to the appliance. The hot water and cooking chamber may be heated by either a single common burner or two individual burners. These units are normally constructed of heavy grade steel and/or cast and can be very heavy. Any flooring used to support this type of appliance shall be capable of supporting its weight when filled with water, including any ancillary controls.

Fig 14.8 Range cooker boiler

14.4.1 Regular non-condensing boilers (standard boilers)

The standard boiler is generally considered the simplest of all the options that we have available to us with regard to supplying heating and hot water. The basic component parts will include the main body which houses the heat exchanger and the combustion chamber.

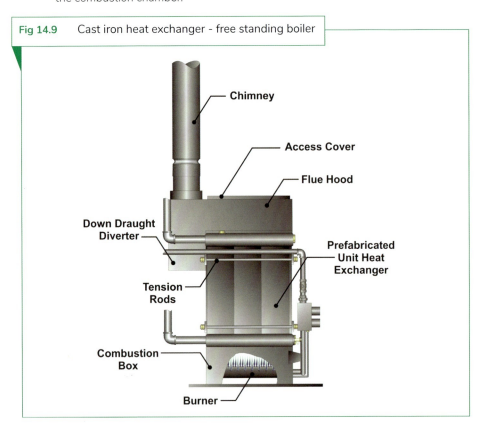

Fig 14.9 Cast iron heat exchanger - free standing boiler

In the past the heat exchanger has mainly comprised of cast iron sections creating water ways through which the primary waters circulate. To enable greater collection of heat the waterways are surrounded by cast fins making the exchange more efficient. It is generally accepted that the efficiency of this type of appliance ranges between 70 % and 80 %. By today's standards this is low and would not be acceptable, except in extreme circumstances, for a new installation. However, this type of heat exchanger has the advantages of providing quieter operation and is also suitable for open vented heating and hot water systems where the hot water may circulate by means of gravity.

It needs to be pointed out that although gravity circulation may be a thing of the past there may still be such systems in operation today. The main disadvantage is the weight. This can prove to be an added difficulty during installation on two fronts; the first being the actual manhandling during transport then manoeuvring into the final installation position. And secondly, the actual location, regardless if it is to be floor standing or wall hung, needs to be able to support not only the weight of the unit, but also the weight of the water when it is in operation.

The cast iron heat exchanger is prone to silting up with the debris from the system and is subject to leakage from gaskets joining the exchanger sections together (although not a common problem).

There are a number of standard boilers which use low water content heat exchangers. The low water content heat exchanger comprises of single run of pipework passing back and forth above the burner. The heat is gathered by means of many collecting fins and transferred into the water. The main advantages of this type are that the heat is able to pass more quickly to the water, the heat exchanger is lighter and is more adaptable to different heating applications. The disadvantages needs to be weighed up as the boiler is considered to be noisier, can only be used on pumped systems, may become partially blocked by system debris and the heating system will normally require a bypass.

Fig 14.10 Low water content heat exchanger

The combustion chamber comprises of an open space in which the gas and air can combust. In order to reduce heat loss and subsequent possible heat damage to the boiler or parts of the building, the combustion chamber is lined with non-combustible insulating panels. The heat produced then passes up through the heat exchanger.

After the products have passed up through the heat exchanger they then pass through to the flue. In open flued appliances the products would pass through the primary flue which is normally part of the boiler's construction, then through to the down draught diverter, again part of the boilers construction. The down draught diverter has three primary functions:

- To divert down draught in the event of adverse weather conditions thus not disturbing the combustion process.
- To allow air from the room to enter the flue and dilute the products of combustion.
- To break excessive draught created by flues that "work too well". This then allows the transfer of heat to the water and prevents the heat being sucked out of the appliance. In extreme cases without the down draught diverter, the flames could be lifted off the burner by the power (pull) of the flue.

The operation of the boiler is controlled by a number of components. The simplest being the appliance isolation valve. This is usually in the form of a tapered plug valve or for more modern appliances, a ball valve. From this point the supply of gas will enter a multifunctional device.

The multifunctional device usually incorporates a flame supervision device (traditional thermoelectric valve with thermocouple), a simple regulator and a solenoid (see Chapter 10, section 10.4). The temperature is regulated by liquid expansion thermostatic switch or disc type run stats (usually only providing high and low options for temperature control to the user), which in turn operates the solenoid allowing the gas through to the burner.

The multifunctional device often provides two test points to enable the commissioning or servicing engineer to record and/or monitor the inlet pressure and/or burner pressure whilst adjustments are made. The gas then passes through the burner injector and into the burner where by doing so, will draw in air from the primary air ports. The gas air mixture is ignited by means of a permanent pilot. For convenience the boiler usually has a piezo single shot ignitor to light the pilot, but it needs to be pointed out that it is the permanent pilot that is the main burner's source of ignition.

Additional controls may be found on more advanced models. These essentially will consist of temperature reactive devices such as overheat stats and TTBs (spillage monitoring devices) which interrupt the thermocouple. Room sealed appliances, which include a fan for removal of the products of combustion will have a differential pressure switch as an additional control. The pressure switch is required to ensure that the boiler does not operate in the event of fan failure.

Standard boilers which are to be used in combination with sealed heating systems shall also have the additional protection of a pressure relief valve, expansion vessel fitted to the installation with uninterrupted connection to the boiler and an overheat device fitted to the boiler itself.

14.4.2 Back boiler units with fire fronts (outset or ILFE)

Back boiler units (BBUs) are 'location specific' standard boilers – only to be installed within a builders opening – that has a chassis design which accommodates the installation of a compatible fire front. Having a fire located on the front of the boiler gives the user the option to boost the heat or have a heat source in the main living area during times when the heating is off as well as providing a focal point for the room.

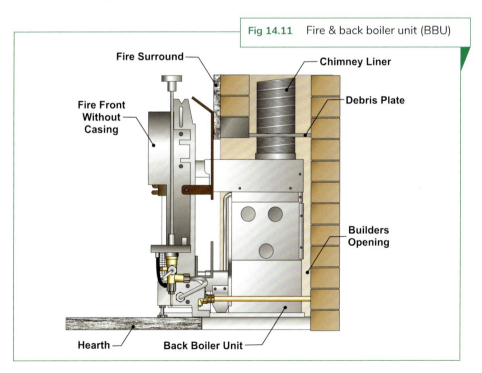

Fig 14.11   Fire & back boiler unit (BBU)

The main difference in controls may include a spillage sensing tube, which supplies air from the down draught diverter to the pilot burner air port. In the event of spillage, the sensing tube will provide the pilot with contaminated air. The pilot flame, being an atmospheric sensing device (see Chapter 10, section 10.6), will then lift from the thermocouple and the thermoelectric flame supervision device (FSD) will shut down. Newer models may have electronic ignitions systems coupled with flame rectification FSD. This of course would replace the permanent pilot and the thermoelectric FSD.

The installation of a BBU has additional considerations to be taken into account; the clearances around the unit shall be large enough to ensure that the movement of air is sufficient to prevent excessive heat build up and more importantly, to provide air for combustion.

The fact that the installation will more than likely be fitted into a builders opening that has previously been used for a solid or oil burning appliance means that there is the possibility of soot and other corrosive materials being present. The reaction between soot and copper can be fairly aggressive and may result in water or gas escapes in a short period of time. It is therefore important that protection is provided on pipework. For similar reasons copper pipe should be installed in such a way that will prevent contact with cement based products.

To comply with the recommendations of BS 5440-1 it is essential that any flue products which enter the builder's opening due to spillage, for whatever reason, are prevented from accessing any other room in the property. Therefore, pipework etc. which pass through the chimney breast structure should be sealed. In the case of a brick built chimney breast then the pipework should be sleeved and sealed.

The dimensions of the builder's opening should comply with the manufacturer's instructions to enable installation, service and maintenance. All BBUs require to be connected to a flue liner which should be installed in accordance with BS 5440-1. The down draught diverter hood of the boiler should be located to enable the spigot of the fire front to engage without undue strain being placed on either component.

14.4.3 System boilers

System boilers are commonly used but not restricted to sealed heating systems and perform the same function as a standard boiler. However, the additional external controls and components that would be found on a traditional sealed system installation are incorporated in the boiler casing.

These additional controls and components would include: the expansion vessel, the pressure relief valve, the heating circuit circulating pump and may also include a low-water content or low-water pressure sensing device to prevent the appliance operating in the event of the system losing water and/or pressure. As with all sealed systems there is a requirement for an overheat thermostat. Some older models of a standard boiler had the ability to be converted to a system boiler with the addition of a conversion kit supplied by the manufacturer.

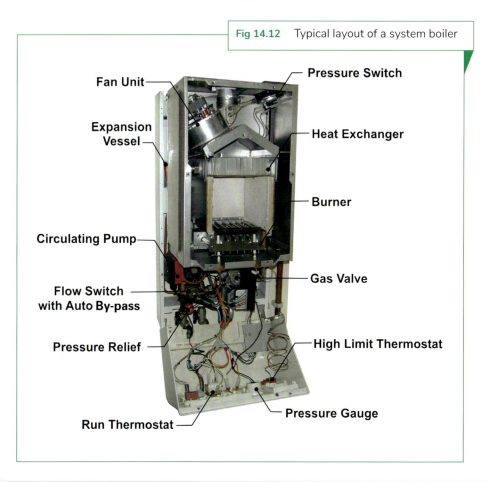

Fig 14.12 Typical layout of a system boiler

14.4.4 Combination boilers

The purpose of a combination boiler or 'combi' boiler as it's more commonly known, is to provide heat for a heating system and instantaneously (opening of a hot tap) heated hot water supply. This provision eliminates the need for a separate storage of hot water, a cold water storage cistern in the roof space and the associated pipework that is required for a traditional hot water system. This system also provides a higher pressure of water at all outlets. However, until recently the flow of water from the combi has been notoriously poor when providing the demand for properties with more than a kitchen and shower room.

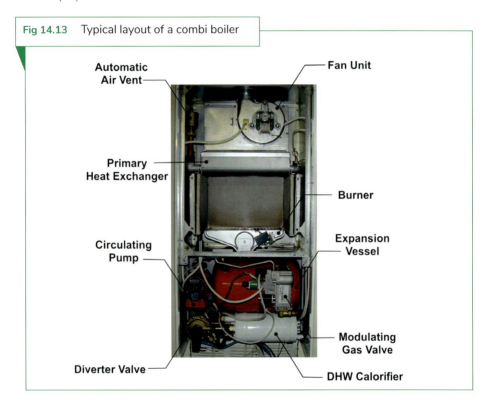

Fig 14.13 Typical layout of a combi boiler

In the past there have been many versions of the combi boiler, however manufacturers now seem to favour a design which incorporates an air-to-water heat exchanger, a water-to-water heat exchanger, a water flow sensing device and a diverter valve in addition to the controls and components described in system boilers.

When there is a heating demand the boiler will operate as previously described. If during the heating cycle there is a demand for hot water the diverter valve in the boiler will operate, diverting the flow of heated water from the air-to-water heat exchanger, passing the heated water through a water-to-water heat exchanger (usually a plate heat exchanger) where the cold water entering the appliance is heated and delivered to the user.

The standard temperature rise that is achieved is 35 °C (see Chapter 19, section 19.16 for the procedure to ascertain flow rates and measuring temperature rise across an appliance). This means that whilst there is a hot water demand there is no heating provision. This is not usually a noticeable problem as the duration of demand for the hot water is normally for short period of time. However, with modern house design, hot water demand is ever increasing with the introduction of multiple en suites, additional toilets, dish washing facilities, etc.

The poor flow rate from the traditional combination boiler does not lend itself well to these installations. Manufacturers' on the other hand are now producing appliances designed to provide this higher demand. With the instantaneous combination boiler the heat input for hot water demand has been increased dramatically, this coupled with more advanced plate heat exchanger design giving faster heat transfer into the domestic hot water, resulting in improved water flow rates. However, even this has its limitations.

Storage combination boilers on the other hand hold a reserve of hot water with some as much as 120 litres (CPSU) to facilitate varying hot water demands. To ensure a continuous supply of hot water most of these units are now designed to operate as an instantaneous combination boiler once the initial stored water has been used up. In this mode there is a notable reduction in flow rate as from that of the stored water.

14.4.5 Condensing boilers

The principal behind a condensing boiler is to recover the lost heat that would be discharged through the flue in the standard type of boiler. During the combustion process some heat is "lost" as energy is required to convert the hydrogen to water vapour. This is true when changing the state of any material, i.e. from solid to liquid, liquid to gas, gas to liquid and liquid to solid.

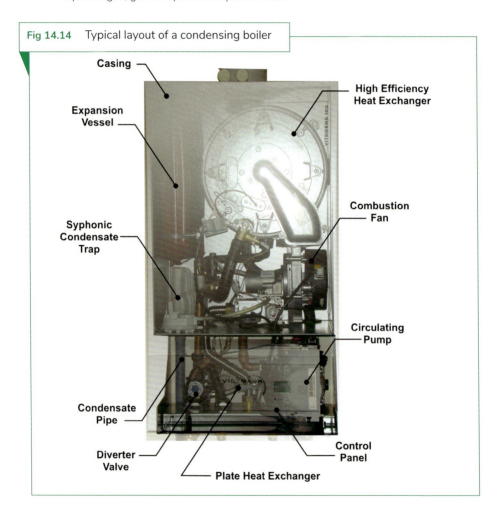

Fig 14.14   Typical layout of a condensing boiler

The condensing boiler captures the lost heat by passing the products through an extended network of heat exchanger fins and/or a second heat exchanger, thus cooling down the flue gases (this generates condensate) whilst extracting the latent heat, which is transferred back into the circulating water.

The transfer of heat back to the circulating water (this can also be used to preheat incoming mains water when satisfying hot water demand on some models or through the use of an additional passive flue gas heat recovery device), means that less energy is used to heat that water to the desired temperature and thereby increasing appliance efficiency (appliance efficiency of 94 % and higher is common).

This of course reduces the flue gas temperatures which can often be seen as pluming from the flue terminal. Typical flue gas temperature ranges between 50 °C to 60 °C, whereas traditional appliance flue gas temperatures range in excess of 200 °C. Flues should be installed in accordance with the manufacturer's instructions where most, if not all, will detail the flue with a gradient of between 2° and 3° running from the flue terminal back to the appliance. The reason for this is to prevent the nuisance of condensate dripping from the flue terminal and so that the condensate can be collected and disposed of in accordance with current guidelines (see sub-section 14.4.5.1 in this Chapter).

The selection of the materials used for a flue is important. Given that the condensate is acidic, most metallic flues would corrode in a short time therefore plastics which are resistant to the acidic corrosion are often used. See Chapter 11 for more information.

14.4.5.1 Condensate removal

The condensate produced by a condensing boiler may be removed from the appliance by either gravity or mechanical means such as a pump. When choosing a condensate discharge point, consideration shall be given to the possibility of the pipe freezing due to prolonged extreme cold weather conditions. It is therefore preferred that the discharge point, where practical, is terminated at an internal foul water drain. The condensate drainage pipe shall be run using a standard drainpipe material such as:

- Poly Vinyl Chloride (PVC).
- Unplasticized Poly Vinyl Chloride (PVC-U)
- Acrylonitrilebutadiene-styrene (ABS)
- Polypropylene (PP)
- Chlorinated Poly Vinyl Chloride (PVC-C).

Most new condensing boilers incorporate a siphon as part of the condensate trap assembly which releases a set quantity of condensate from the boiler at intervals depending on the heat input, frequency of use and volume of the trap. Since the condensate is released intermittently instead of a constant slow stream, as would happen with a normal trap, the risk of an external condensate drainage pipe freezing is greatly reduced. For ease of installation some boiler manufacturers may allow the pressure relief discharge and condensate discharge pipe to be combined either outside the appliance casing or internally within the appliance as part of its design. In these cases further additional conditions apply with the boiler manufacturer's recommendations adhered to at all times.

For boilers manufacturers who allow the pressure relief and condensate discharge pipes to be combined external from the appliance casing, where the pressure relief discharge pipe is metallic, a means to ensure the condensate does not flow back into the metallic pipe shall be employed as specified by the appliance manufacturer.

In all accounts where the pressure relief and condensate discharge pipe are combined (whether within or external from the appliance) any discharge from the pressure relief shall be indirectly or directly visible – directly visible may be by means of a tundish, transparent pipework or external discharge, where as indirectly visible could be audible or visual indication on the boiler of activation such as pressure loss.

Unless otherwise directed by the appliance manufacturer and where the appliance trap has a condensate seal of less than 75 mm or no trap has been incorporated as part of the appliance assembly, a trap with a seal of at least 75 mm shall be installed on the condensate pipe located within the premises; it cannot be located externally. There shall be a visible air break between the appliance and the additional condensate trap.

The size of the condensate drainage pipe shall be such that it allows the condensate to flow freely away from the appliance to a suitable point of discharge. When run internally the minimum internal nominal bore is 19 mm unless stated otherwise by the appliance manufacturer. To reduce the risk of freezing any external condensate drainage pipe shall be increased to a minimum internal nominal bore of 30 mm prior to passing through the wall to outside. It shall be kept as short as possible, preferably less than 3 m, taking the most vertical route – a slope of at least 3° as the pipework passes through a wall should be maintained to ensure a good velocity of condensate – with a minimum number of bends and fittings.

In addition and where run externally (unpreferred), condensate discharge pipes should be fitted with at least one of the following: waterproof insulation (minimum 19 mm thickness) 'O' class PVC coated material, or trace heating installed as per manufacturer's instructions, or the installation of an internal auxiliary siphon as mention previously in this section. Condensate drainage pipework located in unheated areas such as garages, loft spaces or basements downstream of the trap or siphon should be regarded as external.

Where the location of the appliance is such that removal of the condensate by gravity is impractical a condensate pump may be used. The pump shall be installed as per the pump manufacturer's instructions and be proved suitable for the appliance. Special consideration shall be given to the use of condensate pumps for combined pressure relief and condensate discharge due to the increased temperature, volume and pressure of the water discharged by the relief valve. In addition, the discharged water may contain an inhibitor which could have an adverse effect on the pump components. In this case the pump manufacturer shall be consulted as to the suitability of the pump for this purpose and where appropriate, any additional special requirements with regards to discharge pipe material, size and jointing method.

To ensure the condensate is disposed of safely the drainage pipe shall run at a slope of at least 2.5° (45 mm drop per metre run to BS 6891 or the slightly greater drop of 52 mm per meter run which many manufacturer's typically specify) towards the discharge point. The number of bends and fittings should be kept to a minimum with all internal burrs removed to ensure the pipe route is as smooth as possible. The drainage pipe should be supported at a maximum spacing of 0.5 m horizontally and 1 m vertically. Suitable discharge points, in order of preference, are:

1. **Internally via a gravity discharge system** connected to –

    - soil and vent stack,
    - kitchen sink waste,
    - washing machine and dishwasher waste,
    - sanitary waste (bath, shower and sink waste).

2. **Internally via a pumped discharge system** – a condensate pump and internal pipework connect to soil and vent pipe, or if not practical, connect to another internal waste system.

3. **Externally via a gravity discharge system** connected to –

  - soil and vent stack,
  - rainwater downpipe or gully which shall discharge into a foul water system and not that of a surface water or storm drain,
  - a rainwater hopper connected to a combined system i.e. foul and rain water sewer,
  - a purpose designed soakaway.

It should be noted that the connection of the condensate to any waste or drain system may be subject to local building control approval.

The diagrams that follow show different configurations of condensate drain pipe terminations. Where the appliance internal trap does not meet that specified an additional trap shall be installed in the condensate drainage pipe with a minimum height as specified, with a visible air break between the trap and boiler.

When connecting into a soil and vent stack, the distance between the condensate drain connection and soil and vent pipe invert of the tail of the bend, at the foot of the stack, is determined by the number of storeys within the building. Where the invert is not visible this distance is from the lowest visible straight section of the stack:

- Up to 3 storeys - minimum 450 mm.
- Up to and including 5 storeys - minimum 750 mm.
- Greater than 5 storeys but not more than 20 storeys - ground floor appliances shall discharge into their own soil and vent stack or directly to an external drain, gully or rainwater hopper.
- Greater than 20 storeys - ground floor and 1st floor appliances shall discharge into their own soil and vent stack or directly to an external drain, gully or rainwater hopper.

If the condensate is terminating into a cast iron internal soil and vent stack it shall not terminate above the highest existing waste water drain point or any branch which is not used for waste water discharge. This is to minimise the corrosive effects of the condensate on the cast.

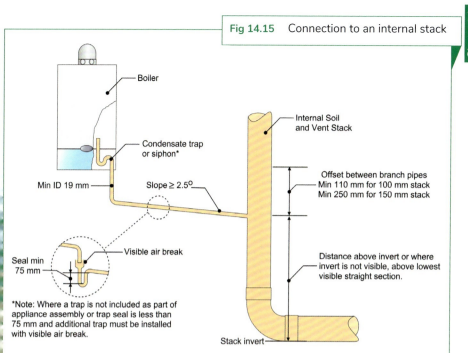

Fig 14.15 Connection to an internal stack

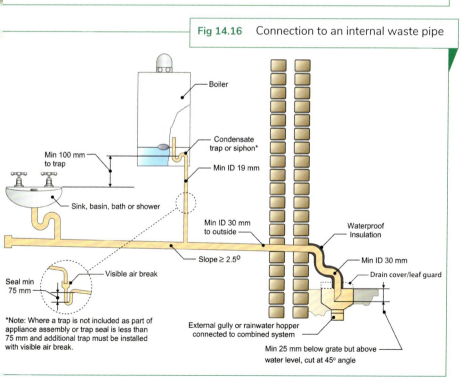

Fig 14.16 Connection to an internal waste pipe

Fig 14.17 Connection before trap on sink, basin, bath or shower

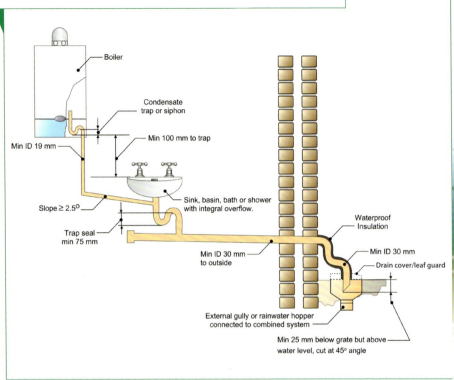

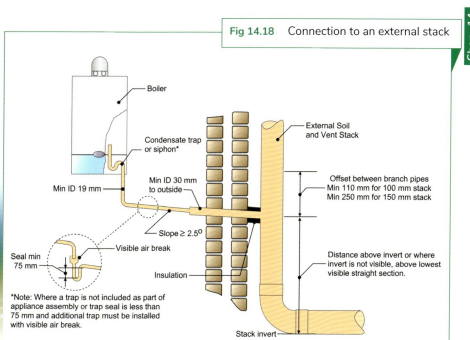

Fig 14.18 Connection to an external stack

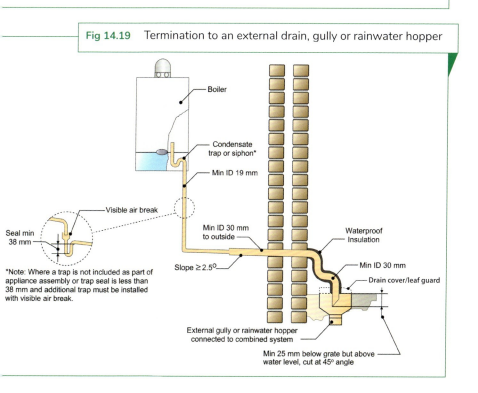

Fig 14.19 Termination to an external drain, gully or rainwater hopper

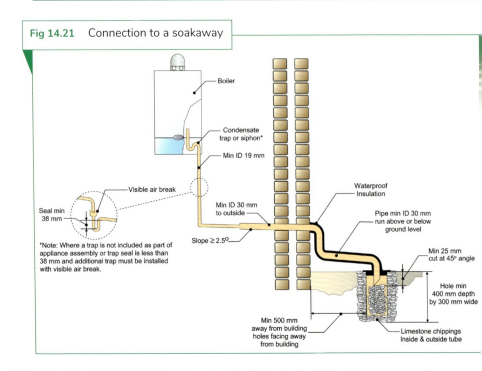

Fig 14.20 Termination to an external rain water drain

Fig 14.21 Connection to a soakaway

*Note: Where a trap is not included as part of appliance assembly or trap seal is less than 38 mm and additional trap must be installed with visible air break.

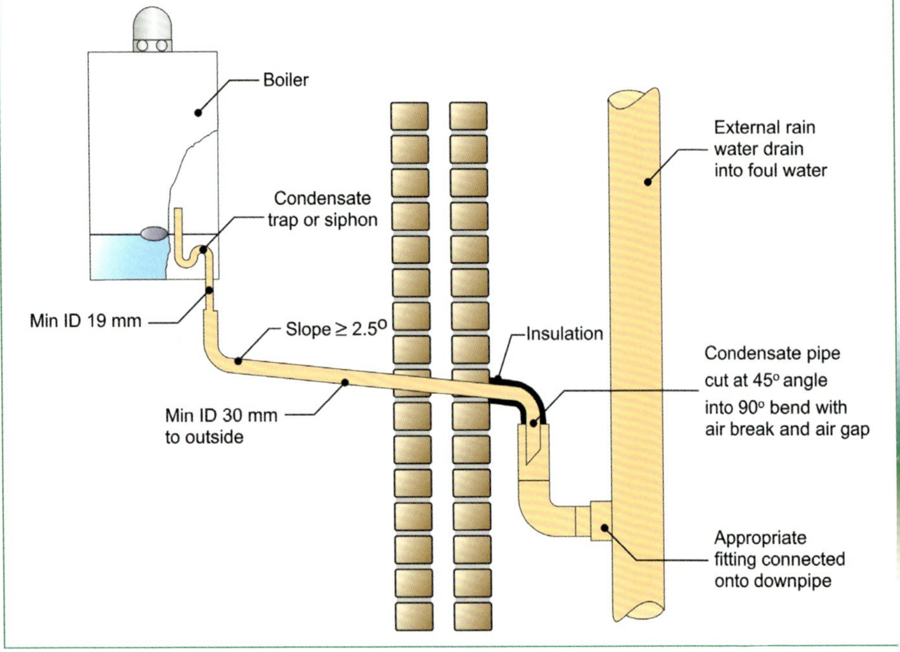

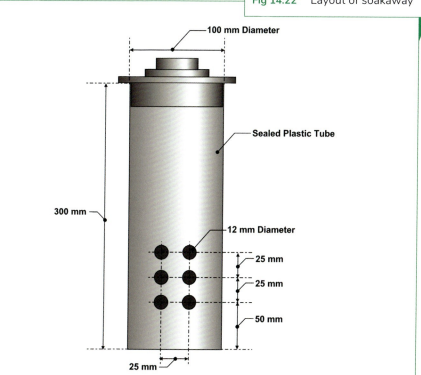

Fig 14.22   Layout of soakaway

If the condensate discharge pipe is terminated into a rainwater downpipe it shall pass into a combined foul and rainwater drainage system. Connection into the downpipe shall be by means of an appropriate fitting such as boss connector. Cutting and pushing the condensate pipe into the rainwater pipe is prohibited due to the likelihood of blocking the flow of water. To avoid a reverse flow of rain water into the boiler if the downpipe becomes blocked or frozen, either an air break external from the building or a non-return valve on the condensate drainage pipe shall be fitted. Disposal of condensate into grey water recovery systems that are intended for reuse is prohibited.

Where a new boiler is being installed into an existing soak away the limestone chips shall be replaced both inside and around the unit.

14.4.5.2 Condensate in-line neutraliser devices

An in-line neutraliser device is fitted downstream of the condensate trap (fig 14.23). It is chemical based, normally by means of renewable cartridges, which reduces the acidic pH levels of the condensate discharge prior to dispersal into the drainage system. These devices can only be installed where the boiler manufacturer permits.

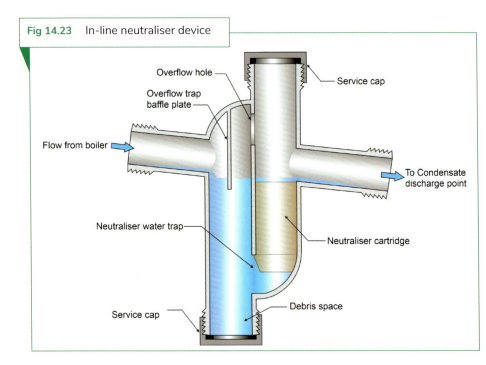

Fig 14.23   In-line neutraliser device

Where a combined pressure relief and condensate discharge pipe is used, the pressure relief discharge point shall be located downstream of the neutraliser outlet unless allowed otherwise by the neutraliser manufacturer.

Where the pressure relief and condensate discharge are connected as part of the appliance assembly in-line neutralisers can only be used if permitted by the neutraliser manufacturer. Inhibitor used within the central heating system can affect the chemicals within the neutraliser when discharged by the pressure relief. Also the neutraliser may not be able to handle the increased water temperature, flow rate and pressure when the pressure relief is activated.

Where an in-line neutraliser is to be fitted it shall not impair the flow rate of condensate from the boiler. Prior to installation reference shall be made to the boiler manufacturer's instructions to ensure the minimum condensate flow rate can be achieved through the device.

The installation instructions supplied by the manufacturer shall include:

- advice on the lifespan of the neutralising agent,
- temperature limitations of the device components and chemicals,
- how to replace the neutralising agent cartridge,
- maintenance requirements.

A label shall be affixed to the outside of the boiler casing stating the life span of the device and the responsibility of the customer to ensure suitable maintenance schedules are in place.

The disposal of the condensate waste shall adhere to the requirements as stated previously. Deviation can only be permitted if the device is so designed that it will automatically shut-down the boiler when the performance of the in-line neutraliser has diminished to such an extent that it is no longer neutralising the condensate waste. The automatic shut off device shall be designed in such a manner that it can only be reset by a suitably qualified operative.

14.5 Room Types and Location

The room type is very important with regards to the installation of a central heating boiler. Always consult with the GS(I&U)R, the manufacturer's instructions and British Standards. The following information should be considered in your design and installation.

14.5.1 General

The installation of the boiler shall provide adequate clearances from combustibles and obstructions in accordance with the manufacturer's minimum requirements. This will assist in the prevention of damage to the building and its internal structures through heat damage from the boiler or indeed the boiler itself.

Room sealed appliances can be installed in any room with little or no restrictions; again awareness of other requirements should be ensured i.e. the current electrical requirements when installations are located in bathrooms, shower rooms and toilet/cloakrooms, in accordance with BS 7671[5].

14.5.2 Boiler compartments

The boiler compartment should be constructed of a fixed rigid structure. The internal walls and floors (where floor mounted) should be made of or lined with non-combustible surfaces. Where the distance between the boiler and the combustible materials are less than 75 mm the surface shall be lined with a non-combustible material unless stated otherwise in the manufacturer's literature.

It is important that the compartment is not allowed to get too hot. It is feared that spontaneous combustion may take place and as such the compartment shall be cooled by purpose provided vents to prevent this likelihood. The size of the vents required are subject to the requirements of the manufacturer's instructions and/or BS 5440-2. These vents shall not communicate with bathrooms or shower rooms and are subject to the requirements of bed rooms/bedsitting rooms. The compartment door/access panel shall allow access for replacement, inspection, maintenance and servicing of the boiler.

14.5.3 Basements

Boilers designed for the use of LPG shall not be installed in basements.

14.5.4 Shower rooms/bathrooms

In line with the GS(I&U)R, open flued boilers and flueless appliances cannot be installed in shower rooms or bathrooms. The primary reason for this regulation is that generally open flued and flueless appliances will require ventilation direct from the outside and it is thought that these ventilators would be covered up in the colder months to reduce the effect of the cold draught on the naked body within the room. This of course could lead to incomplete combustion due to a lack of oxygen, the reduced effectiveness of a flue and subsequent adverse affect on the person in the room.

14.5.5 Bedrooms

Again, in line with the GS(I&U)R, an open flued boiler can be installed in bedrooms/bedsitting rooms however, the heat input is restricted to 14 kW gross (12.7 kW net) and must have an atmospheric sensing device incorporated to prevent the appliance operating if oxygen levels in the room fall dangerously low, possibly affecting occupants whilst they sleep.

14.5.6 Under stairs

Installations of boilers in under stair cupboards are limited to two storey buildings without the need for lining of the cupboard with a non-combustible material. Where the building exceeds this height the internal walls ceiling and floor shall be lined providing at least ½ hr fire resistance (this includes the floor of the cupboard) and the appliance should be of the room sealed type.

14.5.7 Airing cupboards

Where an airing cupboard is being used to house a gas appliance, the installation should be designed to meet the following criteria:

- The airing space should be kept separate from the boiler section by a non-combustible partition.
- The non-combustible partition may be perforated, however any apertures or openings shall not have a major dimension greater than 13 mm.
- Any open flue passing through the airing space shall be either insulated or constructed of double walled components unless surrounded by an air inlet duct (for example a concentric room sealed flue). Single walled chimney/flue systems shall have an air gap of at least 25 mm for a distance of at least 1 m from the outlet of the draught diverter. A suitable non-combustible guard such as expanded metal or rigid wire mesh may be used to form the air gap. The space between the chimney guard and airing area partition shall not exceed 13 mm.
- Open flue appliance down draught diverter and air vents should be located within the cupboard/compartment and not connect with the airing space.
- Where the airing cupboard is no longer used for this purpose the cupboard shall meet the requirements of a normal boiler compartment (see sub-section 14.5.2 in this Chapter). All shelving and clothes storage facilities shall be removed with a suitable durable label affixed indicating the purpose of the cupboard and if reinstated as for the purpose of an airing cupboard, additional measures shall be put in place to ensure the cupboard is safe to use for that purpose. The customer should be made aware of this label and the guidance it contains.

14.5.8 Toilets and cloakrooms

Boilers can be installed in toilets and cloakrooms however, it is only to be considered where there is no other viable alternative. The required ventilation shall only be supplied directly from the outside and not through other single or multiple rooms. This is to prevent the possibility of foul smells from the toilet entering the rest of the property. Awareness of other requirements should be ensured i.e. the current electrical requirements (BS 7671).

14.5.9 Roof space installations

When selecting the roof space as a location for the boiler there are a number of considerations that should be made:

- A floored area which is large enough to allow an engineer to maintain and service the unit shall be provided under and around the boiler.
- The structure shall have sufficient strength to support the unit when filled with water together with the systems associated controls.
- There should be sufficient vertical clearance above the boiler to maintain the requirements for static head if the boiler is installed in an open vented heating/hot water system.
- Fixed lighting at the boiler and along the access route to the boiler is required.
- A permanent purpose provided means of access to the boiler is required and can take the form of a retractable ladder.
- In order that stored combustible materials are not pushed up against the boiler where there would be a risk of spontaneous combustion, it is recommended that a guard is erected around the boiler to prevent such occurrences.
- Where the flue is connected to an existing chimney at a point higher than that previously used, the lower unused part of an unlined chimney should be sectioned off by means of a sealing plate located 250 mm under the flue/chimney connection. Sealed access should be provided for inspection and cleaning. Where the chimney has at least one external face, the lower unused section of chimney should be ventilated to external air at high and low level to prevent the affects of damp.

14.5.10 External installations

The boiler shall be either specifically designed for external installations or housed in a compartment designed for the purpose (i.e. weatherproof). Pipework containing water and the boiler shall be protected against the effects of extreme weather conditions, primarily freezing, with the assistance of a frost thermostat (see sub-section 14.6.3 in this Chapter) and adequate insulation. A fused, double pole electrical switch is to be provide to enable full electrical isolation of the boiler and controls. Cooling air is generally required by providing appropriate vents to prevent the build up of heat within the compartment. These requirements will be stipulated by the appliance manufacturer and/or BS 5440-2.

14.6 System Protection

14.6.1 Open vented systems

For the protection of the system when allowing the release of pressure in fault condition a vent will be provided which has a minimum diameter of 19 mm. The vent pipe should rise continuously to allow air in the system to escape easily and terminate above the feed and expansion cistern which supplies water to the system unless otherwise specified by the boiler manufacturer. The vent shall be connected to the primary flow pipe from the boiler and terminate above the feed and expansion cistern; no controls (i.e. isolation valves) are permitted along its length.

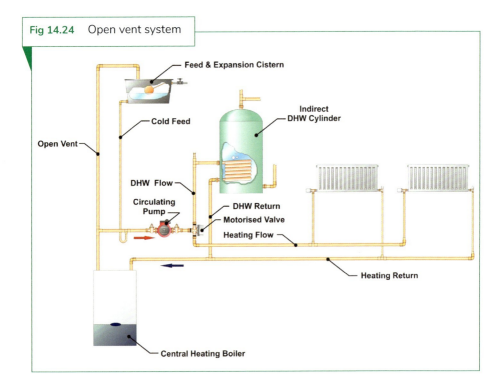

Fig 14.24 Open vent system

14.6.2 Sealed systems

In order to accommodate the expansion of water on heat up the system shall include an appropriately sized expansion vessel which should be precharged per system design. This is usually located in the boiler and should be checked during an annual service with the installation de-pressurised.

A pressure relief valve (PRV) is required to prevent over pressurisation of the installation in the event of a system failure and normally has a maximum relief setting of 3 bar. A manual testing device (usually a lever) should be fitted to the valve and the valve tested during an annual service. The discharge from the PRV should be positioned so as to be visible and prevent danger to persons in the event of operation. These are usually fitted to the appliance by the manufacturer.

As indicated earlier, a boiler supplying heat to a sealed system of heating will also require overheat protection in the from of a hi-limit thermostat. This can usually be found near or on the heat exchanger of the boiler as it monitors the temperature of the water inside.

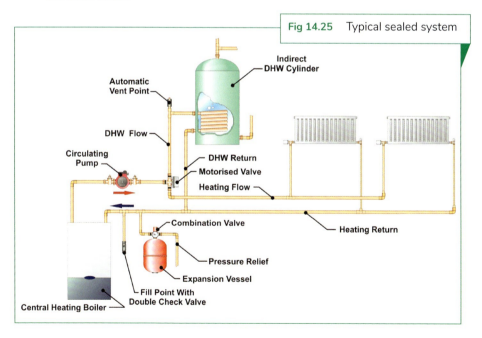

Fig 14.25   Typical sealed system

14.6.3 Frost

The boiler and associated pipework should be protected against the effects of the cold when located in vulnerable positions. This can be achieved by applying insulation in accordance with BS 5422[6] and BS 5970[7]. The protection of the boiler is paramount when vulnerable to cold so a frost thermostat should be installed in the immediate locale. In order to prevent excessive fuel consumption the installation will require a pipe thermostat located on the return pipework of the heating circuit in order to shut down the appliance when the circuit and the boiler have heated up and are no longer at risk from frost damage.

14.6.4 Corrosion

Corrosion inhibitors are normally added to the system after complete flushing of the installation has taken place. The purpose of the inhibitor is to prolong the life and maintain the efficiency of not only the heating circuit but also the boiler. The application of the inhibitor should be noted and displayed in a prominent position (normally on the boiler casing) in the form of a label often provided by the inhibitor manufacturer. The type of inhibitor that is to be used should be checked with the manufacturer to ensure that it has no adverse reactions with the materials used in the construction of the boiler.

By the nature of construction of single feed cylinders, inhibitors can not be use when such cylinders are employed in the system. Where a system has aluminium components, the use of water softeners shall not be used due to the corrosive reaction that will take place resulting in a component failure.

14.7 Ventilation

There are 6 possible location scenarios which we shall consider when assessing the ventilation requirements of a boiler;

1. Open flued boiler located in a room.
2. Open flued boiler located in a compartment venting to a room.
3. Open flued boiler located in a compartment venting directly to the outside
4. Room sealed boiler located in a room.
5. Room sealed boiler located in a compartment venting to a room.
6. Room sealed boiler located in a compartment venting directly to the outside.

Refer to the generic elements of ventilation in Part 1, Chapter 4 and BS 5440-2.

14.8 Gas Supply

The gas supply to the boiler shall be provided with regard to BS 6891 or IGEM/UP/2, as appropriate for natural gas and LPG – see Part 1, Chapter 5 for generic elements relating to natural gas pipework. For LPG reference can be made to the generic elements within the 'Liquefied Petroleum Gas On Site Guide'. Additional standards dealing with LPG are PD 54823[8] & BS EN ISO 10239[9]; IGEM/G/6[10] and Liquid Gas UK CoP 22[11].

Some important points;

- Rigid pipework only to be used when supplying gas to a domestic flued appliance.
- Pipework is correctly sized to meet the demand of the appliance. Under sizing of pipework can lead to difficulties in achieving the design performance of the appliance or even incomplete combustion of the gas being supplied.
- An appliance isolation valve is provided at the inlet to the appliance (usually supplied by the manufacturer).

14.9 Electrical Supply

Electrical work, as with that of gas, requires those undertaking the work to be competent in relation to the work activity being carried out and to work in a manner that promotes safety, whilst not imposing any dangers to both those working on the electrical installation or those who use it.

Electrical work encompasses a multitude of disciplines, but in terms of the scope of this section of the Guide is confined to the low-voltage (LV) AC system from the means of isolation (disconnector) up to and including the gas appliance(s).

> **NOTE:** BS 7671: 2018/A1: 2020 'Requirements for Electrical Installations. Eighteenth Edition IET Wiring Regulations' defines LV AC systems as being above 50 V AC but not exceeding 1000 V AC between live conductors, or 600 V AC between conductors and earth.

Regardless of the various wiring configurations that can be used by central heating and hot water systems, any electrical installation work associated with such systems shall comply with the requirements of BS 7671: 2018 (as amended) and the appliance/equipment manufacturers' instructions.

14.9.1. Legislation

The primary regulations of Great Britain (GB) covering ALL electrical work are:

- the Electricity at Work Regulations 1989 (EWR) – England, Wales & Scotland; and
- the Electricity at Work Regulations (Northern Ireland) 1991.

The EWR dovetail with –

For England, Wales & Scotland the:

- Health and Safety at Work etc. Act 1974 (HSWA), and
- Management of Health and Safety at Work Regulations 1999 (MHSWR).

For Northern Ireland the:

- Health and Safety at Work (Northern Ireland) Order 1978, and
- Management of Health and Safety at Work Regulations (Northern Ireland) 2000.

The HSWA and other appropriate regulations for GB are discussed in Part 1, Chapter 1 of this Guide.

Regulation 16 'Persons to be competent to prevent danger and injury' of the EWR requires that –

"*No person shall be engaged in any work activity where technical knowledge or experience is necessary to prevent danger or, where appropriate, injury, unless he possesses such knowledge or experience, or is under such degree of supervision as may be appropriate having regard to the nature of the work.*"

The Building Regulations further reinforces the EWR and the HSWA by requiring –

Building Regulations 2010 (England and Wales):

P1 -

"*Reasonable provision shall be made in the design and installation of electrical installations in order to protect persons operating, maintaining or altering the installations from fire or injury.*"

Building (Scotland) Regulations 2004:

Schedule 5, 4.5 Electrical safety "*Every building must be designed and constructed in such a way that the electrical installation does not –*

(a) threaten the health and safety of people in, and around, the building; and

(b) become a source of fire."

NOTE: At present there is no Building Regulation equivalent for Northern Ireland.

The legislation provides an overarching framework, i.e. a 'goal setting' approach, but does not provide the technical detail as to what is required. For this reference should be made to technical guidance contained within:

- Approved Document P 'Electrical Safety - Dwellings' 2013 Edition for England,
- Approved Document P 'Electrical Safety - Dwellings' for Wales 2006 Edition incorporating 2010 amendments, or
- Technical Handbook – Domestic 2019 – '4.5 Electrical Safety' for Scotland.

These technical documents ALL share one major commonality (including Northern Ireland by virtue of the Health & Safety Executive Northern Ireland (HSENI)) and that is reference to the detailed requirements of BS 7671: 2018 (as amended).

Whilst the requirements of BS 7671: 2018 (as amended) are non-statutory, they may be used in a court of law in evidence to claim compliance with a statutory requirement. Therefore, if any work carried out complies with the requirements of BS 7671, it is likely to be compliant with the intent of the overarching legislation.

Additionally, Building Regulations place a duty on those undertaking defined electrical work to notify the local Building Control Body (BCB) of the electrical installation (see sub-section 14.9.1.1 of this Chapter).

14.9.1.1. Notification of building work

The GB Building Regulations define certain electrical work as 'building work', requiring that work to be formerly notified to the local BCB as being in compliance. Notification can be either –

- via a member of a Competent Person Scheme (CPS) who can self-certify their installation upon completion, or
- via persons directly notifying the local BCB, before work starts, of the electrical installation work, or
- within England, via third-party certification.

The self-certification route, being the predominant route of notification, has been optimised to make the process quick and cost effective; the CPS provider will facilitate the automated notification process to the local BCB as well as issuing a compliance certificate to the home/building owner.

The other options are also acceptable but this may increase the cost and time involved in certifying the electrical installation.

Electrical work falling under the definition of building work includes –

For England:

- the installation of a new circuit;
- the replacement of a consumer unit;
- the addition or alteration of a circuit in a special location (e.g. in rooms containing a bath or shower, swimming pool, etc.).

For Wales:

Includes the same provisions as for England but in addition also includes:

- the addition or alteration of a circuit within a kitchen; and
- new central heating control wiring.

Scotland has a different approach, requiring a building warrant to be obtained prior to work commencing for certain buildings. For example, buildings above two-storeys and flats require a building warrant for electrical work associated with a new boiler. However, buildings of two-storeys and below do not.

For further guidance for Scotland and to a lesser extent, Northern Ireland, refer to the local BCB.

NOTE: The list of notifiable electrical work is not exhaustive and does not include outbuildings or electrical equipment installed within the curtilage of the premises.

Where the electrical work does not fall under the prescribed definitions of building work – for example the like-for-like replacement of electrical components associated with the heating and hot water system (circulating pump, zone valve(s), etc.) – then this work neither requires to be notified to the local BCB nor does the individual undertaking the work require to be a member of a CPS.

The individual responsible for the electrical work is still required to be competent and/or be under the supervision of a competent individual (skilled person) and ensure their work complies with the requirements of BS 7671 (as amended).

Part 2 'Definitions' of BS 7671 defines a skilled person as a –

"Person who possesses, as appropriate to the nature of the electrical work to be undertaken, adequate education, training and practical skills, and who is able to perceive risks and avoid hazards which electricity can create."

Having provided an overview of the legislative framework, it is necessary to focus on the method of electrical isolation and safe isolation practices.

14.9.2 Means of isolation

Gas appliances that utilise electrical energy, as with all electrical equipment, must have a means of isolating the supply in the event of danger and for maintenance purposes.

In particular, Regulation 12(1) of the EWR states:

"Subject to paragraph (3), where necessary to prevent danger, suitable means (including, where appropriate, methods of identifying circuits) shall be available for –

(a) cutting off the supply of electrical energy to any electrical equipment; and

(b) the isolation of any electrical equipment."

Electrical isolation for a gas appliance is typically provided by one of two methods:

- via a double-pole switched fused connection unit (see Note 2) incorporating a 3 A fuse link complying with BS 1362[12], or
- via a 3-pin plug (again incorporating a 3 A fuse link) connected to an unswitched socket-outlet (see Note 3).

NOTE 1: Where the appliance/equipment is located in a special location, i.e. a room containing a bath or shower, the LV circuit supplying that appliance/equipment shall also be protected by a residual current device (RCD) having a rated residual operating current not exceeding 30 mA.

Other forms of electrical isolation located within the consumer unit for the premises such as residual current operated circuit-breaker with integral overcurrent protection (RCBOs), circuit-breakers (CBs), etc., will be encountered, however this Guide will focus on the two prevalent and local methods of stated isolation for gas appliances.

NOTE 2: BS 6798 requires both line and neutral poles to be disconnected.

NOTE 3: BS 6798 also recommends that the socket-outlet features no switches as this promotes the physical removal of the 3-pin plug in order to isolate the gas appliance and/or installation.

Ideally, there should be a single means of electrical isolation located in close proximity to the equipment it serves – this ensures that it remains under the control of the person undertaking work on the installation. However, it isn't uncommon to find more than one means of electrical isolation for a central heating and hot water system. In such instances, and where two or more points of electrical isolation are provided, they should comply with the following:

- there is no physical connection between parts of the system that are separately isolated; and
- where one isolator is operated, there is no possibility that this isolation can be overridden by activation of parts of the non-isolated electrical system; and
- they are located adjacent to the equipment they serve so as to be readily accessible and obvious to what they isolate; and
- durable labelling is installed at each isolator (and other electrical enclosures deemed reasonable to warn of the dangers) stating that the heating system has multiple points of electrical isolation and stating where these points of isolation are located. The labelling should comply with the Health and Safety (Safety Signs and Signals) Regulations.

Where the means of isolation does not remain under the control of the person undertaking work because it is to be left unattended for any period or because it is located away from the appliance/equipment it serves, then an appropriate means of locking off the isolator shall be employed (see sub-section 14.9.3.5 of this Chapter) as part of the 'safe systems of work' covered in section 14.9.3.

As stated, the location of the isolator should make it obvious as to the appliance and/or equipment it serves. Where it is not obvious or where more than one isolator is located in close proximity (regardless of what it serves), then the means of isolation shall also be labelled. Regulation 537.2.7 of BS 7671 states -

"*Each device used for isolation shall be clearly identified by position or durable marking to indicate the installation or circuit it isolates.*".

It is for these reasons, even where isolation appears to be obvious that we **DO NOT assume** that the isolator(s) is correctly identified or that once switched/unplugged that the electrical installation served by it are de-energised (dead) – it is essential to practice 'safe isolation' including proving dead.

14.9.3 Safe system of work

Working safely requires knowledge and understanding of the work activity at hand and how this impinges upon or is affected by the work environment. Combining a simple risk assessment with industry developed processes, should ensure that personal actions do not lead to harm to ourselves or others who may be affected by that work.

14.9.3.1 Risk assessment

Like all work activities, it is essential that an initial risk assessment of the work environment is undertaken, and the risks posed to both ourselves in undertaking the activity and to those in the vicinity who may be affected by that activity is adequately considered.

The risk assessment should consider, amongst other things:

- personal competence to work on the appliance/equipment concerned or whether, in the case of electrical work, it will be necessary to defer to an individual with the required electrical competence or be under the supervision of an electrically skilled person,
- the work area* –
    - access to and around the appliance/equipment to be worked on, particularly for more restrictive installations in roof spaces, airing cupboards, etc.,
    - adequacy of the lighting available or if additional lighting is required,
    - uncontrolled access by others to the work area,
    - whether barriers and safety signage are required.
- the tools and equipment to be used are suitable, i.e. test instrumentation complying with the guidance of HSE's GS38 'Electrical test equipment for use on low voltage electrical systems' (see sub-section 14.9.3.3 of this Chapter)
- whether any personal protective equipment (PPE) is required - gloves, eye protection, bump cap where working in tight/confined spaces, etc.,
- control of information - keeping the gas user/responsible person informed of the intended work activity, including via the use of suitable signage and temporary barriers (where appropriate), warning others that electrical work is in progress,
- control of the testing process, the means of isolation, exposing of live parts, etc.

* Regulation 15 of the EWR states "For the purposes of enabling injury to be prevented, adequate working space, adequate means of access, and adequate lighting shall be provided at all electrical equipment on which or near which work is being done in circumstances which may give rise to danger."

14.9.3.2 Safe to touch

The simplest method of indicating when voltages may be present (which should mean it's used routinely) is the use of a single-pole non-contact voltage indicator.

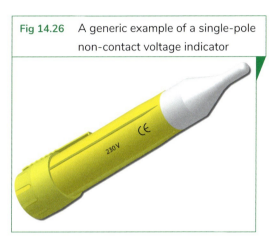

Fig 14.26   A generic example of a single-pole non-contact voltage indicator

Looking mostly like a large pen with an opaque bulbous end these simple devices, when in close proximity to/touching a metallic surface (appliance case or installed pipework) that is electrically 'live' illuminates to warn of the presence of a voltage (see fig 14.26). Some commercially available non-contact voltage indicators also provide an audible warning when a voltage is detected.

Currently there is no published industry standard for the use of a single-pole non-contact voltage indicator and so they should be used as instructed by the manufacturer.

Generally their use will comprise of:

- a visual check of the instruments condition before use - ensure it isn't damaged,
- where batteries are removed between uses, inserting the required batteries (typically 2 x AAA),
- turn on (where an on/off button is included) and where a self-test function is included, check operation of the instrument. After self-test or where the instrument does not have this function, check against a known 'live' source, e.g. back of plug as shown in fig 14.27 (note the illuminated tip showing the presence of a voltage),

- check the metallic component (appliance case, facia, drop door, pipework, etc.) without physically handling the component. The lamp of the single-pole non-contact voltage indicator should remain unlit, indicating that no voltage is present,

- before touching the metallic component, always retest the instrument on a known 'live' source to confirm that it is still functioning correctly – **DO NOT assume** it is working, as for example, the batteries may have been exhausted during initial testing or the instrument may have developed a fault.

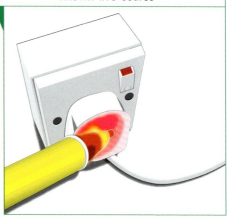

Fig 14.27 Single-pole non-contact voltage indicator checked against a known 'live' source

Should the single-pole non-contact voltage indicator illuminate, **DO NOT touch** the metallic component. Advise the gas user/responsible person and others who may be present in the dwelling of the danger and where appropriate isolate that appliance/component and, if it's within your competence, investigate and rectify the cause for the electrification.

In such an event and where the circuit for the gas appliance/installation concerned can be easily identified (either at the local isolator or at the consumer unit) switch off that circuit and recheck the metallic component with the single-pole non-contact voltage indicator as before following the manufacturer's procedure.

Where the dangerous circuit supplying the appliance/equipment cannot be identified/isolated or isolation of the circuit does not result in the voltage being no longer present on the metallic components, with the responsible persons permission, isolate the entire electrical supply of the dwelling at the main switch of the consumer unit.

Once isolated, appropriate documentation (Electrical Danger Notification for example) should be completed and presented to the responsible person advising that the supply is to remain off until inspected & tested by an electrically competent person.

It is important to note that single-pole non-contact voltage indicators only detect the presence of a voltage, not a measured value which would require more dedicated instrumentation. It is also important to stress that these 'indicators' are only a simple aid and must not be used to prove the absence of voltage; this can only be done when a safe isolation procedure in conjunction with a suitable test instrument is followed (see sub-section 14.9.3.3 in this Chapter).

NOTE: Other voltage indicators such as the ubiquitous neon screwdriver shall not be used as a 'safe to touch' indicator.

14.9.3.3. Test instrumentation

To prove safe isolation, it is necessary to use a suitable test instrument - NOT a single-pole non-contact voltage indicator as discussed in 14.9.3.1 of this Chapter, which has a narrow and defined purpose.

The HSE, via GS38 'Electrical test equipment for use on low voltage electrical systems' provides guidance on the selection and use of:

- test probes,
- leads,
- lamps,
- voltage detecting devices; and
- measuring equipment for circuits whose rated voltage does not exceed 1000 V AC.

NOTE: The guidance in this section of the Guide is specific to the determination of the absence of voltage in ensuring continued safety when working on appliance(s) and equipment, and as such other test parameters (current, resistance, etc.) are not discussed.

Test probes, clips and leads

The test probes, clips and leads that come with the test instrument must be in good condition and conform to BS EN 61010-031[13] or in the case of a two-pole voltage detector, to BS EN 61243-3[14]. Additionally, the probes, clips and leads should be marked with the rated installation category (CAT** II, III or IV) and the manufacturer's name or identifier.

*** CAT II is for measurements of LV circuits (appliances and ancillary components), CAT III for measurements associated with the premises fixed electrical installation and CAT IV is for measurements performed at the source of the LV installation (meters, consumer units, etc.).*

The test probes and clips should have the following features:

- finger barriers or be so shaped that inadvertent hand contact with the live parts under test is avoided,
- uninsulated tips of probes do not exceed 4 mm, but preferably should not exceed 2 mm or less, or be fully enclosed by a spring-loaded retractable screen.

The test leads should have the following features:

- be adequately insulated,
- be distinguishable by the use of colour from one lead to another (brown, blue and green or red & black on older leads) – colouration doesn't typically apply to two-pole voltage detectors as they use a single colour of black,
- be flexible and of sufficient capacity for the intended testing,
- be sheathed to protect against mechanical damage,
- be of sufficient length for the testing activity, but not overly long that they become unwieldly, and
- have no accessible exposed conductors should the leads be detached from test probes, clips or instrument (voltage detector leads and probes are held captive and do not detach from each other or from the instrument).

NOTE: Older test instruments complying with previous British Standards may be suitable for continued use, but they must be in good condition and their test leads, probes and clips should include the features discussed above.

Two-pole voltage detectors

Equipment used solely for testing for the presence or absence of voltage can be either a:

- test lamp (fig 14.28),
- a voltage detector with an LED meter scale (fig 14.29),
- a multimeter (unpreferred as they can be set incorrectly by the user and as such are not discussed in this Chapter).

Fig 14.28   An example of a test lamp

Fig 14.29   An example of a voltage detector

Two-pole voltage detectors need to comply with BS EN 61243-3 and will typically use internal circuitry to limit the current and energy entering the detector. The lead and connection to the two testing probes is held captive and cannot therefore be disconnected from each other.

Test lamps fitted with glass bulbs should not give rise to danger should the bulb be broken, and all voltage detectors should be clearly marked with the maximum voltage and category (CAT II, III or IV) that may be tested by the device. Where the device has a short-term maximum current rating, this should be stated on the device and not exceeded during use.

As these devices are used to prove 'dead' (no voltage present) they should be proved before and after use to ensure they continue to function correctly, preferably on a voltage proving unit (see fig 14.30), unless an inbuilt test facility is provided. Alternatively, the test lamp or meter scale voltage indicator can be proved against a known live source of similar voltage under test, with the necessary safety precautions in place.

Fig 14.30   An example of a proving unit

14.9.3.4 Safe isolation procedure

Before any work is undertaken on a gas appliance, especially where covers to electrical enclosures need to be removed, the appliance and its ancillary controls must be safely isolated from the electrical supply.

Regulation 14 'Work on or near live conductors' of the EWR states –

> *No person shall be engaged in any work activity on or so near any live conductor (other than one suitably covered with insulating material so as to prevent danger) that danger may arise unless –*
>
> *(a) it is unreasonable in all the circumstances for it to be dead; and*
>
> *(b) it is reasonable in all circumstances for him to be at work on or near it while it is live; and*
>
> *(c) suitable precautions (including where necessary the provision of suitable protective equipment) are taken to prevent injury.*

Having previously satisfied ourselves that metallic surfaces of the installation can be safely handled and that we are going to prove dead before carrying out electrical work, we can now think about the process for safe isolation in its entirety.

The following simple procedure is used in conjunction with the local means of isolation for the appliance and equipment concerned.

Procedure

Step 1

- Check it is safe and acceptable to the gas user/responsible person to isolate the appliance and equipment in question. Turn off the appliance at its controls so that no demand (load) is called for and for a:
  - fused connection unit - operate the switch to the off position to remove the electrical load, or
  - socket-outlet and 3-pin plug - withdraw the 3-pin plug from the socket-outlet (where switched, it is good practice to turn off the switch, but this is not regarded as being critical).

Where the local means of isolation is under your full control whilst work is carried out, proceed to Step 2.

If for any reason you will be out-of-sight of the means of isolation, remove the fuse link from the fuse carrier or if the fuse carrier can be removed, remove the fuse carrier (keeping the fuse link/carrier on your person at all times) and place suitable signage warning of electrical work in progress. Alternatively, secure the isolator via the use of a suitable safety lock-off device (see sub-section 14.9.3.5 of this Chapter).

Step 2
- Prove the correct operation of a suitable voltage detector against a known voltage source.

Step 3
- Whilst exercising caution, remove the necessary covers to gain access to the electrical connections of the appliance or equipment. Using the voltage detector check that there is no dangerous voltage present on any circuit conductor to be worked on. Check terminal voltages between:

1. earth and line,
2. neutral and line, and
3. earth and neutral

NOTE 1: When checking for a voltage between an earth terminal and live (including neutral) terminals, the test probe should make contact with the earth terminal first, to reduce the risk of the remaining probe becoming live.

NOTE 2: Testing terminal voltages will also prove that the means of isolation has been correctly identified – even if obvious or otherwise marked as being the means of isolation, DO NOT assume this is the case.

Step 4
- Prove the voltage detector again against the known source to check that it was functioning correctly when the circuit(s) were tested for the presence of voltage.

Once safely isolated (electrically) work can commence on the installation.

Upon satisfactory completion of works, replace electrical covers and remove tools from around the work area. If means of locking off have been used, remove lock(s) or where a fuse link has been withdrawn, replace the fuse link to the fuse carrier and insert back into the fuse connection unit/3-pin plug. Operate isolator to re-energise the appliance/installation.

Temporarily set controls so that appliance comes into operation and confirm satisfactory operation. Once satisfied, reset controls to user preference and complete all necessary documentation.

14.9.3.5 Means of locking off

Where the means of isolation is not under the full control of the individual carrying out the work, steps should be taken to secure the means of isolation against inadvertent re-energisation.

Securing the isolator can be as simple as withdrawing the fuse link and its carrier on a fused connection unit and keeping it on your person. If the carrier cannot be removed, i.e. stays captive once open, insert a small padlock through the carrier's frame to prevent anyone inserting a new fuse and re-energising the appliance/installation.

Likewise and for a 3-pin plug, once the plug is withdrawn from the socket-outlet, the fuse link and fuse carrier on a moulded plug can be removed and kept on your person or for a traditional plug, open the plug top and remove the fuse link before resecuring.

Alternatively and for both forms of isolator there are commercially available options that will place the switching mechanism of the isolator within a lockable enclosure – fig 14.31 illustrates a box that can be attached on to the face plate of a fused connection unit then locked & fig 14.32 shows a lock plate encasing a 3-pin plug. A 3-pin plug can also be placed within a lockable box (not shown).

Fig 14.31 Example of a lock box for a fused connection unit

Fig 14.32 Example of a 3-pin plug lock plate

Regardless of the method of locking off, suitable warning signage should be posted advising that work is in progress, which can include temporary barriers if required, and those present within the premises should be kept informed of the work activity.

14.10 Controls

The common controls that would normally be found on boilers are listed below in there relevant categories. Refer to Chapter 10 for further guidance.

Flow

- taper plug valve,
- ball valve,
- solenoid.

Flame supervision

- thermoelectric,
- flame rectification,
- vapour pressure.

Pressure

- simple regulator,
- modulating regulator,
- air/gas ratio control valve.

Ignition

- permanent pilot,
- electronic/electrical,
- hot surface

Temperature

- liquid expansion thermostatic switch,
- thermistors,
- bimetallic switch,
- rod type,
- wax capsule.

Safety

- TTB,
- Interrupted thermocouple,
- vitiation sensing,
- pressure switch,
- hi-limit thermostat.

Multifunctional components - many, if not all, appliance manufacturers will employ a multifunctional component within the appliance. The component will, no doubt, include two of more of the controls previously listed. There is a large variety of components used across the many different appliance manufacturers.

14.10.1 Air/gas ratio valve

The use of an air/gas ratio valve in these appliances assists in obtaining the high levels of efficiency. The temperatures of the primary flow and the primary return coupled with the monitoring of the flue gas temperatures allows the boiler to calculate the optimum fan speed for that moment in time. This means that the boilers heat input modulates in direct relation to the demand at that moment, again contributing to a higher level of efficiency. (See Chapter 7 for further information).

14.10.2 Operating sequence for fan assisted boilers with automatic ignition

1. The boiler receives a demand for heat usually through external controls such as a time switch or a programmer together with a room thermostat.
2. The pressure switch is then checked to ensure it returned to the normally closed position after the boiler switched off at the end of the last cycle.
3. When the boiler is satisfied that the pressure switch returned to the normally closed position, it will energise the flue fan otherwise the boiler will go straight to lockout (often the manufacturer may incorporate indicators which will assist the engineer to diagnose the faults).
4. With the flue fan now running the pressure switch will activate and switch from the normally closed position to the normally open position.
5. When the boiler is satisfied that the pressure switch has been activated it will start the ignition sequence and send a spark to the ignition electrode and allowing the gas to flow to the burner by opening the solenoid, otherwise the fan will continue to run but the ignition sequence and the solenoid operation will not be activated (the flue fan may continue to run until the boiler is switched off manually).
6. The flame rectification FSD will constantly monitor the presence of the flame during the cycle whilst the thermostat in the boiler will control the temperature within the boiler during the timed period.

14.11 Commissioning and Servicing

In all cases the manufacturer's commissioning procedure shall be complied with. A generic procedure is detailed as follows:

14.11.1 Commissioning procedure

1. Check site –
   1.1 Suitability of location (BS 6798).
   1.2 Clearances from obstacles.
   1.3 Proximity to combustibles.
   1.4 Visual inspection of flue;
      1.4.1 route (length, support, bends, size, materials, etc.),

NOTE: For fan draught room sealed appliances check for the provision of inspection hatches when routed through voids.

   1.4.2 terminal position,
   1.4.3 sealing and proximity to combustibles,
   1.4.4 flue flow test (OF appliances).
   1.5 Ventilation requirements (combustion and compartment).
   1.6 Assembly and fixing (casing seals, panel seals, wall fixing, etc.).
   1.7 Packaging removal.
   1.8 Adequate supplies;
      1.8.1 gas,
      1.8.2 water,
      1.8.3 electricity.
2. Test for tightness –
   2.1 Gas (using appropriate standard for gas type and location).
   2.2 Water.
3. Purge supplies –
   3.1 Gas.
   3.2 Water (add cleanser).
4. Test operation and performance –
   4.1 Control devices;
      4.1.1 isolation valves
         4.1.1.1 gas,
         4.1.1.2 water.
      4.1.2 control knob,

- 4.1.3 ignition system,
- 4.1.4 boiler thermostat,
- 4.1.5 air/gas ratio control valve.
- 4.2 Safety devices (where fitted);
    - 4.2.1 flame safety device,
    - 4.2.2 gas escapes,
    - 4.2.3 spillage test,
    - 4.2.4 spillage sensor,
    - 4.2.5 fan flow proving or pressure proving,
    - 4.2.6 hi-limit thermostat.
- 4.3 Set burner pressure and check heat input.
- 4.4 Check flame picture;
    - 4.4.1 pilot,
    - 4.4.2 main,
    - 4.4.3 measure the combustion performance as required (now mandatory for commissioning new condensing appliances with air/gas ratio control valves)).
- 4.5 Commission heating circuits;
    - 4.5.1 check operation of heating and control system,
        - 4.5.1.1 reverse circulation,
        - 4.5.1.2 programmer, room/cylinder 'stats, pump speed/overrun, motorised valves).
    - 4.5.2 hot flush and corrosion inhibitor (install insulation).
5. Electrical checks –

These will be dependent on what alterations/installations have been carried out. Basically the central heating circuits need to be checked for;

- 5.1 Conformity with BS 7671;
    - 5.1.1 supplementary bonding,
    - 5.1.2 provision of safe isolation of whole system from single point,
    - 5.1.3 fuse/mcb/cable sizes,
    - 5.1.4 jointing/securing/colour coding.
- 5.2 Earth continuity (<1 Ohm).
- 5.3 Resistance to earth (L-E, N-E).
- 5.4 Polarity.
- 5.5 Correct operation of circuits.

Operatives shall be suitably qualified and have adequate test equipment.

6. Instruct customer (leave manufacturers' instructions) –
    - 6.1 Correct usage.
    - 6.2 Maintenance requirements.
    - 6.3 Gas emergency procedure.
    - 6.4 Complete benchmark documentation (typically forms part of MI's).
    - 6.5 Frost protection.

Depending on whether the system is open vented or sealed, other checks will be necessary such as feed & expansion cistern water level, cold fill pressure, PRV operation, pumping over/air entrainment, filling loop.

14.11.2 Servicing procedure

1. Initial Investigation –
    - 1.1 Ask customer about the operation of appliance.
    - 1.2 Test operation and visually inspect for obvious defects.
    - 1.3 Suitability of location (BS 6798).
    - 1.4 Clearances from obstacles.
    - 1.5 Proximity to combustibles.
    - 1.6 Visual inspection of flue;
        - 1.6.1 route (length, support, bends, size, materials, voids, etc.),
        - 1.6.2 terminal position,
        - 1.6.3 sealing and proximity to combustibles,
        - 1.6.4 flue flow test (open flue appliances).
    - 1.7 Ventilation requirements (combustion and compartment).
    - 1.8 Assembly and fixing (casing seal, wall fixing, etc.).
    - 1.9 Adequate supplies;
        - 1.9.1 gas,
        - 1.9.2 water,
        - 1.9.3 electricity.
2. Test for tightness –
    - 2.1 Gas (using appropriate standard for gas type and location).
    - 2.2 Water.
3. Dismantle and clean (as fitted) –
    - 3.1 Remove casing/panels, inspect seals.
    - 3.2 Remove main/pilot burners/injectors and clean/inspect.
    - 3.3 Brush clean heat exchanger/combustion chamber.
    - 3.4 Clean flueways and inspect insulation panels for damage.
    - 3.5 Remove and clean fan assembly.
    - 3.6 Reassemble.

4. Test Operation and performance –
   4.1 Control devices;
      4.1.1 isolation valves,
         4.1.1.1 gas,
         4.1.1.2 water.
      4.1.2 control knob,
      4.1.3 ignition system,
      4.1.4 boiler thermostat.
   4.2 Safety devices;
      4.2.1 flame safety device;
      4.2.2 gas escapes
      4.2.3 spillage test,
      4.2.4 spillage sensor,
      4.2.5 fan flow proving or pressure proving,
      4.2.6 hi-limit thermostat.
   4.3 Set burner pressure and check heat input.
   4.4 Check flame picture;
      4.4.1 pilot,
      4.4.2 main burner,
      4.4.3 measure the combustion performance as required.
   4.5 Commission heating circuits;
      4.5.1 check operation of heating and control system,
         4.5.1.1 reverse circulation,
         4.5.1.2 programmer, room/cylinder 'stats, pump speed/overrun, motorised valves.
      4.5.2 hot flush and corrosion inhibitor (install insulation).
5. Electrical checks –

Inspect and test as follows

   5.1 Conformity with BS 7671;
      5.1.1 supplementary bonding,
      5.1.2 provision of safe isolation of whole system from single point,
      5.1.3 fuse/mcb/cable sizes.
   5.2 Earth continuity (<1 Ohm).
   5.3 Resistance to earth (L-E, N-E).
   5.4 Polarity.
   5.5 Correct operation of circuits.

Operatives shall be suitably qualified and have adequate test equipment.

6. Advise customer –
   - 6.1 Correct usage.
   - 6.2 ID or AR encountered.
   - 6.3 Gas emergency procedure.
   - 6.4 Complete benchmark documentation (typically forms part of MI's).
   - 6.5 Frost protection.

Depending on whether the system is open vented or sealed, other checks will be necessary such as feed & expansion cistern water level, cold fill pressure, PRV operation, pumping over/air entrainment, filling loop.

Chapter 15
Carbon Monoxide/Dioxide Atmosphere Sampling

			Page No.
15.1	Introduction		15.1
15.2	Combustion Products and Their Movement Within Dwellings		15.3
	15.2.1	Constituents of complete and incomplete combustion	15.3
	15.2.2	Movement of carbon monoxide/dioxide within dwellings	15.4
5.3	Basic Safety Principles		15.7
15.4	Dwelling Investigation		15.8
	15.4.1	General	15.8
	15.4.2	Types of electronic portable gas analysers	15.9
		15.4.2.1 Analyser operational checks	15.11
	15.4.3	Sweep testing appliances	15.12
	15.4.4	Detailed discussion with customer	15.13
	15.4.5	Initial test to determine levels of CO and CO_2 within dwelling with no appliances in operation	15.14

Chapter 15
Carbon Monoxide/Dioxide Atmosphere Sampling

	Page No.
15.4.6 Testing ambient air with appliances in operation	**15.15**
15.4.6.1 Testing "Type A" appliances - cookers	**15.16**
15.4.6.2 Testing "Type A" appliances - Flueless water heaters	**15.17**
15.4.6.3 Testing "Type A" appliances - flueless space heaters (Including LPG cabinet heaters)	**15.17**
15.4.6.4 Testing "Type B" appliances - open flue	**15.17**
15.4.6.5 Testing "Type C" appliances - room sealed	**15.18**
15.4.7 Appliance examination	**15.19**
15.4.8 CO detector activation	**15.20**
15.4.9 Reports	**15.20**
15.4.10 Final completion of investigation and leaving the property	**15.21**

References in this Chapter

[1] BS 7967-5: 2010 Guide for using electronic portable combustion gas analysers in non-domestic premises for the measurement of carbon monoxide and carbon dioxide levels and the determination of combustion performance'

[2] BS EN 50379-3: 2012 Specification for portable electrical apparatus designed to measure combustion flue gas parameters of heating appliances. Performance requirements for apparatus used in non-statutory servicing of gas fired heating appliances.

[3] BS EN 50543: 2011 Electronic portable and transportable apparatus designed to detect and measure carbon dioxide and/or carbon monoxide in indoor ambient air. Requirements and test methods.

15.1 Introduction

Gas engineers may be required to respond to a number of different situations such as CO detector activation, a report of suspected fumes/smells by a customer or a follow up call to a gas emergency where an appliance(s) has been classified as a cause for concern by an ESP. These types of situation warrant the gas engineer to "investigate" and subsequently identify and, where applicable, rectify the source of any problem.

Guidance to help the gas engineer perform these duties is provided in the British Standard (BS) 7967: 2015 'Guide for the use of electronic combustion gas analysers for the measurement of carbon monoxide in dwellings and the combustion performance of gas-fired appliances'. This standard which was introduced February 2015 combines and replaces the previous four parts into one standard, whilst leaving part 5[1] as a separate but associated document.

NOTE: Within this section, further reference to BS 7967 means the current 2015 edition, unless otherwise specified.

BS 7967 covers 1st, 2nd, and 3rd family gases and further normative reference is used to compliment both parts of the standard, namely:

○ HSL 56 - Safety in the installation and use of gas systems and appliances approved codes of practice and guidance,
○ IGEM/G/11 - Gas Industry Unsafe Situations Procedure (see Chapter 8 of Part 1 of this Guide),
○ EH40 - Health and Safety workplace exposure limits,
○ Individual appliance manufacturer's instructions (MIs).

Although BS 7967 specifies that an investigation is to be carried out, it does not extend its scope to include the duties and responsibilities of the emergency service provider as specified by the Gas Safety (Management) Regulations or as detailed in Regulation 11.1 under RIDDOR for the investigation of gas incidents.

In the context of this section a gas incident is where it is known or suspected that exposure to CO has resulted in a person(s) losing consciousness or having acute illness requiring medical treatment or death. It is imperative where a gas engineer is in attendance at a gas related incident that they ensure minimum disturbance of the incident scene and, where safe to do so, the gas supply to the installation is isolated with the premises adequately ventilated.

Incident investigation shall only be performed by suitably trained and competent personnel. The customer shall be advised that any tests or remedial work cannot be performed until as such times as the investigation has been completed and authorisation to proceed is given. Where doubt exists contact the local HSE office.

This section deals with the use of electronic portable combustion gas analysers to investigate and identify the source of fumes, smells, spillage/leakage of PoC's and the reason for CO detector activation. It does not cover the use of gas analysers for the combustion performance analysis of individual appliances (see Part 1, Chapter 3 of this Guide).

For domestic dwellings, BS 7967 applies where the term dwelling is defined as a "unit of residential accommodation" which includes:

- flats,
- bedsits,
- maisonettes,
- terraced, semi-detached and detached houses,
- residential park homes (RPH),
- residential properties situated within, or forming part of, commercial, industrial or agricultural premises,
- leisure accommodation vehicles (LAV),
- boats (B) - excluding vessels with an international load line certificate.

This standard enforces the fact that combustion gas analysers are used as a tool to complement normal service and maintenance of appliances and not a substitute. However, they are invaluable for investigative purposes, not only to identify the source of any problems, but also confirmation of a safe environment within a dwelling.

15.2 Combustion Products and Their Movement Within Dwellings

15.2.1 Constituents of complete and incomplete combustion

As we are aware when we have complete combustion of a fuel gas (in our case natural gas) the main constituents of the combustion process are carbon dioxide (CO_2) and water vapour (H_2O). It is also important to recognise that the combustion products will also contain varying levels of other gases such as nitrogen oxides (NOx), predominantly of which are nitric oxide or nitrogen monoxide (NO) and nitrogen dioxide (NO_2), also aldehydes (simplest of which is methanal commonly known as formaldehyde (CH_2O)).

The quantities of these gases is dependent on the combustion efficiency of each appliance and as such can prove irritant and in some cases extremely harmful. Albeit we do not include these gases as part of the investigation they can lead to symptoms and, in some cases smells, which can help identify any problems that may exist. For example, Formaldehyde is an irritant with a very distinct acrid smell where very low levels (down to as little as 2 parts per million (ppm)) causing severe irritation of the nose, eye's and throat.

Higher levels of formaldehyde are produced during incomplete combustion and as such its effects may complement that of the toxic carbon monoxide (CO). For example, customers complaining of fumes may indicate the usual symptoms associated with CO such as headaches, nausea, dizziness and tiredness. However, they may also complain about an acrid smell with streaming eyes, runny nose and a sore throat which are symptoms associated with formaldehyde rather than the CO.

It is recognised that the production of formaldehyde from incomplete combustion is beneficial given that it makes the customer more aware of fumes. CO is commonly referred to as the "silent killer" as it has no smell, taste or colour, therefore if produced with no formation of formaldehyde, it can build up in sufficient quantities to incapacitate the occupants before they recognise any problem exists.

15.2.2 Movement of carbon monoxide/dioxide within dwellings

Carbon monoxide has a relative density slightly less than that of air whereas carbon dioxide is about 1.5 times that of air. As these gases are produced during the combustion process they are normally at a temperature significantly higher than that of the surrounding air making them more buoyant and therefore, would tend to rise to high level. As they cool they will become less buoyant. With CO, given that it has a density close to that of the surrounding air, it will start to distribute itself evenly throughout the room.

The extent of which it mixes with the surrounding air will be dependent on the thermal convection currents that are within the room. For example, if the room contained appliances which are designed to heat a room through convection such as gas fires, air heaters, etc., the CO will mix more readily throughout the room whereas with a central heating boiler which is not designed as a convective appliance will allow the CO to stratify (form layers) at high level, resulting in higher concentrations in that area (see fig's 15.1 & 15.2).

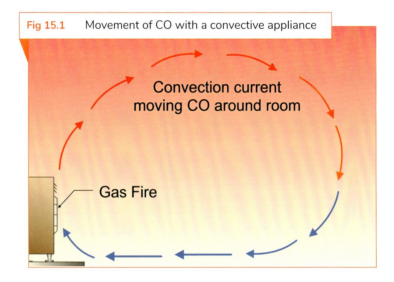

Fig 15.1   Movement of CO with a convective appliance

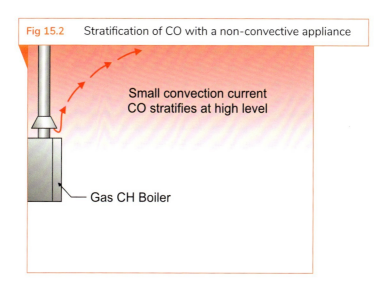

Fig 15.2   Stratification of CO with a non-convective appliance

It should be noted that even though the CO stratifies, as it cools it will fall to low level such that after a period of time the concentrations will start to increase at lower levels but not as fast as that of the convective appliance.

The Department of Health specifies that CO levels within a room must not exceed 10 ppm and thus is used within BS 7967, with the limited exception of gas cookers (see sub-section 15.4.6.1 in this Chapter). Carbon dioxide (CO_2) on the other hand, as it cools increases in density and will generally fall to low level due to its higher specific gravity.

To think outside the "box" we have to appreciate that not in all situations will spillage lead to incomplete combustion of the appliance(s). Take for example a compartment which contains an open flue boiler. If this compartment is adequately ventilated direct to outside with correct configuration of the ventilators at high and low level, any PoC which are released into the internal space will rise due to the temperature difference between them and the surrounding air.

These products may then be vented to outside air by means of the high level vents with clean fresh air for combustion coming into the boiler from the low level vent. As long as this cycle is not disturbed the convective current generated within the compartment by the high and low level ventilation would not allow the atmosphere within the compartment to degrade to such a level as to affect the combustion process.

However, if the CO_2 were allowed to build up, as it cools the highest concentration would be at lower level where it could then be entrained into the combustion air stream. If the concentration were to build up in excess of 1.5 % volume per volume of the combustion air it would dramatically affect the combustion process causing accelerated production of toxic CO. The gas industry specifies a maximum indoor level of 2,800 ppm CO_2 in atmosphere whereas the world health organisation (WHO) and the HSE specify a maximum exposure level for any person of 5,000 ppm over a weighted 8 hour day.

Where an appliance is spilling products of combustion either by means of the draught diverter or through faulty casing seals, concentrations of both CO_2 and/or CO would generally be higher within the room in which the appliance is installed. However, it can migrate to other parts of the dwelling or adjacent dwellings through openings such as doors, windows, vents, boxing in, flooring or other building defects.

On the other hand where the combustion products enter the building through a defective chimney or flue, depending on the route of the chimney and the location of the defect, higher concentrations of CO_2 and/or CO may be found in other parts of the dwelling or adjacent dwellings rather than at the appliance. Given this, it is important to check throughout a dwelling and where applicable, adjacent dwellings, for any signs that combustion products may be entering into the property, especially along chimney/flue routes. This includes monitoring not only for CO, but also CO_2 as incomplete combustion may not have occurred.

It should also be taken into consideration that CO_2 and/or CO may be entering the premises not just from gas-fired appliances but from other sources such as smoking, other fuel burning appliances, vehicles or generators in attached buildings or dwellings and engines on boats.

5.3 Basic Safety Principles

Within the gas industry all gas engineers have what we call a duty of care. This duty of care involves a number of safety principles that must be adhered to and are listed in order of priority below:

1. **Protect life.**
2. **Protect property.**
3. Locate all fuel burning appliances.
4. Locate any escape of gas, fumes, smells or spillage/leakage of combustion products.
5. Confirm the safe operation and installation of all suspect gas appliances.
6. Make safe any identified unsafe appliance/installation in accordance with IGEM/G/11 - the Gas Industry Unsafe Situations Procedure (GIUSP).
7. Advise the customer of any remedial action.
8. Complete all necessary reports, documentation and actions as per GIUSP.

In general terms the gas engineer through initial evidence and inspection is required to determine the safety of an installation, or conversely, any 'suspect' appliance before proceeding; the level of risk will determine the course of action taken, for example high levels of CO in atmosphere (above 30 ppm) will warrant immediate evacuation of the premises, isolation and ventilation to safeguard life (including your own).

Appliances that may be regarded as "suspect" are those which after initial appraisal:

- Are showing signs of distress in, on or around the appliance and/or chimney/flue system.
- When operated are spilling/leaking products of combustion into the dwelling normally evident due to unusual smells, strange tastes, humidity, etc.
- Have an unusual flame picture which may show signs of incomplete combustion.
- Have installation problems such as incorrect flueing, ventilation or location.
- Have previously been regarded as unsafe, for example a warning notice has been attached with no signs that the problem has been rectified and the appliance is in operation.
- Have been turned off by the emergency services.

It should be noted that this can also be applied to other fuel burning appliances such as oil and solid fuel.

15.4 Dwelling Investigation

15.4.1 General

It should be noted that a gas engineer is invited into a customer's premises and as such it is imperative that any actions that the engineer may require to take shall be done with consent of the customer before proceeding.

Having taken all necessary steps to ensure the safety of life and property, the gas engineer shall decide on whether an investigation is required before proceeding; has an incident occurred (loss of consciousness, acute illness requiring medical treatment or death) and if so have the relevant authorities been contacted.

Where it is safe to continue, remembering the basic safety principles, a preliminary discussion with the customer may help to establish the reason for attending:

1. Customer feeling the effect of exposure to CO – dizziness, nausea, chest pains, etc.
2. Presence of strange tastes, smells, unusual atmosphere's, humidity when appliances have been or are in use.
3. Sooty marks/stains in, on or around appliances and flues.
4. CO detector activation.
5. Referral from ESP or an agent acting on behalf of the customer.
6. There is a presence of CO and/or CO_2 (this will only be found by atmospheric analysis). Maximum levels of CO permitted is 10 ppm (with the possible exclusion of gas cookers, see sub-section 15.4.6.1 in this Chapter) and for CO_2, 2,800 ppm.

In addition and where it is safe to continue, a relatively quick sweep test of 'in use' appliances can be conducted to help identify the possible presence of CO (see sub-section 15.4.3 in this Chapter); this may also serve to priorities 'suspect' appliances.

15.4.2 Types of electronic portable gas analysers

Gas analysers used during the investigation shall conform to the following standards:

- BS EN 50379[2] part 3 which supersedes BS 7927 (analysers to this standard are still acceptable). This type of analyser is used for combustion analysis and normally measures both oxygen (O_2) and carbon monoxide (CO) levels. Carbon dioxide (CO_2) is calculated from the O_2 measurement and is normally displayed as a percentage with a resolution of ± 0.1 % (± 1,000 ppm).

- BS EN 50543[3] which supersedes BS 8494 analysers are specifically designed for measuring concentrations of CO_2 in indoor ambient air. They directly measure CO_2 and, depending on manufacturer, include CO measurement. They shall not be used for combustion performance analysis and as such do not meet all the requirements, if necessary, to complete an investigation. In most accounts they are used to complement the BS EN 50379 part 3 analyser due to their accuracy of measurement of CO_2.

Fig 15.3 Example of a BS EN 50379-3 analyser

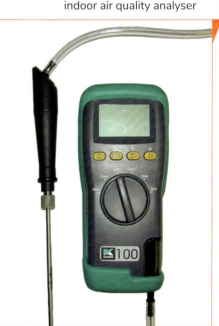

Fig 15.4 Example of a BS EN 50543 indoor air quality analyser

Both types of analyser are suitable for use when measuring CO concentrations in atmosphere. They shall have an accuracy of ± 3 ppm when measuring at or below 20 ppm CO and ± 5 ppm above this. Be careful when the analyser does not record the maximum CO levels as a peak value may be missed.

When measuring ambient CO_2 a BS EN 50543 compliant analyser should be used. This type of analyser shall have a range of at least 0 to 5,000 ppm CO_2 with a resolution of 50 ppm or higher, or 5,000 to 20,000 ppm with a resolution of 2 % of the displayed reading or higher.

Combustion gas analysers can use different methods of measurement when used to sample indoor air quality. Some analysers only measure an increase above background levels i.e. they "zero" in outdoor air and only display levels above this, whilst others measure absolute levels (actual levels including background).

An analyser measuring from absolute zero displays the actual concentrations of CO & CO_2 in the atmosphere and as such do not require to be zeroed in outside air. It should be noted, however, that it is advisable in all accounts to purge in outside air to obtain a background reference reading and check sensor operation. Analysers which do not "zero" or display unusual readings in outside air can indicate either a faulty analyser or sensor.

Reference shall be made to the manufacturer's instructions to ensure correct operation and diagnostic procedures are followed.

15.4.2.1 Analyser operational checks

As with any measuring instrument it is essential that they are operated, maintained and calibrated in accordance with the manufacturer's recommendations to ensure accuracy. Any analyser which is out of calibration should not be used.

Before use, the following general checks should be performed:

1. The batteries have enough charge for the duration of the test(s) and are in a suitable condition for use. It is advisable where non-rechargeable batteries are used that some NEW spare batteries are available before commencing with the test(s). Confirm with the manufacturer or, where practical, look in the battery compartment to confirm battery type. If the analyser switches off during the test, you need to re-purge and zero in outside air before continuing.

2. Check for damage to the instrument casing, filter housing, probe connections, display, hoses, sampling probe (remove any protective boots which may hide damage). Damaged can cause the analyser to give inaccurate readings either due to hardware malfunction or air ingress diluting the sample.

3. Check the water traps area is empty and the filters are clean and dry. Some analysers have a small plug which is used to drain the water out of the trap. Ensure that these are in place before operation as air entering these points will dilute any sample taken.

4. Check that the analyser and probes are assembled correctly.

5. Turn the analyser on and purge in fresh air. On start-up check the display is functioning correctly and the pump is operating. Never turn on an analyser in contaminated air or in the combustion gas stream.

6. Where available, after prepurge check the oxygen level. This should read approximately 20.9 % in fresh air. Readings that fluctuate or deviate from this may indicate a faulty sensor. In addition, where a machine has been exposed to high levels of CO (unless designed otherwise) the sensor can become "flooded" with the sample gas and in some instances may take a long time to clear, even when purged with fresh air. These excessive exposure levels can cause irreparable damage to the CO sensor. This can also happen when the analyser is turned off before a full fresh air purge has had time to clear the sensors. Always purge in fresh air and check the readings have "zeroed" back to background levels before turning off.

7. Check the analyser has been set to the correct fuel.

15.4.3 Sweep testing appliances

After preliminary discussion with the customer and where it is safe to continue, the gas engineer can perform a sweep test around any open flue or room sealed appliances to establish if CO is present.

Flueless appliances, for obvious reasons cannot be tested using this method and will therefore, need to have their combustion ratio (CO/CO_2) measured. The ratio needs to be within the manufacturers specified limits, or where no information is given, in accordance with BS 7967 (see Part 1, Chapter 3 for further guidance).

The test, at this stage may help to establish if CO is present and if so, the possible 'suspect' appliance before moving into more involved atmosphere and appliance testing. The test per appliance should be for a minimum of 2 minutes, with a minimum of 2 passes:

1. Prepare the analyser as instructed by the manufacturer.
2. For open flue appliance ensure any windows or doors to the room in which the appliance is installed are closed.
3. With the appliance operating, slowly sweep the probe of the analyser around the appliance and its chimney/flue – maintain a distance of approximately 100 mm from the probe tip to the appliance & chimney/flue;
   - On open flue ensure that the sweep test also includes the draught diverter.
   - On room sealed sweep around appliance case seals, particularly any sealing grommets for the combustion chamber that thermocouples, ignition leads, etc., pass through.
   - For both open flue and room sealed, sample near to chimney/flue joints (where joints cannot be accessed, a sweep test will not be appropriate and further detailed examination will be required).
4. Record any measured maximum levels of CO, before turning off the appliance and moving to the next. Before each appliance, ensure the analyser returns to zero.

As well as helping to identify any suspect appliance, a visual examination may also alert you to any obvious visual defects (appliance or surrounding materials showing signs of distress, for example).

15.4.4 Detailed discussion with customer

After conducting the necessary sweep testing, a further detailed discussion with the customer will ascertain any pattern to the occurrence. They can provide invaluable information when carrying out an investigation.

1. Does the problem only happen when the appliance/appliances are in operation.
2. How many times and how long has the problem occurred, is there specific times of the day.
3. What are/were the weather conditions at the time when the problem has or is occurring.
4. Appliance history – has there been any problems; servicing, when was the last time the appliance was serviced; have any of the appliances been subject to the requirements of GIUSP (i.e. warning labels, notices).
5. Does the customer only feel unwell inside the property with the symptoms either going away or less acute when outside the property (what are the symptoms – remember some other illnesses might show similar symptoms as that of exposure to CO).
6. Where inside the property do the symptoms become worse – a particular room or is it in the whole house.
7. Were any house hold or other chemicals used for cleaning at the time of the occurrence (note a mixture of some household cleaning agents can cause a chemical reaction emitting vapours which can be both an irritant and dangerous to health – this can be found from advice on the chemicals label).
8. Who within the household is affected.
9. What is their daily routine - are they out, working from home, housebound, etc.
10. Are there any other fuel burning appliances such as biomass, wood burners, oil and solid fuel.
11. Does the customer take medication for any illness.

This list is not exhaustive, each premises is different and given the situation at the time, other influences may be evident and require further information from the customer. Spending time and effort discussing the problem can save time and effort later.

15.4.5 Initial test to determine levels of CO and CO_2 within dwelling with no appliances in operation

It is recognised that of the two gases CO has a greater toxicity than that of CO_2 and as such BS 7967 procedures lean more to the detection of the CO rather than that of CO_2. This standard, however, does recognise the importance of measuring the CO_2 in atmosphere and using this as an indicator for the presence of combustion products within the dwelling, especially where low concentrations are involved.

The following procedures recognise the importance in the measurement of both gases to ensure a thorough investigation has been carried out and all potential risks have been assessed.

1. It is recommended that only the person carrying out the work is present within the room at the time of the test. Do not smoke before and during the tests, even in adjacent rooms as this can affect the accuracy of any readings. For personal safety reasons it is recommended that a personal CO alarm be worn at all times whilst carrying out any test for ambient CO.

NOTE: Ensure that any personal CO alarm is in good condition, including any model specific operational checks/tests recommended by the manufacturer before use.

2. Turn off or extinguish all fuel burning appliances.
3. Ventilate the room by opening doors and windows direct to outside.
4. Turn on analyser and calibrate to outside air. Outdoor levels of CO_2 are generally between 350 to 450 ppm with normally no or very low levels of CO (this will depend on the location of the dwelling, where it is located near busy roads levels can be higher). Record initial outdoor readings for reference.
5. Position the probe in the centre of the room at approximately 2 m above floor level and at least 1 m from the suspect appliance(s).
6. Check indoor levels until they are the same as outside. Once this has been achieved close all external doors and windows.
7. Record the levels of CO and CO_2 over a 15 minute period.
8. If the readings begin to rise during the test period check for CO, and where appropriate CO_2, migration from other sources either from outside or other rooms within the premises or adjacent properties.

9. Where no rise is recorded within the room move through dwelling checking for any rise in CO and where appropriate CO_2. This will ensure that migration is not affecting other parts of the dwelling.

15.4.6 Testing ambient air with appliances in operation

Once it has been established from the initial test that there has been no ingress into the property each appliance requires to be operated one at a time to establish whether or not that the operation of that appliance is the source of the problem. From the initial inspection of each appliance we can determine which poses the highest risk. Normally we would regard flueless appliances as the highest risk due to their design and operation whereas open flue would be medium risk and ultimately room sealed as low.

It is critical that we make a judgement not only on flueing methods but also with respect to additional factors which may be present at the time of the inspection, such as condition, signs of distress, damage, etc. Additional influences shall also be taken into consideration when testing each appliance such as mechanical ventilation/extract systems, passive stack, the operation of other appliances and weather. One single test may not positively conclude what is the cause of the problem.

Each different appliance requires to be tested in a different manner due to their method of operation. Each test should be carried out in sequence from the highest down to the lowest risk appliance. Once this has been completed it is necessary, where no evidence of the source has been located, that where more than one fuel burning appliance is within the premises, that they are operated in combination until the problem has been identified or resolved.

With the exception of cookers where higher intermittent levels are accepted, if at any time during the test the CO reading exceed 30 ppm, stop the test, turn off all appliances and ventilate the room. At this time leave the room (it is prudent to go outside at this point) and do not re-enter until the CO limits decrease to an acceptable level (less than 10 ppm). When re-entering the premises test from the entry point inwards ensuring CO levels are at a level which will allow safe entry into the premises.

It is important that after any test that we check that the original complaint has been rectified and that ALL appliances have been included. Do not assume that by rectifying the fault on one appliance that the problem has been resolved; we need to ensure that the FULL installation is safe.

Where the source of the problem is an appliance other than a gas appliance, advise the customer to seek expert advice from the likes of OFTEC for oil, HETAS for biomass and solid fuel, local environmental health for suspected landfill gas, etc.

Each different type of appliance has specific test method as shown in the following sections. The result of each test shall be recorded within a report and made available to the responsible person for the dwelling such as owner, landlord or their agent.

15.4.6.1   Testing "Type A" appliances - cookers

1. Check that any permanent ventilation is unobstructed.
2. Place a flat base saucepan with diameter between 160 mm and 220 mm above the two largest burners. Each saucepan should contain approximately 1 litre of water and be covered by a lid.
3. Place the grill pan in its highest position.
4. Open/operate any customer adjustable ventilation such as windows, extractor fans, etc.
5. Light the grill, oven and the two hotplate burners at maximum. Turn down oven to mid-range (gas mark 5).
6. Begin monitoring the atmosphere and record levels at 1 minute intervals.
7. Once the saucepans begin to boil, turn down to simmer rate. Do not allow the saucepans to boil dry.
8. Do not operate the grill in excess of 30 minutes.
9. If during the test levels of CO begin to fall below 30 ppm and stay there, or do not exceed 90 ppm at any time during the test and 30 ppm at any time for a duration no longer than 20 minutes, the cooker has been found satisfactory.

Fig 15.5   Typical readings from a faulty cooker installation

ROOM CO TEST

LOG END   15:40   01 10/08/08

TEST	CO ppm
0	00
1	00
2	00
3	03
4	16
5	20
6	29
7	32
8	35
9	34
10	32
11	34
12	35
13	36
14	38
15	39
16	39
17	41
18	41
19	42
20	42
21	43
22	43
23	43
24	40
25	45
26	24

MAXIMUM CO   45

10. If the CO exceeds 90 ppm at any time, the test shall be suspended, room ventilated with the cause investigated. Once rectified the test shall be repeated.
11. It should be noted that readings may "bounce" during this test due to air movement, be aware of readings which are consistently high or rapidly increasing.

15.4.6.2 Testing "Type A" appliances - Flueless water heaters

1. Check that any permanent ventilation is unobstructed.
2. CLOSE all customer adjustable ventilation such as windows, extractor fans, etc., located within the room in which the appliance is installed.
3. Operate the appliance for a maximum of 5 minutes (advise customer on the maximum duration of operation, check for 5 minute label).
4. Begin monitoring the atmosphere and record levels at 1 minute intervals.

15.4.6.3 Testing "Type A" appliances - flueless space heaters (Including LPG cabinet heaters)

1. Check that any permanent ventilation is unobstructed.
2. CLOSE all customer adjustable ventilation such as windows, extractor fans, etc., located within the room that the appliance is installed.
3. Operate the appliance at maximum for 30 minutes.
4. Begin monitoring the atmosphere and record levels at 1 minute intervals.

15.4.6.4 Testing "Type B" appliances - open flue

1. Operate the appliance at full rate.
2. Test ambient air until the CO readings stabilise or the levels begin to fall, whichever occurs first,
3. Be aware that any increase above outdoor levels may indicate spillage from this appliance. Albeit CO_2 is not specified within BS 7967 it is a good indicator that products of combustion are entering the room. Further tests would confirm any deficiencies such as flue flow or spillage test.
4. There is no time limit on this test however common sense should be used for example consistently high readings or levels of both CO and CO_2 would indicate a problem exists, even after a short period of time has elapsed.

15.4.6.5 Testing "Type C" appliances - room sealed

Room sealed appliances are recognised as the least risk appliances due to the fact that, if the appliance and flue system are installed correctly, the appliance is completely sealed from the internal space.

It should also be recognised that given the flexibility of flue systems available that the jointing methods of these systems may cause concern due to inadequate support or installation methods.

In general terms most modern flueless and open flue appliances now have additional safety devices which recognise either insufficient air quality (ASD's or oxy pilots) or spillage (spillage monitoring devices) whereas room sealed appliances do not. Deterioration of the flue system or incorrect installation may not stop the appliance operating therefore, high levels of CO may be produced and evacuated into the internal space with no effect on the operation of the appliance.

The following tests should be performed.

1. Operate the appliance at full rate.
2. Test ambient air until the CO readings stabilise or the levels begin to fall, whichever occurs first.
3. There is no time limit on this test. However, common sense should be used for example consistently high readings or levels of both CO and CO_2 would indicate a problem exists, even after a short period of time has elapsed.
4. Additional tests shall be done along the length of the flue system where it runs from one room to another.

15.4.7 Appliance examination

If during ambient air tests it is evident that an appliance(s) has been deemed suspect that further investigation into the route of the problem is assessed. This will include.

1. Where the appliance is open flue carry out a flue flow and spillage test as specified by the appliance manufacturer.
2. Check the burner pressure or heat input or where necessary both against manufacturers recommended settings.
3. Check the flame picture, where applicable.
4. Carry out a combustion analysis with reference to the manufacturer's instruction or BS 7967 (see Part 1, Chapter 3).
5. Where a combustion analysis cannot be performed or the combustion performance exceeds manufacturers recommendations the following actions shall be performed:

   - Inspect appliance and replace any damaged parts which may affect combustion.
   - Inspect and clean the burner and pilot injectors, venturies, lint guards, air paths to the combustion chamber and any other items the manufacturer recommends.
   - Inspect and clean heat exchanger, flue hood and flueways.
   - Check any seals and fastenings.
   - Ensure flame picture is satisfactory.

6. Carry out a further combustion analysis (if able to do so) after any remedial works to confirm all problems have been resolved.

15.4.8 CO detector activation

There are generally two types of detector namely:

- Card indicator which has a small spot containing a chemical that reacts to exposure to CO by changing colour normally from a pale light brown to black. There is no audible alarm and as such **they are not recommended for use in sleeping accommodation**.
- Electronic alarms which may be either battery or mains powered. These detectors have both a visual and audible alarm. The manufacturer's instructions are invaluable to interpret the different tones and their meaning.

Fig 15.6 Example of CO card indicator

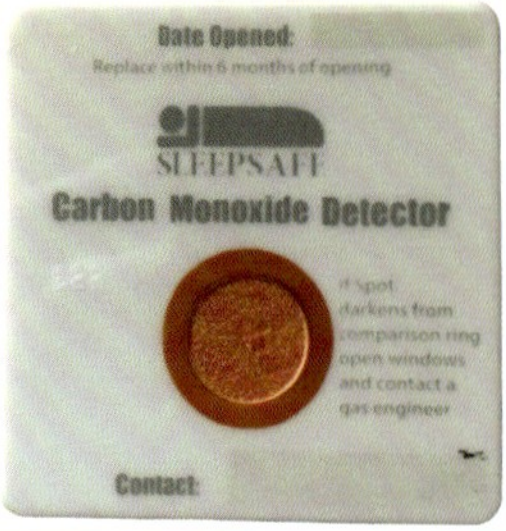

Both types of CO detector are susceptible to activation by house hold chemicals such as aerosol sprays. If it has been proven through ambient testing that CO is not present and all appliances including the installation have been checked for safe operation and found satisfactory, especially if the customer(s) is not experiencing any signs of CO exposure, the detector may be faulty or activated by other products. It is also important to ensure that activation is not a result of migration from other sources.

Further information on types, operation and installation of CO detectors can be found in Part 1, Chapter 3 of this Guide.

The procedure (see flowchart overleaf) is applied where a customer has reported activation of a CO detector.

15.4.9 Reports

A full dwelling and investigation report shall be completed by the gas engineer in all circumstances detailing all tests carried out, including their results. Details on the safety of all appliances and any remedial actions such as outstanding works, recommendation for the installation of CO alarms, servicing of appliances and advice on the safe use of appliances should also be included. A copy of this report should be left with the customer.

Where the customer does not allow an investigation to proceed on suspect appliances, this should also be documented.

If the source of the CO is from a source other than from a gas-fired appliance the customer and, where necessary, other persons who may be potentially affected (for example neighbouring properties especially if they are the suspected origin of the CO) should be made aware of any problems which may exist and advised accordingly to ensure the necessary follow up action is carried out.

Any advice given requires to be documented.

15.4.10 Final completion of investigation and leaving the property

Prior to leaving the premises all gas appliances must be left in a safe condition. Where any defects have been found which affect the safe operation of an installation and/or appliance(s) and where an effective repair cannot be made there and then, the requirements of GIUSP shall be applied.

Where high levels of CO are still within the dwelling and it has been confirmed that it has not been attributed to a gas-fired appliance, contact and advise the relevant authorities (for example the local environmental health) and the property remain evacuated until as such times as that authority has deemed it safe to reenter.

If no faults have been found after a thorough investigation the installation may be turned back on. However, if this has not been the first report and on this and previous occasions no fault has been found, the installation may be re-instated with a recommendation for further investigation and long term monitoring. If the customer feels unwell and no source of CO has been found, the customer should be advised to seek medical attention to establish the cause of their illness and whether or not that it has been as a result of CO exposure.

Customers should also be advised on the safety benefits of CO alarms where there are none fitted and also regular servicing arrangements for their gas appliances.

Procedure for carrying out checks due to a report of CO detector activation

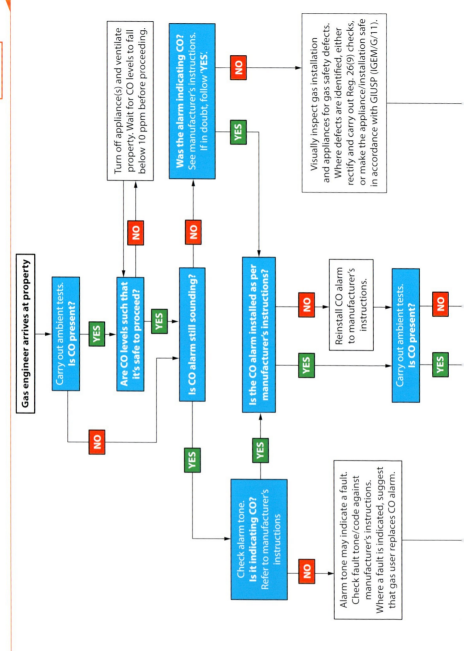

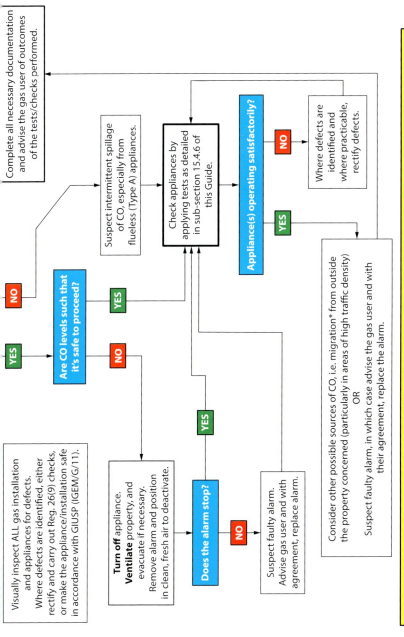

Chap. 15

Chapter 16
Cookers

		Page No.
16.1	Introduction	16.1
16.2	Scope	16.1
16.3	Design Considerations	16.1
16.4	Appliance Selection	16.2
16.5	Installation Requirements - Room Types	16.4
16.6	Location	16.5
16.7	Ventilation	16.8
	16.7.1 Wet rooms	16.9
16.8	Gas Supply	16.11
16.9	Stability Devices	16.15
	16.9.1 Method 1 – stability bracket	16.15
	16.9.2 Method 2 – chain (where no facility has been provided for bracket)	16.16
	16.9.3 Method 3 – leg bracket	16.17
16.10	Electrical Supply	16.17
16.11	Burner Types	16.18
	16.11.1 Hotplate	16.18
	16.11.2 Grill	16.19
	16.11.3 Sola grill	16.20
	16.11.4 Oven	16.20

Chapter 16
Cookers

	Page No.
16.12 Controls	**16.20**
16.12.1 User controls	16.20
16.12.1.1 Isolation valve (self-sealing bayonet)	16.20
16.12.1.2 Gas taps (hotplate and grill)	16.22
16.12.1.3 Liquid expansion thermostat	16.23
16.12.2 Safety controls	16.25
16.12.2.1 Cooker lid safety shut off (valve or SBS mechanism)	16.25
16.12.2.2 Vapour pressure flame supervision devices	16.26
16.12.2.3 Thermoelectric flame supervision devices	16.27
16.12.2.4 Solenoid valve (only on cookers with automatic facilities)	16.28
16.13 Other Features	**16.29**
16.13.1 Ignition	16.29
16.13.1.1 Piezo spark	16.29
16.13.1.2 Single shot (capacitor discharge)	16.30
16.13.1.3 Repetitive spark	16.30
16.13.1.4 Reignition	16.31
16.13.1.5 Automatic Cooking	16.32
16.13.2 Additional features	16.32
16.14 Commissioning	**16.33**
16.15 Maintenance	**16.35**
16.16 Additional information on CO levels for cookers	**16.37**

Chapter 16
Cookers

Page No.

References in this Chapter

[1] BS 6172: 2010 + A1: 2017 Specification for installation, servicing and maintenance of domestic gas cooking appliances (2nd and 3rd family gases).

[2] IGEM/G/5 Edition 2 Gas in multi-occupancy buildings

[3] BS 6173: 2020 Installation and maintenance of gas-fired catering appliances for use in all types of catering establishments (2nd and 3rd family gases) – Specification.

[4] IGEM/UP/11 Edition 3. Gas installations for educational establishments.

[5] BS 669-1: 1998 Flexible hoses, end fittings and sockets for gas burning appliances. Specification for strip-wound metallic flexible hoses, covers, end fittings and sockets for domestic appliances burning 1st, 2nd and 3rd family gases.

[6] BS 669-2: 1997 Flexible hoses, end fittings and sockets for gas burning appliances. Specification for corrugated metallic flexible hoses, covers, end fittings and sockets for catering appliances burning 1st, 2nd and 3rd family gases.

Chapter 16
Cookers

16.1 Introduction

The information in this section has been prepared in relation to domestic, natural gas and LPG flueless cooking appliances (Type A). The installation should be in accordance with BS 6172[1] and the GS(I&U)R. Throughout this section any reference to a "cooker" also means oven, grill, hob or any combination thereof.

16.2 Scope

Work activities will include installation, commissioning, repair and maintenance of new, previously used and second hand domestic cooking appliances. Normally, work will be performed in domestic premises including permanently sited leisure accommodation vehicles (LAV), residential park homes (RPH) and permanently moored boats (B).

BS 6172 also applies to domestic type installations in commercial or industrial premises including educational establishments. There may be additional requirements in these situations with regard to the likes of installation pipework, ventilation, extraction, tightness testing and purging, etc., and as such engineers shall be appropriately qualified for the scope of work that they perform. Examples include staff kitchens, home economics classrooms, small scale catering facilities such as B&B, etc.

BS 6172 does not specify any maximum net heat input limit, most engineers would accept 70 kW as being the domestic limit (reference can be made to BS 5440-2 which gives a maximum rated input for cooking appliances as 70 kW net); the average cooker is usually rated at 16 kW net.

Combined cooking and heating appliances (cooker boilers, e.g. AGA ranges) are not covered by BS 6172, reference should be made to BS 6798.

16.3 Design Considerations

It is essential that kitchen fitters are aware of the clearances specified by a cooking appliance Manufacturer prior to the installation of kitchen units. Often the kitchen is fitted prior to the installation of the cooker, normally before the make and model has been determined. Alterations post kitchen fitting could be expensive and collaboration between customer, architect, local building control and tradesmen should avoid this situation.

Other considerations will include:

- ○ Gas and electrical supply requirements.
- ○ Room type, size and layout.
- ○ Ventilation requirements including windows and/or extraction system.

16.4 Appliance Selection

Types of cooking appliances are shown below:

Fig 16.1 Free standing slot in

Fig 16.2 Free standing eye level grill

Fig 16.3 Range

Fig 16.4 Built in hob

Fig 16.5 Built in oven

New appliances shall be CE marked and supplied with installation, servicing and user instructions. Previously used or "Second hand" appliances may only be installed if they are in a serviceable safe condition, suitable for the gas type being used and have the manufacturer's installation and maintenance instructions supplied.

Where the appliance has been previously used and the manufacturer's instructions are not available they may be obtained by contacting the manufacturer. Where these are not available from the Manufacturer the appliance may be installed in accordance with current standard. For second hand appliances the manufacturer's instructions shall be available otherwise the appliance cannot be installed.

With reference to the above paragraphs a previously used appliance is one which is owned by the customer, but is being relocated either in the same kitchen or moved to another premises when the customer has moved house. A second hand appliance is one which is purchased either used or refurbished and installed for the first time by this particular customer.

The appliance must be suitable for the gas type supplied. If a conversion is required this shall be performed in accordance with the manufacturer's instructions using their approved conversion kit (ad hoc conversion is not permitted).

All appliances must have a readable data plate which provides important information in relation to:

- Gas type:
  - G20 is nat. gas @ 20 mbar.
  - G30 is butane @ 29 mbar.
  - G31 is propane @ 37 mbar.
- Intended country of use (GB).
- Supply pressure.
- The appliance manufacturer, make, model, serial number and colour (this data is essential when ordering spare parts).

Fig 16.6   Example of data badge

16.5 Installation Requirements - Room Types

Cooking appliances are intended for use in kitchens. However, they may be installed in other areas as long as it meets the installation requirements set by the manufacturer, Building Regulations and BS 6172.

Installation in a room or internal space which is, or intended to be used as a bathroom, shower room or bedroom is not permitted.

Unless the appliance is a single burner, installation in bed sitting rooms is only permitted provided the room volume is not less than 20 m^3.

LPG cookers are not permitted in a basement or cellar. Where an LPG cooker is installed at low level in a boat, a gas detector which is interlocked to the gas supply shall be installed.

Installation in any room which is part of a protected passageway is not permitted within flatted property and multi-storey dwellings.

New and unused cookers to be installed in multi-occupancy dwellings **shall have flame supervision devices on all burners (except for cooker oven burners of uncontrolled heat input less than 0.6 kW)** see IGE/G/5[2].

Consideration shall be given with any alteration to a premises as this can have an impact on the safety of the installation.

16.6 Location

Beware of the possible adverse effects of draughts (windows) and doors (room and kitchen units) when deciding on the appliance location.

The manufacturer will give guidance with regard to specific clearance requirements from combustible materials and obstacles. Where no specification is given, observe the clearances given in fig's 16.7 & 16.8.

NOTE: The clearances for a wall mounted grill are the same dimensions as indicated for the grill on the free standing cooker.

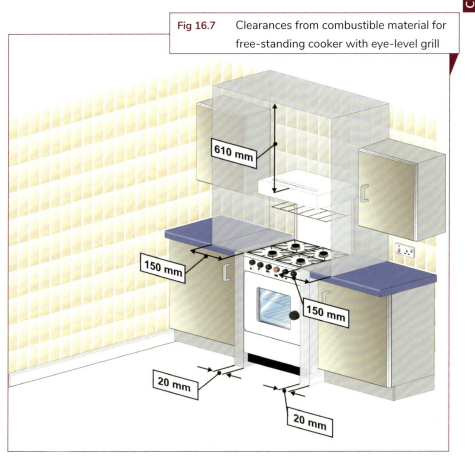

Fig 16.7   Clearances from combustible material for free-standing cooker with eye-level grill

Fig 16.8 Clearances from combustible material for hob

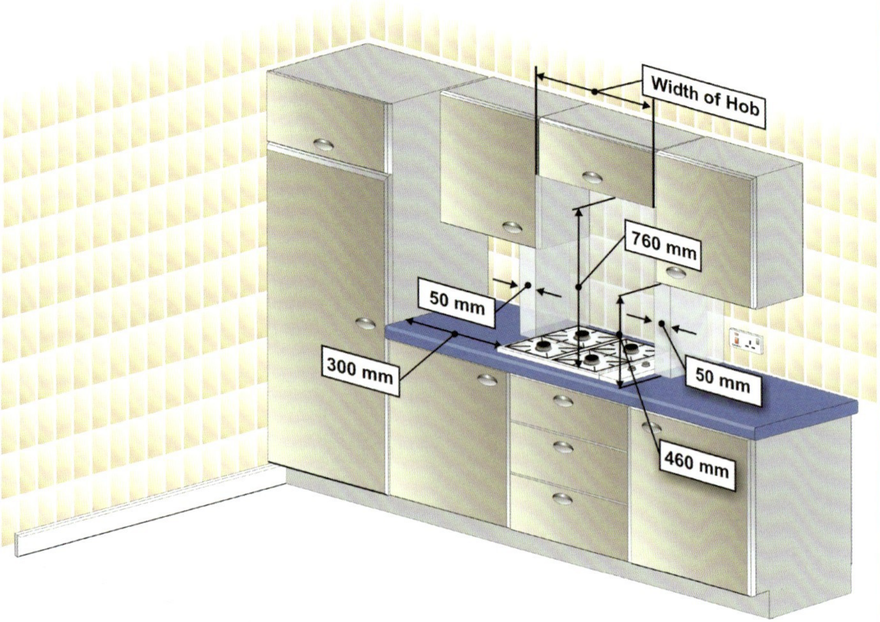

Any floor or base upon which freestanding cookers are sited shall be capable of supporting the weight of the cooker and allow for adjustment of wheels, castors or feet to enable the cooker to be level and stable. This requirement also applies to plinths used to raise the height of the cooker.

Built in and built under cooking appliances shall be installed in accordance with the manufacturer's instructions with particular attention being paid to combustible material, fixing methods and ventilation.

When installing a cooker extract hood, the manufacturer's installation instructions of both the cooker and hood shall be adhered to. Where the installation instructions of both documents indicate different distances for height x, as given in the fig 16.9, the greater of the two dimensions shall be used.

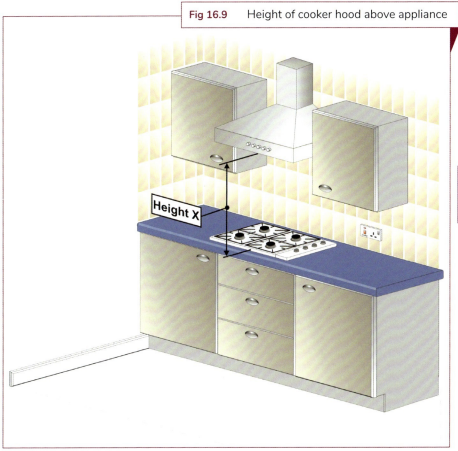

Fig 16.9 Height of cooker hood above appliance

16.7 Ventilation

On face value, providing combustion ventilation via purposes provided vents presents gas engineers little difficulty. Any combustion ventilation shall be direct to outside air and be sized in accordance with the manufacturer's instructions (MIs), or where none is stated or the MIs defer, in accordance with the minimum requirements of BS 5440-2 (see Chapter 4 of this Guide).

Table 16.1 provides the minimum ventilation requirements for gas cooking appliances based on the volume of the kitchen concerned.

Table 16.1 Minimum ventilation requirements for gas cooking appliances

Room Volume	Ventilation Provision (cm^2)	Additional Requirements
Less than 5 m^3	100	Openable window or similar
5 m^3 up to & including 10 m^3	50*	Openable window or similar
Greater than 10 m^3	No ventilation required	Openable window or similar

*Purpose provided ventilation not required if a door opens directly to external air.

Note: Louvres, hinged panels or mechanical extraction systems may be an acceptable alternative to a window

It is worth noting that unlike other forms of flueless appliance, there is no maximum heat input for a given room volume and therefore, no restriction on the size of gas cooking appliance that can be installed (see Note 1) – this does not apply to bed/sitting rooms, which shall have a minimum room volume of 20 m^3 otherwise the appliance shall be a single burner hotplate or boiling ring.

NOTE 1: Caution needs to be exercised when discussing semi-professional/professional cooking appliances that many gas users favour as these larger heat output appliances may require provisions (and possibly competencies) for ventilation and/or extraction in accordance with a commercial catering standard, i.e. BS 6173[3].

NOTE 2: Domestic cooking appliances will also be found in educational establishments (food technology classrooms). These may or may not require ventilation provision in line with typical domestic standards or require more specialist arrangements found in commercial catering environment. This and other specific safety considerations relating to a teaching environment will be found in IGEM/UP/11[4].

As can be seen, room volumes greater than 10 m^3 do not require additional purpose provided ventilation unless otherwise directed by the appliance manufacturer. Room volumes between 5 and 10 m^3 also do not require purposes provided ventilation if a door opens directly to external air. If not, a minimum ventilation provision of 50 cm^2 will be required.

The additional requirements of an 'openable window or similar', address concerns with maintaining a healthy internal environment during cooking activities, as required under Building Regulations. This provision is known as 'purge' ventilation, which is user controlled, and is required in areas classed as 'wet' rooms, i.e. rooms used for domestic activities such as cooking, washing and bathing (kitchens, bath and shower rooms, WCs and Utility rooms).

16.7.1 Wet rooms

The kitchen of a NEW dwelling or refurbishment of an existing dwelling requires extract ventilation to be provided in addition to whole house background ventilation and purge ventilation by windows, doors or similar (a requirement of Building Regulations). The building designer and/or the designer for the refurbishment should determine the ventilation provision based on the air permeability of the structure and as such isn't the direct concern of the gas engineer.

The engineer does need to be mindful of the requirements however, in order to ensure compliance when installing and maintaining gas cooking appliances in **existing** kitchens. Gas engineers are permitted to install and otherwise maintain flueless gas cooking appliances – they are not classed as a 'controlled service' under current Building Regulations* – without kitchen extraction provision being present, although its provision is encouraged for obvious reasons.

Controlled services shall comply fully with Building Regulations and be notified to Building Control prior to installation or, where applicable, under a competent person scheme (CPS) framework. Note that flued cooker boilers are a controlled service and shall be both notified and comply fully with the provisions of Building Regulations.

Extract ventilation can be provided in the form of:

- Natural means of extraction and ventilation – Passive Stack Ventilation system (see Chapter 4; sub-section 4.3.4 of this Guide) combined with background ventilation (trickle vents)' or
- Mechanical means of extraction and ventilation –
  - Intermittent extraction (for example a cooker hood) combined with natural background trickle ventilation.
  - Continuous extraction combined with natural background trickle ventilation – this may be decentralised, i.e. individual extract in each wet room (termed dMEV) or centralised with extraction ducted back to a single unit (MEV).
  - Continuous extraction combined with mechanical ventilation – a balanced system of Mechanical Ventilation with Heat Recovery (MVHR).

It can be argued that the use of a cooker hood/kitchen extractor is favoured by most gas users, particularly for existing dwellings due to ease of installation and the lower costs involved and as such is the focus of the guidance here.

The extraction is intermittent depending on the cooking activity and this can be controlled either manually (gas user turning on and off, as required, via switch or pull cord) or automatically (operation of the kitchen light switch, sensor, etc.). If the kitchen has a window or similar opening that does not open direct to outside air or is an internal kitchen (see Chapter 4, sub-section 4.6.2 of this Guide), the extraction shall also have the provision of a 15 minute overrun.

Background ventilation may be within the kitchen (typically in the head of a window or door frame) or via other habitable rooms, provided that a ventilation path is provided – this normally takes the form of an undercut of the internal doors of 10 mm from floor finishes (20 mm from floor boards if no finish), which provides 7600 mm^2 of equivalent area for a standard 760 mm wide door.

For Great Britain (England & Wales, Scotland and Northern Ireland) the intermittent extract rate should be:

- 30 l/s adjacent to a hob**
- 60 l/s elsewhere.

** Adjacent to a hob can be taken to mean within a cooker hood over the hob or located near the ceiling within 300 mm of the centre line of the space for the hob.

16.8 Gas Supply

Internal pipework shall be in accordance with BS 6891 or IGEM/UP/2, as appropriate. 15 mm copper is normally an adequate size of pipe for gas cookers. Most appliances are provided with an Rc½ connection (½ inch BSP female).

Appliances which are not intended to be removed by the customer for cleaning purposes should be installed by rigid pipework and be provided with an appliance isolation valve (AIV) and a disconnecting union.

Built-in gas hobs and ovens can be installed using rigid pipework or where permitted by the appliance manufacturer, connected using a flexible pipe and self-sealing coupling conforming to BS 669[5] part 1 or BS EN 14800, or pliable corrugated stainless steel tube conforming to BS 7838 or BS EN 15266 (see Chapter 5) – maximum length of pliable CSST not to exceed 500 mm between AIV and appliance.

Freestanding cookers shall be connected by means of a flexible pipe and self-sealing bayonet type connector conforming to BS 669-1 or BS EN 14800.

The flexible connection should not come into contact with hot cooker parts where the surface temperature will exceed 95 °C for flexible connectors conforming to BS 669-1 or BS 7838 (pliable CSST), or 60 °C for flexible connectors conforming to BS EN 14800 or BS EN 15266 (pliable CSST).

If it cannot be verified that the cooker will not cause a temperature rise exceeding these stated values, the connection should be by means of rigid pipework (other flexible connections such as a commercial catering flexible connection conforming to BS 669[6] part 2 may be acceptable provided that the temperature range of that connection is not exceeded). The manufacturer's instructions shall be followed in this regard so as to avoid possible heat related damage to the flexible connection. LPG flexible connections have their specification indicated by a red stripe along the length of the pipe, natural gas flexible connections are not suitable for use with LPG.

The cooker bayonet fitting should face downwards to reduce the entry of airborne dust and fittings should be selected which will allow the appliance to be positioned close to the rear wall, so that the front of the appliance will be in line with kitchen units without compromising the minimum clearances specified by the manufacturer.

Where no guidance is given, the bayonet connector should be positioned at a height of 750 mm above floor level provided this results in easy access for the customer.

Wall brackets are available in either angled or straight, compression or capillary, bottom strapped or side strapped.

The connection of the hose to the appliance shall be sealed in accordance with the manufacturer's instructions – some prohibit the use of jointing compound.

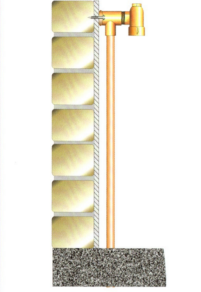

Fig 16.10   **CORRECT** – self-sealing bayonet on supply pipe

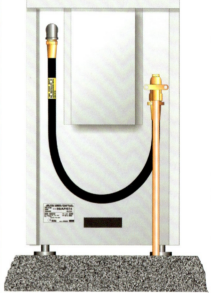

Fig 16.11   **CORRECT** – the hose should form a natural "U" shaped bend

| Fig 16.12 | INCORRECT – avoid sharp bends | Fig 16.13 | INCORRECT – do not allow hose to touch floor |

| Fig 16.14 | INCORRECT – avoid twisting the hose | Fig 16.15 | INCORRECT – self-sealing bayonet on appliance |

Fig 16.16 INCORRECT – appliance connection and bayonet too close

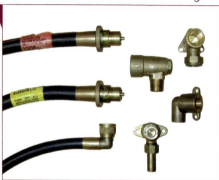

Fig 16.17 Selection of approved flexible connections and wall fittings

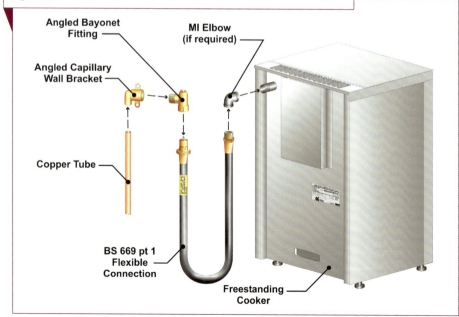

Fig 16.18 Installation detail for cooker and flexible connection

16.9 Stability Devices

Free standing cookers connected by means of a flexible connection shall be secured in order to prevent movement which could result in spillage of saucepan contents from the hotplate, this is in addition to the commissioning engineer ensuring that the cooker is level and stable.

There are two method of securing the cooker in common practice (see fig's 16.19 to 16.23); although some manufacturers have devised their own particular methods, an example being method 3 as illustrated in fig 16.24.

16.9.1   Method 1 – stability bracket

Fig 16.19   Wall mounted stability bracket

Fig 16.20   Floor mounted stability bracket

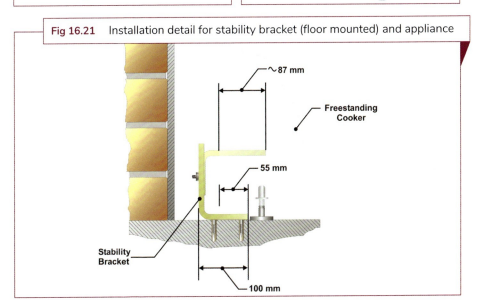

Fig 16.21   Installation detail for stability bracket (floor mounted) and appliance

16.9.2 Method 2 – chain
(where no facility has been provided for bracket)

Fig 16.22   Stability chain kit

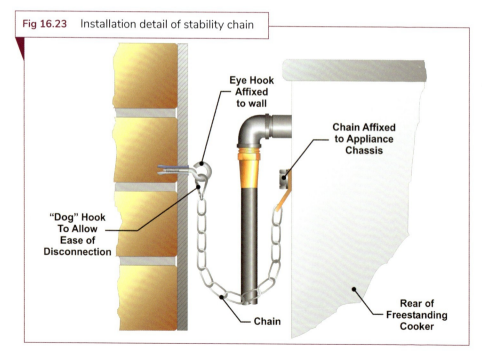

Fig 16.23   Installation detail of stability chain

16.9.3 Method 3 – leg bracket

Fig 16.24   Position of leg bracket

16.10 Electrical Supply

Cooking appliances which require an electrical supply shall be installed in accordance with the BS 7671.

The cable size and fuse rating shall be in accordance with the manufacturer's instructions; cookers are normally protected by a fuse rated at 3 amperes.

The means of isolation may be by:

- A three pin plug and an unswitched socket-outlet (in order to encourage physical disconnection when work is performed).
- A fused, double pole, switched connection unit (spur box).
- Utilising the connection provided for an electric cooker. In this case the fuse or mcb at the consumer unit will need to be down rated.

All electrical equipment will require to be positioned outside the clearance zones detailed earlier in this Chapter. See also Chapter 14; section 14.9.2 for detailed guidance on safe isolation of gas appliances.

16.11 Burner Types

16.11.1 Hotplate

There are normally four circular, pre-aerated, natural draught hotplate burners which may be equally rated, but more often there is one small burner (1 kW), two medium burners (2 kW) and one large burner (3 kW). Some hotplate's are now supplied with five burners, the fifth being a "wok burner" for stir fry applications and is rated in the region of 4 kW.

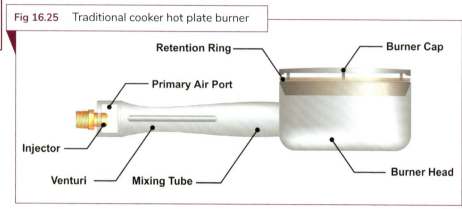

Fig 16.25 Traditional cooker hot plate burner

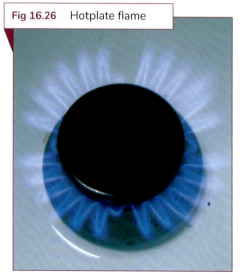

Fig 16.26 Hotplate flame

The primary aeration port is unadjustable. The mixing tube is constructed from stainless steel and the burners are cast iron or aluminium. Older appliances may use a separate flame retention ring which should be kept clean to avoid flame lift. The injector is normally brass with a single orifice and can be screwed directly into the gas tap or located closer to the burner if so designed.

The flame picture (fig 16.26) should be crisp, stable, vibrant and blue in colour with a distinct inner flame cone.

Some manufacturers provide a fitting which replaces a burner injector and then serves as a temporary test point. Alternatively the gas supply test point may be at the end of the gas rail, on the FSD or at the gas connection at the rear of the cooker.

Fig 16.27   Temporary test point

Fig 16.28   Test point fitted to hotplate

16.11.2   Grill

The grill cooks food by radiant heat transfer; the burner causes a fret to become incandescent and heat the food below.

The traditional design is shown in fig 16.29. Where the burner is located centrally between two frets it is important that the cross-lighting plate is kept clean otherwise the gas will ignite only on one side.

Fig 16.29   Flame on grill fret

16.11.3 Sola grill

The sola grill was developed to produce a uniform intensity of radiant heat. The burner and the fret are one item (layers of fine mesh). The flame forms as a blanket and as the mesh heats the flame becomes more stable.

Fig 16.30   Sola grill burner

16.11.4 Oven

The oven burner is located centrally at the bottom rear of the oven. Different Manufacturers' have designed their burners to burn with more or less primary air than others, but a yellow flame does not necessarily mean incomplete combustion.

The oven door seal is normally constructed from neoprene and often there is no seal at the base of the oven door.

16.12 Controls

The controls found on gas cookers can be placed into one of two categories; user controls or safety controls.

16.12.1 User controls
16.12.1.1 Isolation valve (self-sealing bayonet)

A self-sealing valve (bayonet plug in socket) is the arrangement most often encountered (fig 16.31). The "micropoint" gas pipework system also uses this type of valve at each wall socket.

When rigid pipe connection is employed (range or hob) a taper plug valve is the preferred choice (fig 16.32) but a ball valve (fig 16.33) is equally suitable. The provision of a test point will prove useful.

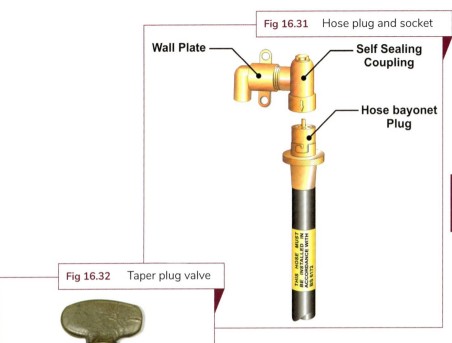

Fig 16.31 Hose plug and socket

Fig 16.32 Taper plug valve

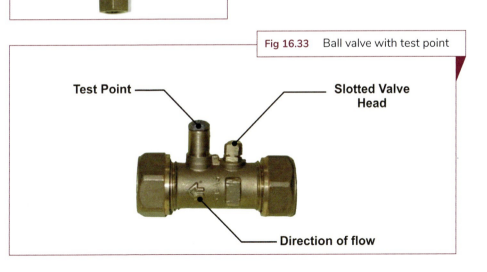

Fig 16.33 Ball valve with test point

16.12.1.2 Gas taps (hotplate and grill)

The gas tap is the control provided for the hotplate and grill burners. This control allows the customer to manually adjust the gas rate to the burners to suit their particular requirements.

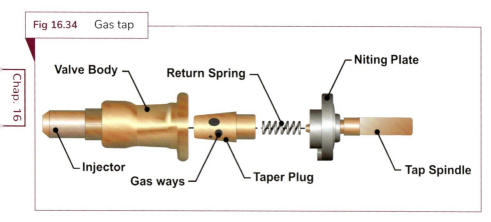

Fig 16.34   Gas tap

Taps may incorporate a thermoelectric FSD as shown in fig 16.35.

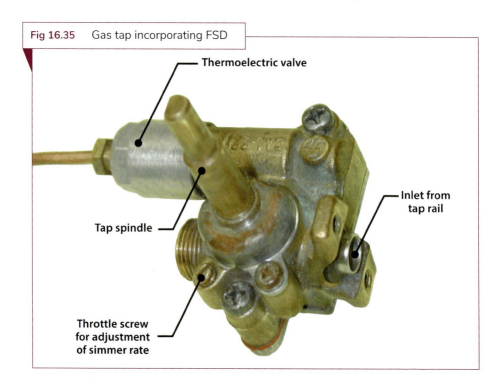

Fig 16.35   Gas tap incorporating FSD

A combined grill tap and oven thermostat may be encountered which includes thermoelectric FSDs (fig 16.36).

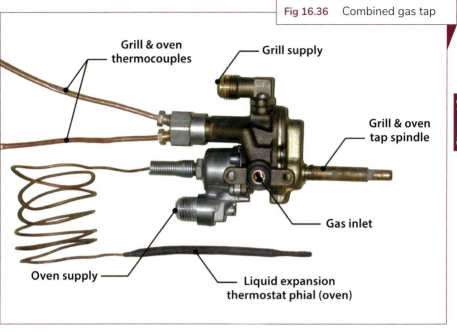

Fig 16.36   Combined gas tap

16.12.1.3 Liquid expansion thermostat

This valve is most commonly found as part of the thermo tap assembly on gas cooker ovens (fig's 16.37 & 16.38). The regulo or thermo tap is actually two devices in one assembly; a gas tap and a thermostat.

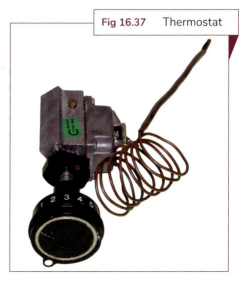

Fig 16.37   Thermostat

Fig 16.38 Thermostat bare

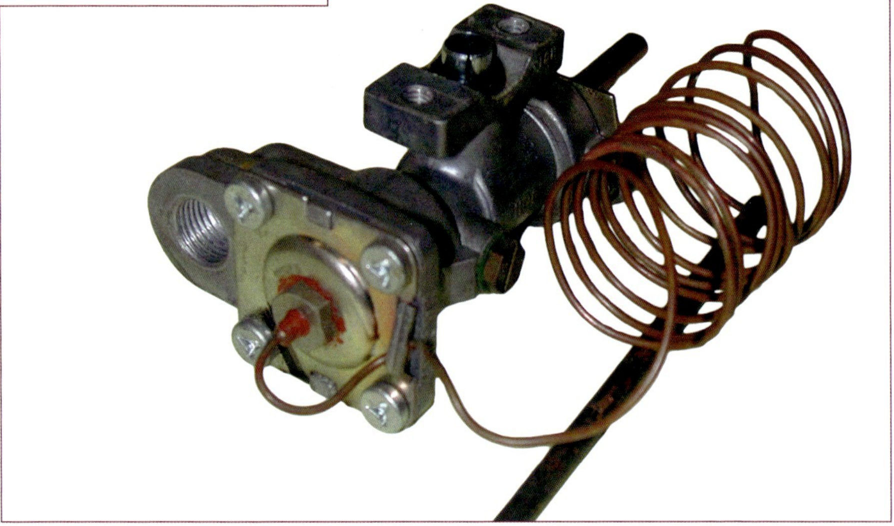

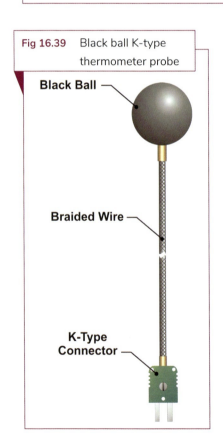

Fig 16.39 Black ball K-type thermometer probe

- Black Ball
- Braided Wire
- K-Type Connector

The calibration of the thermostat can be checked if the customer complains of the oven being to hot or to cold by measuring the temperature control at specific gas mark settings. The preferred sensor is the "black ball" type used in conjunction with a digital thermometer (fig 16.39); the ball should be placed in the centre of the oven.

Although calibration of the thermostat can be performed on site it is normal practice to exchange the complete fitting due to cost restrictions.

Table 16.2 Average oven temperatures

Gas Mark	Averaged Temperature (± 10°)	
	°C	°F
¼	105	221
½	120	248
1	135	275
2	150	302
3	165	329
4	175	347
5	190	374
6	205	401
7	220	428
8	230	446
9	245	473

To convert degrees Celsius to degrees Fahrenheit – °F = (°C × 1.8) + 32

16.12.2 Safety controls

16.12.2.1 Cooker lid safety shut off (valve or SBS mechanism)

This mechanism (fig's 16.40 & 16.41) is unique to gas cookers with drop down lids.

There are many different valve designs including systems which utilises a drive mechanism instead of a valve – referred to by the manufacturer as "Switch Back System (SBS)" – but the common feature is that if the lid is dropped without the hotplate burners being turned off this valve will extinguish the burners.

Some valves once activated will reset the burner controls whilst others may require to be manually reset.

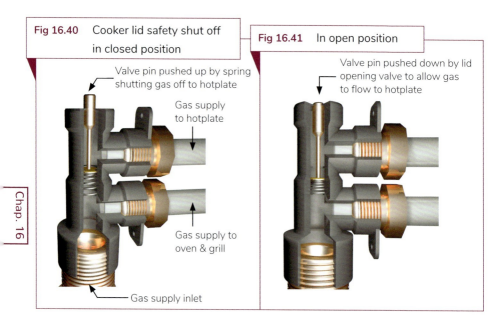

Fig 16.40 Cooker lid safety shut off in closed position

Fig 16.41 In open position

16.12.2.2 Vapour pressure flame supervision devices

Natural gas cooker ovens tend to be fitted with vapour pressure FSDs (fig's 16.42 to 16.44) whereas LPG cookers use the thermoelectric type. With the moves by manufacturers' to provide flame protection to all burners, thermoelectric is now commonplace on natural gas hotplates and grills (see sub-section 16.12.2.3 in this Chapter and Chapter 10 for more in depth details of operation).

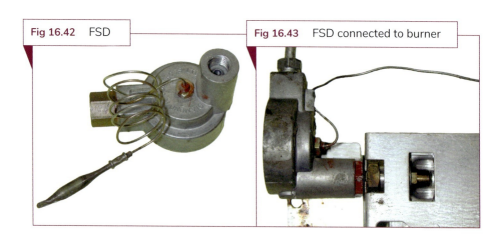

Fig 16.42 FSD

Fig 16.43 FSD connected to burner

Fig 16.44 Phial

The appliance test point may be connected to the FSD as shown in fig 16.45 or the oven burner injector may be used as a test point instead.

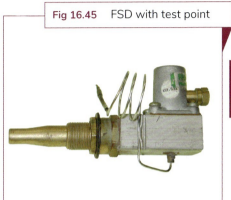

Fig 16.45 FSD with test point

16.12.2.3 Thermoelectric flame supervision devices

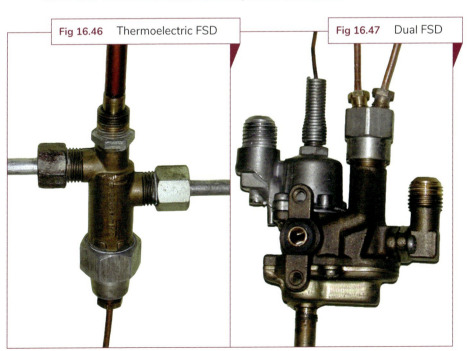

Fig 16.46 Thermoelectric FSD

Fig 16.47 Dual FSD

Fig 16.48 FSD gas tap

16.12.2.4 Solenoid valve (only on cookers with automatic facilities)

Where automatic cooking is provided, there will be a miniature solenoid valve as an integral part of the FSD. Other components of this system will be a digital timer, a microswitch mounted on the tap spindle of the oven regulo and an automatic reignition system.

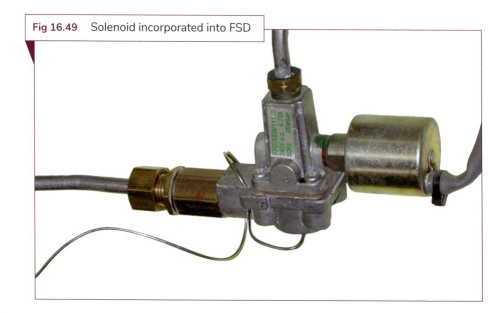

Fig 16.49 Solenoid incorporated into FSD

16.13 Other Features

There are many options available with cookers, ultimately it is up to the customer which they select.

16.13.1 Ignition

All but the most basic of cookers will be provided with an ignition system. Spark ignition is the most reliable and may be battery or mains powered. There are different types available.

16.13.1.1 Piezo spark

Certain crystals when subjected to pressure will generate a potential difference (p.d.). These crystals are contained in a unit along with a spring loaded piston which is operated by the customer to produce a single spark each time the mechanism is operated. A high tension (HT) lead is taken from the unit to the electrode where the electricity is conducted through the air in the form of a spark. This is known as the spark gap and is generally in the order of 3 to 4 mm. The electrode is insulated from the earthed burner by a ceramic sleeve. The spark is of a sufficiently high temperature to ignite the gas. The voltage of the p.d. is around 5,000 volts but the current is very low, it may cause pain but will not be fatal.

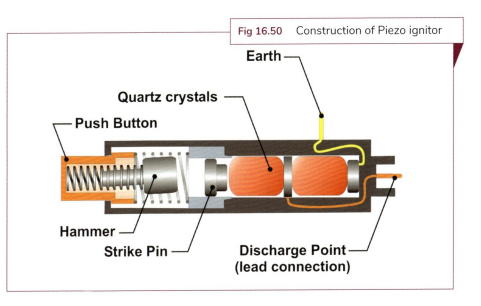

Fig 16.50 Construction of Piezo ignitor

16.13.1.2 Single shot (capacitor discharge)

This system uses electronic devices (PCB) to produce a single spark at each electrode connected to the system and can be battery or mains powered. When the ignition switch is pressed in, it charges the electronic circuitry. When the switch is released the circuitry discharges as a single spark at each electrode.

16.13.1.3 Repetitive spark

This system uses electronic devices (PCB) to produce a pulsed spark and can be battery or mains powered. It produces sparks (approximately three per second) at each electrode connected to the system as long as the ignition switch is depressed. It does not matter which electrode is connected to which outlet on the ignition unit.

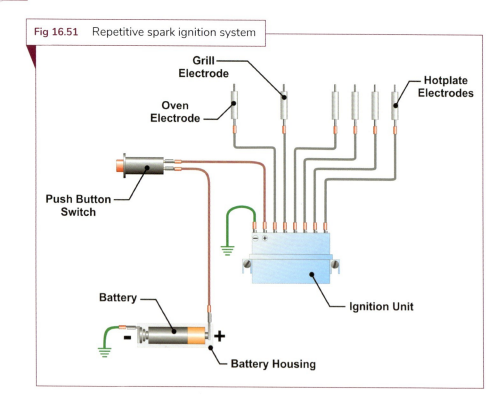

Fig 16.51 Repetitive spark ignition system

16.13.1.4 Reignition

Reignition is so called because if the flame goes out, the system will start sparking again in an attempt to reignite the flame. It is not a flame safety device. It is often found on cooker ovens and is usually incorporated into the same ignition unit that serves the hotplate and grill with repetitive sparks.

The switch which energises the oven spark reignition system is usually mounted on the regulo spindle and is turned on as soon as the customer operates the control knob and remains on as long as the oven is turned on. As soon as the switch is made, the sparking will commence at the oven electrode (and the hotplate and grill). When the oven burner lights, the flame will envelope the spark gap, the ignition unit senses this and the sparking is suppressed. The supply voltage and the oven electrode shall be connected to the correct terminals on the ignition unit otherwise the system will not operate correctly.

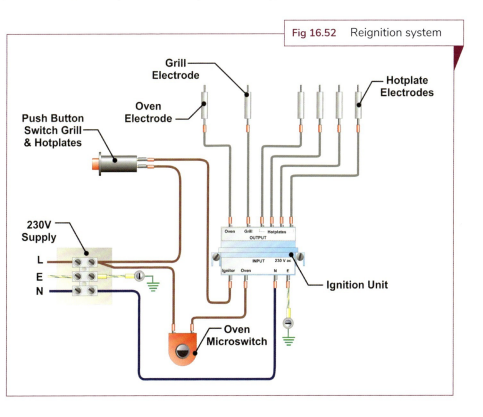

Fig 16.52   Reignition system

16.13.1.5 Automatic Cooking

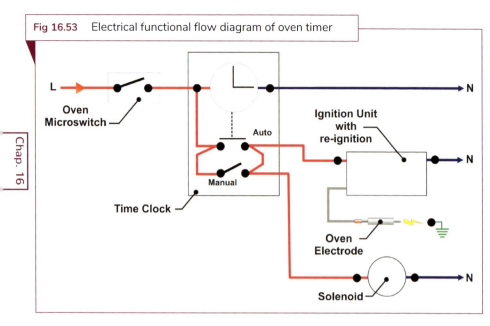

Fig 16.53   Electrical functional flow diagram of oven timer

16.13.2 Additional features

- Oven and fascia lights – usually fluorescent tubes or the fascia and high temperature filament MES bulbs in the oven.
- Rotisserie – electrically powered motor for grilling kebab style.
- Griddle plate – solid plate with burner underneath.
- Rotating hotplate burner – small burner shaped like a cam with the burner ports at the end. A synchronous motor causes the burner to rotate. Useful for gentle simmering of sauces and the like.
- Thermostatically controlled hotplate burner – liquid expansion sensor located in the centre of a hotplate burner. When selected temperature is reached the burner goes to by-pass rate. Useful when heating milk, etc.

16.14 Commissioning

In all cases the manufacturer's commissioning procedure shall be complied with.

A generic procedure is detailed below:

Commissioning procedure for cookers
1. Check site (BS 6172) –
    1.1 Suitability of location.
    1.2 Clearances from obstacles.
    1.3 Proximity to combustibles.
    1.4 Suitability of room (size, type and openable window required - see also BS 5440-2).
    1.5 Ventilation requirements (direct to outside – BS 5440-2).
    1.6 Assembly and fixing (level and stable).
    1.7 Packaging removal.
    1.8 Stability bracket or chain.
    1.9 Adequate supplies:
        1.9.1 gas,
        1.9.2 electricity.
2. Test for tightness –
    2.1 Gas installation.
3. Purge supply –
    3.1 Gas.
4. Test operation and performance –
    4.1 Control devices:
        4.1.1 isolation valve or bayonet/flexible connection,
        4.1.2 gas taps (high and simmer),
        4.1.3 ignition systems,
        4.1.4 oven ON/OFF and thermostat (regulo or thermo tap) including door seal,
        4.1.5 operation of automatic cooking facility (if fitted).
    4.2 Safety Devices:
        4.2.1 flame supervision devices (vapour pressure or thermoelectric),
        4.2.2 gas escapes,
        4.2.3 test for correct operation of lid cut-off device (SBS or valve).
    4.3 Set burner pressure and/or check heat input (test point or injector).

4.4 Check flame pictures –
   4.4.1 hotplate/grill/oven:
   - stability (throughout turndown range)
   - colour.
4.5 Where required by the manufacturer's instruction carry out a combustion performance analysis (see sub-clause 16.16 in this Chapter)
4.6 Check the safe operation of appliance is not affected by extract fans or re-circulatory fans.

5. Electrical checks (BS 7671) –
   5.1 Check for correct cable (condition and fuse size).
   5.2 Check for correct earth and polarity.
   5.3 Check for correct provision of isolation of supply.

6. Instruct customer –
   6.1 Correct usage (leave all manufacturer's instructions with customer).
   6.2 Maintenance requirements (owner of appliance advised in writing).
   6.3 Advise user on the benefits and limitations of a CO detector. Indicate that it is not a substitute for proper installation and maintenance of the appliance.
   6.4 Gas emergency procedure.

16.15 Maintenance

In all cases the manufacturer's maintenance and servicing procedures shall be complied with.

A generic procedure is detailed below:

Servicing procedure for cookers
1. Initial investigation –
    1.1 Ask customer about the operation of appliance.
    1.2 Test operation and visually inspect for obvious defects.
    1.3 Suitability of location (BS 6172).
    1.4 Clearances from obstacles.
    1.5 Proximity to combustibles.
    1.6 Ventilation requirements.
    1.7 Assembly and fixing (door seal, stability, level, etc.).
    1.8 Adequate supplies:
        1.8.1 gas,
        1.8.3 electricity.
2. Test for tightness –
    2.1 Gas installation.
3. Dismantle and clean –
    3.1 Remove panels.
    3.2 Remove burners/retention rings/injectors and clean/inspect.
    3.3 Clean oven flueway.
    3.4 Strip, clean and grease taps.
    3.5 Inspect/clean/check spark electrodes (gap, ceramic, corrosion).
    3.6 Reassemble.
4. Test operation and performance –
    4.1 Control devices:
        4.1.1 isolation valve or bayonet/flexible connection,
        4.1.2 gas taps (high and simmer),
        4.1.3 ignition systems,
        4.1.4 oven ON/OFF and thermostat (regulo or thermo tap) including door seal,
        4.1.5 operation of automatic cooking facility (if fitted).

4.2 Safety devices:
   4.2.1 flame supervision devices (vapour pressure or thermoelectric),
   4.2.2 gas escapes,
   4.2.3 test for correct operation of lid cut-off device (SBS or valve).
4.3 Set burner pressure and/or check heat input.
4.4 Check flame pictures:
   4.4.1 hotplate/grill/oven:
      ❏ stability (throughout turndown range),
      ❏ colour.
4.5 Where required by the manufacturer's instruction carry out a combustion performance analysis (see sub-clause 16.16 in this Chapter).

5. Electrical checks (BS 7671) –
   Inspect and test as follows:
   5.1 Check for correct cable (condition and fuse size).
   5.2 Check for correct earth and polarity.
   5.3 Check for correct provision of isolation of supply.

6. Advise customer and landlord –
   6.1 Correct usage.
   6.2 Maintenance requirements (in writing).
   6.3 Gas emergency procedure.
   6.4 Advise user on the benefits and limitations of a CO detector. Indicate that it is not a substitute for proper installation and maintenance of the appliance.
   6.5 Advise on any necessary repairs or operational issues.

16.16 Additional information on CO levels for cookers

The following text is provided for information purposes on the initial operation of gas cookers when measuring the combustion process using a suitable electronic combustion gas analyser; this supplements the information contained in Part 1, Chapter 3, sub-section 3.9 of this Guide.

Gas engineers are reminded that investigating a report of fumes, which is both more in depth and includes the extensive sampling of the internal atmosphere, requires specific knowledge and skills, and these are demonstrated by holding CMDDA1 accreditation. For detailed guidance on sampling of the internal atmosphere for both Carbon Monoxide (CO) and Carbon Dioxide (CO_2), refer to Part 2, Chapter 15 of this Guide.

Gas cookers during normal operation should not generate CO levels in excess of 10 ppm. However, burner assemblies (particularly those of grills) can become contaminated with food particles and fats, which on initial ignition can generate CO levels in excess of 10 ppm for **short periods of time**. Concentrations in excess of 10 ppm may be allowed provided that the cooker conforms to the guidance of BS 7967 (see Chapter 15) and the cooker is installed in accordance with the manufacturer's instructions and BS 6172.

Note that should CO concentrations exceed **90 ppm AT ANY TIME**, turn off the cooker and leave the area – open doors/windows as you leave. **DO NOT** re-enter the area or allow others to, until CO levels fall to below 10 ppm.

Use engineering judgement when reading an analyser. If levels rapidly increase above 10 ppm toward the 90 ppm threshold, do not wait for confirmation of the fact; suspend the test immediately, turn off the cooker and ventilate the area. Once outside, purge the analyser's sensors in fresh air before turning off (this can take a number of minutes depending on how 'flooded' the analyser is).

The cause of the elevated CO readings shall be investigated and where appropriate, rectified and the cooker re-tested to confirm CO levels remain below 10 ppm.

Where, for any reason, rectification work cannot be undertaken implement the Gas Industry Unsafe Situations Procedure (IGEM/G/11) and with the gas users permission, disconnect the cooker and seal with an appropriate fitting (self-sealing bayonet fittings shall be removed and the gas point sealed with a cap or plug, as necessary).

Chapter 17
Ducted Air Heaters

		Page No.
17.1	Introduction	17.1
17.2	Scope	17.1
17.3	Design Considerations	17.2
17.4	Appliance Selection	17.2
	17.4.1 Condensing appliances	17.7
	17.4.1.1 Specific installation requirements for condensing appliances	17.9
17.5	Installation Requirements – Room Types	17.10
17.6	Location	17.10
	17.6.1 Slot fix	17.10
	17.6.2 Compartment installations	17.11
	17.6.3 Airing cupboards	17.12
	17.6.4 Under-stairs cupboards	17.12
	17.6.5 Roof space installations	17.12
	17.6.6 Multi-occupancy dwellings	17.13
	17.6.7 Timber and steel frame properties	17.14
	17.6.8 Location of room thermostats or thermistorstats	17.15
17.7	Flueing	17.15
	17.7.1 Type B	17.15
	17.7.2 Type C	17.15
17.8	Ventilation	17.16
17.9	Gas Supply	17.18

Chapter 17
Ducted Air Heaters

	Page No.
17.10 Electrical Supply	17.19
17.11 Warm Air Distribution	17.19
17.11.1 Diffusers and registers	17.21
17.11.2 Return air	17.21
17.11.3 Duct systems	17.22
17.11.4 Plenum	17.22
17.12 Controls Systems	17.23
17.12.1 Room stat	17.23
17.12.2 Transformer	17.25
17.12.3 Fan stat	17.25
17.12.4 Limit stat	17.26
17.12.5 General controls	17.26
17.13 Commissioning	17.28
17.13.1 Commissioning procedure for ducted warm air units	17.28
17.14 Maintenance	17.30
17.14.1 Servicing procedure for conventional open flued warm air units	17.30
17.15 Heat Exchanger Safety Checks	17.32
17.15.1 Visual inspection of the heat exchanger	17.32
17.15.2 Checking the heat exchanger using a smoke pellet	17.34
17.15.3 Checking the heat exchanger using an indoor air quality analyser	17.35

Chapter 17
Ducted Air Heaters

Page No.

References in this Chapter

[1] BS 5864: 2019 Installation and maintenance of gas-fired ducted air heaters of rated heat input not exceeding 70 kW net (2nd and 3rd family gases). Specification.

[2] IGE/UP/7 Edition 2 +A: 2008 Gas installations in timber framed and light steel framed buildings.

Chapter 17
Ducted Air Heaters

17.1 Introduction

This section has been prepared in relation to domestic, natural gas and LPG gas-fired ducted air heating appliances with flue types B and C. They include combined air heaters with an integral hot water circulator and heaters which circulate air by either forced or natural convection.

The installation shall be in accordance with BS 5864[1] and the GS(I&U)R. Further additional information on gas installations within timber and light steel framed buildings is given in IGE/UP/7[2] and for multi-occupancy dwellings, IGEM/G/5. Throughout this section, gas-fired, ducted air heater(s) will be referred to as "warm air unit(s)".

17.2 Scope

Work activities will include installation, commissioning, repair and maintenance of both new and previously used appliances. Normally, work will be performed in domestic premises including permanently sited leisure accommodation vehicles (LAV), residential park homes (RPH) and permanently moored boats (B). It does not include air heaters in towed or motorised leisure accommodation vehicles.

BS 5864 also applies to domestic type installations in commercial premises. There may be additional requirements in these situations with regard to the likes of installation pipework, ventilation, flueing, tightness testing and purging, etc., and as such engineers shall be appropriately qualified for the scope of work that they perform.

BS 5864 specifies a maximum net heat input limit of 70 kW net as being the domestic limit.

17.3 Design Considerations

The type of property will have an effect on the selection and design of the warm air heating system. The rated output of the appliance shall be adequate for the heat requirements of the building, including any duct heat losses.

Considerations will include;

- Number of storeys in the building including structure, size and location.
- Gas, water and electrical supply requirements.
- Room type.
- Ventilation and chimney requirements.
- Installation of ductwork size, route and termination.
- Condensate removal from condensing appliances.

The British System Design Manual for gas-fired warm air heating is highly recommended if readers are involved in the design of warm air heating systems.

17.4 Appliance Selection

Any appliance which is to be installed must have a readable data plate and the relevant manufacturer's installation and maintenance instructions. Where the manufacturer's instructions are not available, they should be acquired from either the appliance manufacturer or their agent prior to installation. It is imperative that the appliance is proved suitable for the gas pressure and type supplied. Where there is any doubt the appliance shall not be installed. If a conversion is required this shall be performed in accordance with the manufacturer's instruction using an approved conversion kit; ad hoc conversion is not permitted.

Previously used heaters, with or without a CE mark, may be installed although industry advises against it. The installer shall ensure that these types of appliances are in a safe and serviceable condition.

New appliances must meet the requirements of the Gas Appliance (Safety) Regulations and carry a CE mark.

The data plates provides important information in relation to:

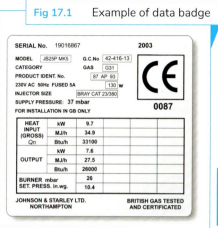

Fig 17.1   Example of data badge

- Gas type and inlet pressure –
  - G20 is nat. gas @ 20 mbar.
  - G30 is butane @ 29 mbar.
  - G31 is propane @ 37 mbar.
- Intended country of use (GB).
- Operating (burner) pressure.

The appliance serial number (along with the make, model and colour) is essential if any spare parts have to be ordered.

Forced convection air heating appliances are normally categorised by the direction of air flow through the appliance. Most domestic heaters are of the "down-flow" type, i.e. the fan which generates the air flow is located at the top of the appliance pushing the air down, over the heat exchanger and into the plenum (distribution box).

Figures 17.2 to 17.4 overleaf show some common configurations. It is also commonplace to have an integral, storage circulator fitted within the unit (fig 17.5).

Fig 17.2 Down flow heater

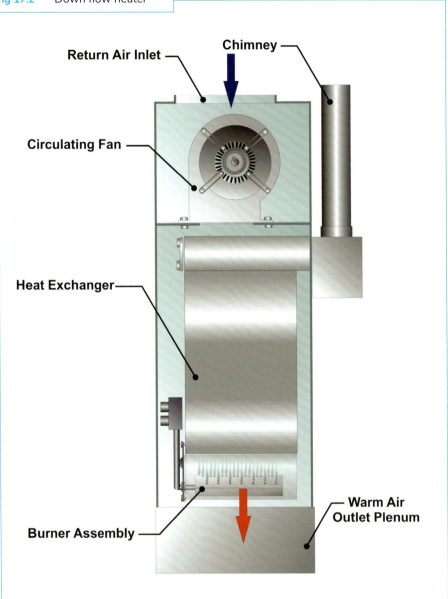

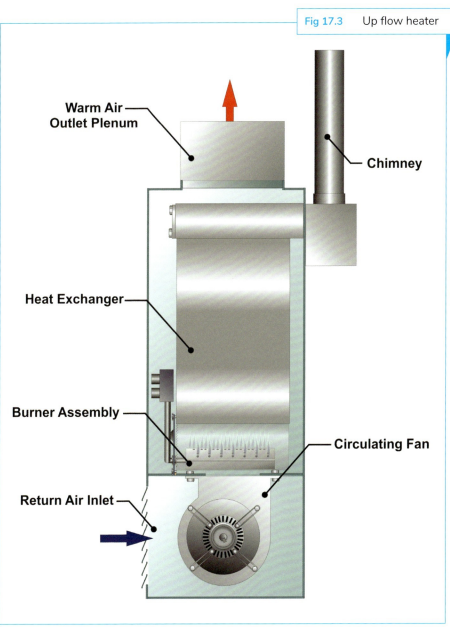

Fig 17.3 Up flow heater

Fig 17.4 Horizontal flow heater

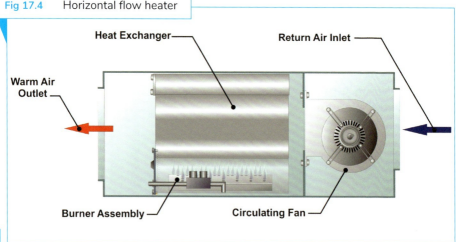

Fig 17.5 Heater with integral circulator

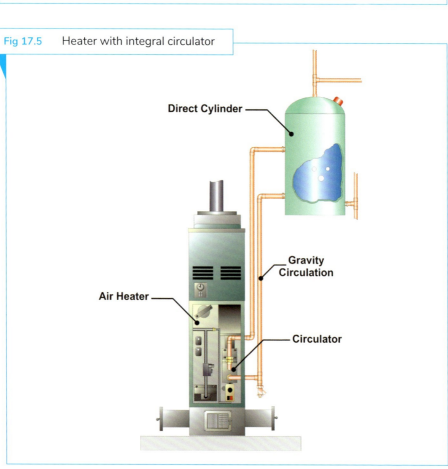

17.4.1 Condensing appliances

With the requirements for greater fuel efficiency, gas-fired air heaters are now moving in the same direction as hot water boilers with high efficiency condensing models being developed. To achieve this high efficiency manufacturers have developed a number of heat exchanger and burner designs which offer a more effective means of heat transfer to the circulation air.

Figure 17.6 illustrates an example of one manufacturers design.

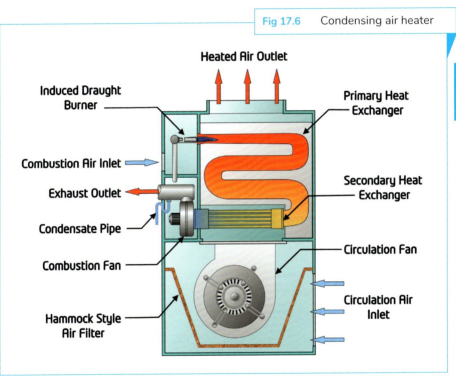

Fig 17.6 Condensing air heater

The secondary heat exchanger in this example is a multipass unit which, due to its design, offers a large surface area in which to distribute the heat in to the circulation air, preheating it before passing it over the primary heat exchanger. This high heat loss effectively reduces the temperature of the flue gases below the dew point allowing the water vapour to condense.

The primary heat exchanger on the other hand is designed to slow the combustion gases down by diverting them along a number of "passes" before entering the secondary unit. An additional flat plate is attached to heat exchanger not only for rigidity but also to further increasing the effective surface area of the heat exchanger allowing a greater distribution of heat into the circulation air. The air heater contains a number of these heat exchangers laid side by side along the unit's width.

Due to the highly restrictive heat exchanger and the mode of operation of air heaters, it is preferable for safety reasons to have a burner which works on the induced draught principle.

With central heating boilers an air/gas ratio valve is used in conjunction with a combustion fan to ensure the correct air/gas mixture is present at the burner. Since the fan is located upstream of the heat exchanger, the combustion chamber is normally above atmospheric pressure. This pressure pushes the combustion products through the heat exchanger into the flue and finally to the termination point.

With an induced draught system a fan is located downstream of the heat exchanger at the flue outlet. The fan is used to suck the products of combustion through the heat exchanger. The negative pressure generated pulls combustion air into the appliance then through to the burner. The pressure within the burner/combustion chamber is monitored by a pressure switch. If the fan were to fail or the heat exchangers became blocked the negative pressure would decrease resulting in burner shut down.

An additional safety benefit of the induced draught system is the negative pressure within the heat exchangers. If the heat exchangers were to fail this system reduces the risk of combustion gases passing into the circulation air and also, depending on the level of failure, the pressure generated by the circulation fan entering the flue gas route would result in burner shut down.

17.4.1.1 Specific installation requirements for condensing appliances

Any heaters, including their water heating facility, which operate in a condensing mode shall be installed as per the manufacturer's instruction or, where there is no specific information, to BS 5864. Chimney/flue installation, condensate disposal, setting up combustion (air/gas ratio control adjustment), etc., shall be done in strict accordance with the manufacturer (see appropriate Chapters within this Guide with regards to chimney/flues, controls and checking and setting regulators).

The chimney outlet shall be positioned such that the plume does not cause a nuisance either to the user or neighbouring properties. Where this may be a problem the manufacturer will provide additional information including any adaptation which may be available for the chimney outlet to redirect the plume.

This can be achieved by, for example:

- Rotation of the chimney outlet.
- Installation of a deflector elbow.
- Use of a plume kit for high level termination of the exhaust outlet.

The termination point shall allow free dispersal of any plume. It shall not be located within carports or where any flue gases will be directed towards openings, doorways or windows or close to adjacent structures such as walls, boundary fences and buildings.

The condensate pipe shall be constructed of a material which is resistant to the slightly acidic condensate such as PVC, PVC-U, ABS, etc. The condensate pipe shall be sized and installed in accordance with the manufacturer's instruction. See Chapter 14; sub-section 14.4.5.1 for more detailed information on the installation and termination of condensate drainage pipe.

17.5 Installation Requirements – Room Types

Open flue heaters must not be installed in a room or internal space which contains or is intended to contain a bath or shower. If the open flue heater has a heat input greater than 12.7 kW net (14 kW gross) they must not be installed in a room used or intended to be used as sleeping accommodation.

Where the heat input is less than 12.7 kW net and the heater is to be installed within a room used or intended to be used as sleeping accommodation it must have a device which is designed to shut down the appliance before there is a dangerous build up of products of combustion in the room space. Where it is not known if the heater has such a device it must not be installed.

Heaters burning 3rd family gases, which have automatic ignition or a permanent pilot must not be installed in any room or internal space below ground level.

Room sealed heaters may be installed in bathrooms, shower rooms, bedrooms or bed sitting rooms only if no other viable alternative exists. The manufacturer's instructions shall be observed as to the suitability of the heater for these locations. Air Heaters may be installed in private garages unless specified otherwise by the manufacturer.

17.6 Location

The manufacturer will give guidance with regard to clearance requirements from combustible materials and obstacles. There shall be enough space to allow easy access for installation, maintenance and repair. Where no specific information is given by the manufacturer, a minimum clearance of 75 mm should be maintained between the heater casing and any combustible materials.

17.6.1 Slot fix

Only units designed for this type of installation should be installed in this way otherwise the operation of the draught diverter will be compromised.

17.6.2 Compartment installations

It is probably true to say that warm air units are more likely than any other appliance type to be encountered within compartments. If the warm air unit is open flued there are two distinct aspects that readers should be aware of:

a). The return air connection of the warm air unit shall be ducted to a point outside the compartment, otherwise spillage of products of combustion may occur.

b). Access to the draught diverter is often compromised by inadequate clearances being provided around the unit. Some manufacturers may give additional guidance regarding spillage testing in this eventuality.

See Chapter 14 for general specifications for compartments housing gas appliances. Beware of the possible adverse affects of draughts from windows or doors on an open flue appliance.

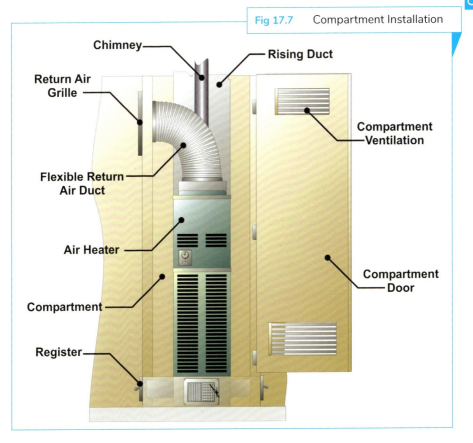

Fig 17.7   Compartment Installation

17.6.3 Airing cupboards

Where an air heater is installed within an airing cupboard the airing space and heater require to be separated by a fire-resistant partition. Where the partition is constructed of perforated materials any major dimension of the apertures shall not be greater than 13 mm.

If the flue passes through the airing space it shall have a suitable guard to prevent any clothing being aired touching the hot flue surface. A minimum clearance of 25 mm should be maintained between any single wall flue pipe and the guard. The guard shall not be more than 13 mm from the partition.

The airing cupboard shall be constructed to the same specification as a compartment.

17.6.4 Under-stairs cupboards

Installation of air heaters in under stairs cupboards presents a fire risk to occupants as the heater is located below what is regarded as the main means of egress from upstairs in the event of a fire. This type of installation should only be considered where there is no viable alternative.

Where the building consists of more than two storeys the internal walls, ceiling and floor must be fire-resistant or lined to provide at least a ½ hour fire resistance.

Where ventilation of the cupboard direct to outside is not practicable for buildings of three or more storeys, advice should be sought from the local building control for the installation of intumescent air vents for ventilation into the internal space. It is preferable that any heater installed in these areas be of the room sealed type.

17.6.5 Roof space installations

Where the appliance is installed in a roof space the following criteria shall be met:

- The floor area shall be large enough to allow access around the heater for maintenance and repair.
- The area in which the heater is installed shall be capable of supporting the weight of the appliance, ductwork, associated pipework and controls.
- If the appliance is supported by combustible materials such as a wooden floor, a non-combustible base at least 12 mm thick shall be affixed directly underneath the heater (this includes the plenum).

- Purpose designed access shall be made available into the roof space such as a permanently fixed loft ladder. The access hatch should have a safety barrier installed around it.
- Adequate fixed lighting shall be installed at both the heater and access to it.
- To ensure stored materials do not come into contact with the heater, associated pipework and chimney/flue system a guard needs to be erected around the heater. The guard will reduce the risk of stored materials becoming a fire hazard or affecting the safe operation of the appliance.
- Where the heater incorporates a circulator, sufficient height needs to be provided above the unit to allow for the minimum static head of water for satisfactory operation of the circulator as required by the manufacturer.

17.6.6 Multi-occupancy dwellings

By design, multi-occupancy dwellings – either of single or multiple storeys – include 'protected areas' whereby the construction of the walls enclosing the area are from materials that will resist the effects of fire for a specified period of time, providing safe evacuation route(s) for the residents.

These protected* areas will be common areas for access to or egress from the building:

- **Protected stairway** – a stair leading to a final exit to a place of safety and that is adequately enclosed with fire resisting construction (includes the passageway from the foot of the stair to the exit);
- **Protected shaft** – a shaft that enables people, air or objects to pass from one compartment to another, and which is enclosed with fire resistant construction;
- **Protected corridor or lobby** – a corridor or lobby that is adequately protected from fire in adjoining areas by fire resisting construction.

They can also include areas within individual dwellings of a multi-occupancy building:

- **Protected entrance hall or landing** – a circulation area, consisting of a hall or space in a flat, that is enclosed with fire resisting construction other than an external wall of a building.

Definitions are drawn from Approved Document B: Fire Safety. Volume 1: Dwellings

Therefore and given the above, new multi-occupancy dwellings with a system of ducted warm air heating and having a storey at a height of more than 4.5 m above ground or access level, or a basement storey, need to comply with the appropriate building regulation as well as BS 9991: 2015 'Fire safety in the design, management and use of residential buildings. Code of practice' and as applicable, IGEM/G/5 Edition 2 'Gas in multi-occupancy buildings'.

Amongst the recommendations of BS 9991:

- Transfer grilles should not be fitted between any room and the entrance hall or stair; and
- Supply and return grilles should be not more than 450 mm above floor level; and
- Where warm air is ducted to an entrance hall or stair, the return air should be ducted back to the heater; and
- Where a duct passes through any wall, floor, or ceiling of an entrance hall or stair, all joints between the duct and the surrounding construction should be sealed (fire stopped).

The bullet points listed do not apply to dwellings with two or more storeys above 4.5 m and which have their own means of access either at ground or 1st floor level, or a dwelling with a floor level less than 4.5 m above ground or access level.

Nor do the bullets apply where an existing unit is being replaced by a new heater with a similar heat output in an existing dwelling and where that installation does not involve extensive alteration and/or extension to any ductwork. The manufacturer's instructions shall be consulted to any special requirements in these circumstances.

17.6.7 Timber and steel frame properties

Installation within these types of property shall be in accordance with the manufacturer's instruction and IGE/UP/7.

17.6.8 Location of room thermostats or thermistorstats

The location of compatible room thermostats or thermistorstats are important considerations for the engineer, as incorrect placement can lead to wildly fluctuating comfort conditions for the gas user. In general, it is recommended that thermostats/thermistorstats be located:

- on an inside wall;
- away from any localised heat source or direct sunlight;
- in a room or space heated by the warm air unit; and
- at a height of between 1,200 mm to 1,500 mm above floor level.

Note that for dwellings of two or more storeys with access at ground level (town house for example), a thermostat or thermistorstat should be located either on the ground floor or 1st floor wall.

17.7 Flueing

The design, installation and commissioning of the flue system shall be in accordance with the manufacturer's instructions and BS 5440-1. Warm air units may be type B (open flue) or type C (room sealed).

17.7.1 Type B

In the United Kingdom, open flued warm air units tend to be type B_{11} (natural draught with a draught diverter). Due to the height of warm air units it may not be possible to achieve 600 mm of vertical flue pipe above the draught diverter before the first bend. The manufacturer may give guidance regarding this situation. Further guidance is also given in BS 5440-1.

17.7.2 Type C

The most common types encountered are units designed for SE ducts or U ducts. Units may be encountered which are room sealed fan assisted or balanced flue, natural draught.

17.8 Ventilation

Ventilation shall be in accordance with BS 5440 part 1. Where there is a water heater and warm air unit combined in one appliance, the ventilation shall be calculated on the sum of the maximum net heat inputs.

Some units may have a mechanical air supply, i.e. the warm air circulation fan also provides air for combustion (and compartment ventilation, if required). Air can be taken from a ventilated roof space or from a grille fitted to an outside wall and ducted directly into the air heaters return air duct or return plenum.

Where the air is taken from the roof space the air inlet shall be sited not less than 300 mm above the joists or 150 mm above any insulation, whichever is the greater. A bird guard shall be installed on the air inlet to prevent debris entering the ventilation duct (fig 17.8).

A lockable damper shall be installed to allow adjustment of the air flow to the heater. The air flow rate shall be a minimum of 2.2 m^3h^{-1} per kW net of the appliances rated input. This air is then delivered to the heated space via a non-closable heat outlet grille located in the same space as the heater or in the same space as the compartment vents.

Remember that the air circulation fan may cause depressurisation and can have an adverse effect (spillage) on any open flued appliances.

Fig 17.8 Open flued vented through roof space

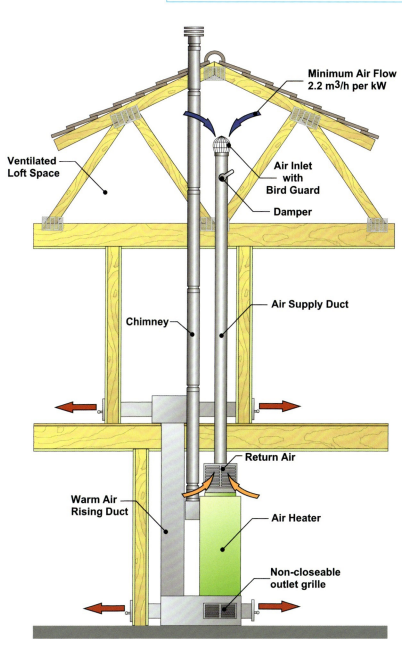

17.9 Gas Supply

Internal pipework shall be in accordance with BS 6891. 15 mm copper is normally adequate for natural gas warm air units. The supply pressure shall be measured with the appliance operating. A pressure tolerance may be permitted by the manufacturer.

Most appliances are provided with a union type appliance isolation valve with an Rc ½ connection (½ inch BSP female).

Warm air units shall be supplied by rigid pipework.

Often, the plenum box is provided with a circular duct which will accommodate the gas supply pipe to the unit. Alternatively, the gas supply may enter via a knockout in the side of the unit (either LHS or RHS).

Note the sealing strip (fig 17.9) on the top of the plenum, it is essential that open flued units are properly fixed and sealed to the plenum in order to avoid problems with combustion. When fixing a new unit to an existing plenum all openings in the plenum shall be made good using metal plate no less substantial than that of the existing plenum; the plates shall be mechanically fixed and sealed to the plenum.

Fig 17.9   Plenum

Manufacturers may provide a drop hole plate for use with LPG (fig 17.10).

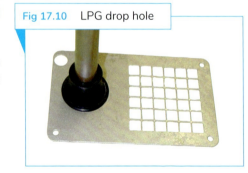

Fig 17.10   LPG drop hole

17.10 Electrical Supply

The electrical supply shall be installed in accordance with BS 7671. The cable size and fuse rating shall be in accordance with the manufacturer's instructions; warm air units are normally protected by a fuse rated at 3 amperes. The means of isolation may be by:

- a three pin plug and an unswitched socket-outlet (in order to encourage physical disconnection when work is performed),
- a fused, double pole, switched connection unit (spur box).

See also Chapter 14; section 14.9.2 for detailed guidance on safe isolation of gas appliances.

17.11 Warm Air Distribution

There are different designs of ductwork for warm air distribution. More detailed guidance can be obtained from the "British system design manual for gas fired warm air heating"; this publication provides guidance on types of registers and grilles, their location, installation and commissioning. The most common system of warm air distribution is the stub duct system (fig 17.11), but other systems may be encountered (fig's 17.12 to 17.14).

Fig 17.11 Stub duct system

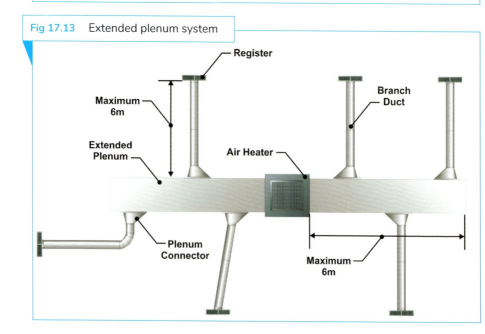

Fig 17.12 Radial system

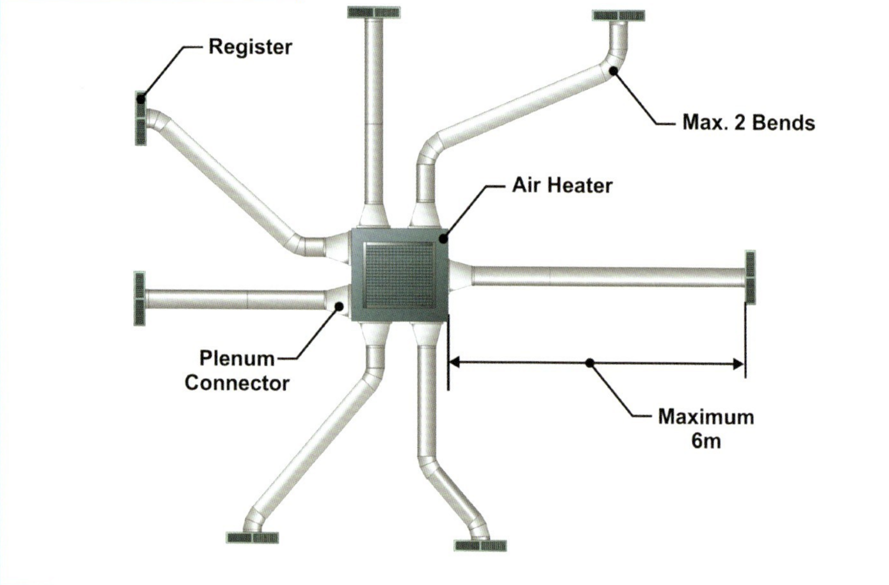

Fig 17.13 Extended plenum system

The main ducts are usually rectangular in cross section whereas the branch ducts are circular. The branch ducts are connected to the air terminal devices (diffusers or registers) by a "boot".

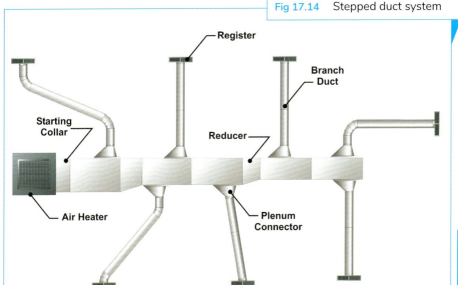

Fig 17.14 Stepped duct system

17.11.1 Diffusers and registers

Diffusers are fitted in the floor or ceiling whereas registers are fitted in the wall (high or low level). Careful design and commissioning is critical to achieve an even heat distribution. They are fitted with a mechanism which permits opening or closing. A multibladed balancing damper may be fitted to enable air flow adjustment.

17.11.2 Return air

In the same way that a wet central heating system requires a return pipe to return the water to the boiler, a dry heating system (ducted warm air) requires a return path for the air to the warm air unit. This is achieved by transfer air openings being installed from heated spaces often to the hall and the return grille of the unit being taken from the hall; the hall acts as a duct. Return air and transfer air shall not be taken from bathrooms, shower rooms, toilets and kitchens. Transfer air openings shall not connect between bedrooms.

The return air duct from the unit to the return air grille may be solid or flexible ducting. An open flued unit in a compartment requires a return air duct whereas a room sealed unit in a compartment does not.

The return air duct shall be intact and adequately sealed to both the unit and return air grille. Defective seals and/or damage to the duct can result in spillage with combustion products entering the circulating air stream.

17.11.3 Duct systems

Ductwork shall be fire resistant and dimensionally stable at temperatures up to 120 °C. If joist spaces are used they shall be lined with fire resistant material.

All joints shall be mechanically sound and leak free, they are normally sealed by duct tape. Where it does not pass through a heated space, heating ducting shall be insulated to prevent wasteful heat loss. Insulation should be a minimum of 50 mm thick and have a vapour barrier; any insulation within 2 m of the unit shall be thermally stable up to a temperature of 120 °C.

17.11.4 Plenum

The plenum shall be constructed of a fire resistant material which is strong enough to support the heater. Normally the heater manufacturer will supply a plenum suitable for the appliance model being installed. Where the plenum has to be adapted to facilitate any distribution ductwork care shall be given when cutting into the plenum walls such that any opening(s) do not impair its mechanical strength. Adaptors shall be mechanically jointed and adequately sealed to the plenum wall.

A self-adhesive sealing strip is normally used to seal the base of the appliance to the plenum, The appliance is then mechanically affixed using the likes of rivets or self-tapping screws. Any self-adhesive tapes used for this purpose shall be of a type suitable for the surface material and be capable of maintaining the seal through the operational parameters of the heater. An inadequately sealed plenum can result in flame disturbance.

Where an existing plenum is to be reused when installing a new heater and the heater plan is different from that of the old heater, an adaptor plate supplied or recommended by the manufacturer shall be used to infill any gaps on the top of the plenum (fig 17.15). The adaptor plate shall again be appropriately sealed and mechanically attached to the plenum. Care shall be taken when installing the new unit as to ensure that any sealing tape is not damaged when mounting the appliance onto the plenum; inspect the seal after fitting, especially at the rear of the appliance.

Normally the existing plenum is adapted to allow the back left hand side of the new heater to be placed to the back left hand side of the plenum. Manufacturer's instructions shall be followed at all times.

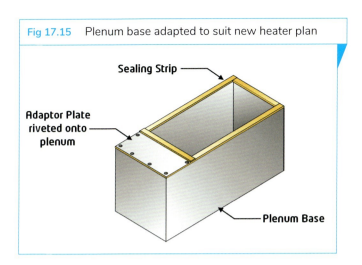

Fig 17.15 Plenum base adapted to suit new heater plan

17.12 Controls Systems

17.12.1 Room stat

Warm air units can operate in conventional ON/OFF mode or MODULATING mode.

The ON/OFF system utilises a make/break electrical thermostat which switches the gas flow on or off – the air circulating fan operates likewise.

The 24 V room stat will have a series wired, adjustable anticipator, this shall be set to match the current rating of the solenoid for proper heat anticipation

Fig 17.16 24 Volt stat with magnet assisted switch contacts

Fig 17.17 24 Volt stat with mercury phial switch

The MODULATING system utilises a thermistor based temperature sensor (thermistastat) which modulates the gas flow between high and low rates, the air circulating fan speed also modulates.

Fig 17.18 Modairflow room stat

17.12.2 Transformer

The unit contains a multi-tapped transformer which allows different fan speeds (and therefore air flow rates) to be achieved; much the same as altering the pump speed on a wet central heating system. During balancing of the system, the fan speed should be set to provide the design temperature increase across the heater, usually 50 °C.

The transformer also has a secondary winding rated at 24 volts; this supplies the time clock switch, the room thermostat, limit stat and solenoid valve. Often these controls will not have a circuit protective conductor (earth wire).

Fig 17.19 Transformer

17.12.3 Fan stat

There is a fan switch (or fan stat) fitted which delays the operation of the fan until the heat exchanger is warm; this can be activated directly by the heat exchanger or it may be activated by a 24 V heater, usually resistor wire wrapped around a bimetallic armature. Figure 17.20 shows the type whose sensor is inserted into the heat exchanger.

Fig 17.20 Fan stat

17.12.4 Limit stat

The heat exchanger is protected from overheating (due to fan failure or a blocked air filter resulting in no or low air flow) by a limit stat which interrupts the power supply to the solenoid; this device resets automatically if activated.

Fig 17.21 Limit stat

17.12.5 General controls

The more conventional gas controls comprise of a:

- time clock (fig 17.22),
- appliance isolation valve (fig 17.23),
- 24 Volt multifunctional gas valve (fig 17.24).

Fig 17.22 Mechanical time clock

Fig 17.23 Appliance isolation valve

Fig 17.24 Multifunctional gas valve

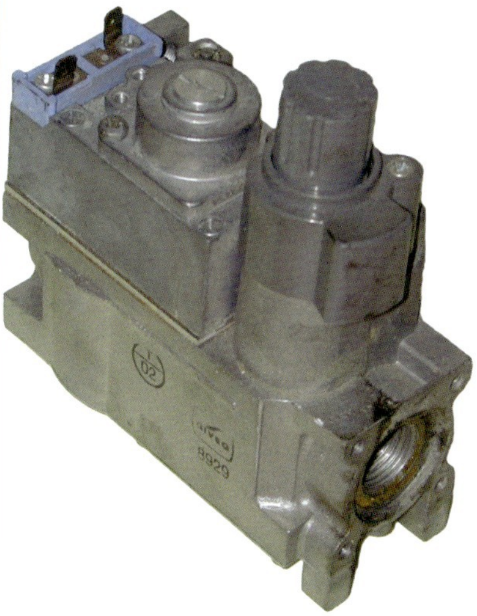

Fig 17.25 Fan unit

The air circulation fan is housed in its own compartment (fig 17.25) and down flow units may have an overheat stat attached to the fan which protects it from excessive heat; often this device has to be manually reset if it activates. The air filter (fig 17.26) reduces particles from being drawn into the fan housing and shall be cleaned regularly by the customer – a blocked air filter will reduce the effectiveness of the heater by restricting air flow across the heat exchanger, resulting in poor heating performance and eventually causing the heat exchanger to overheat. Overheating will result in nuisance burner shut down and premature heat exchanger failure.

Fig 17.26 Removable air filter

17.13 Commissioning

In all cases the manufacturer's commissioning procedure shall be complied with. A generic procedure is detailed below.

17.13.1 Commissioning procedure for ducted warm air units

1. Check site –
    1.1 Suitability of location (BS 5864).
    1.2 Clearances from obstacles.
    1.3 Proximity to combustibles.
    1.4 Suitability of room.
    1.5 Ventilation requirements (compartment and/or room).
    1.6 Visual inspection of flue:
        1.6.1 route (support, bends, size, materials, etc.),
        1.6.2 terminal position,
        1.6.3 sealing and proximity to combustibles.
    1.7 Flue flow test.
    1.8 Assembly and fixing (level and stable and secured/sealed to plenum).
    1.9 Assembly and fixing of positive return air duct/grille.
    1.10 Packaging removal.
    1.11 Adequate supplies:
        1.11.1 gas,
        1.11.2 electricity.
2. Test for tightness and purge –
    2.1 Gas.
3. Test operation and performance –
    3.1 Control devices:
        3.1.1 gas isolation valve,
        3.1.2 control knob,
        3.1.3 ignition system,
        3.1.4 room thermostat/time clock,
        3.1.5 summer/winter switch.

- 3.2 Safety devices:
    - 3.2.1 flame safety device,
    - 3.2.2 gas escapes,
    - 3.2.3 spillage test (repeat test with warm air circulation fan operating),
    - 3.2.4 spillage sensor.
    - 3.2.5 limit and/or overheat thermostat.
- 3.3 Set burner pressure and/or check heat input.
- 3.4 Check flame picture (with circulating fan OFF and ON):
    - 3.4.1 pilot,
    - 3.4.2 burner.
- 3.5 Inspect/test ducting for leakage/insulation.
- 3.6 Inspect/test operation of registers/diffusers.
- 3.7 If required by the manufacturer, carry out a combustion analysis.

4. Electrical tests –

    Inspect and test as follows.

    - 4.1 Conformity with BS 7671.
    - 4.2 Provision of safe isolation of whole system from single point.
    - 4.3 Fuse/mcb/cable sizes.
    - 4.4 Earth continuity.
    - 4.5 Polarity.
    - 4.6 Correct operation of circuits.
    - 4.7 Set anticipator current rating to match solenoid.

5. Balance –
    - 5.1 Adjust air flow rate at each outlet to design specification.
    - 5.2 Adjust fan speed to give design temperature across unit.

    System design information is required along with balancing cone and velocity meter.

6. Advise customer –
    - 6.1 Correct usage.
    - 6.2 ID or AR encountered.
    - 6.3 Gas emergency procedure.

17.14 Maintenance

In all cases the manufacturer's maintenance and servicing procedures shall be complied with. A generic procedure is detailed below.

17.14.1 Servicing procedure for conventional open flued warm air units

1. Initial investigation –
    1.1 Ask customer in operation of appliance.
    1.2 Test operation and visually inspect for obvious defects.
    1.3 Suitability of location (BS 5864).
    1.4 Clearances from obstacles.
    1.5 Proximity to combustibles.
    1.6 Visual inspection of flue:
        1.6.1 route (support, bends, size, materials, etc.),
        1.6.2 terminal position,
        1.6.3 sealing and proximity to combustibles.
    1.7 Flue flow test.
    1.8 Ventilation requirements (combustion and compartment).
    1.9 Assembly and fixing (level and stable and secured/sealed to plenum).
    1.10 Assembly and fixing of positive return air duct/grille.
    1.11 Adequate supplies:
        1.11.1 gas,
        1.11.2 water (circulator),
        1.11.3 electricity.
2. Test for tightness –
    2.1 Gas.
3. Dismantle and clean –
    3.1 Remove casing/panels, inspect seals.
    3.2 Remove main/pilot burners/injectors and clean/inspect.
    3.3 Brush clean heat exchanger/combustion chamber/baffles.
    3.4 Clean flueways.
    3.5 Visual (mirror and torch) and smoke test heat exchanger.
    3.6 Remove and clean fan and air filter.
    3.7 Reassemble.

4. Test operation and performance –
   4.1 Control devices:
      4.1.1 isolation valves,
      4.1.2 control knob,
      4.1.3 ignition system,
      4.1.4 room thermostat/time clock,
      4.1.5 fan stat,
      4.1.6 summer switch.
   4.2 Safety devices:
      4.2.1 flame safety device,
      4.2.2 gas escapes,
      4.2.3 spillage test (repeat test with warm air circulation fan operating),
      4.2.4 spillage sensor,
      4.2.5 limit and/or overheat thermostat.
   4.3 Set burner pressure and check heat input.
   4.4 Check flame picture (with circulating fan OFF and ON):
      4.4.1 pilot,
      4.4.2 burner.
   4.5 If required by the manufacturer carry out a combustion analysis.
   4.6 Inspect/test ducting for leakage/insulation.
   4.7 Inspect/test operation of registers.
5. Electrical checks –

   Inspect and test as follows.

   5.1 Conformity with BS 7671.
   5.2 Provision of safe isolation of whole system from single point.
   5.3 Fuse/mcb/cable sizes.
   5.4 Earth continuity.
   5.5 Polarity.
   5.6 Correct operation of circuits.

   Operatives shall be suitably qualified and have adequate test equipment when testing fixed wiring.

6. Advise customer –
   6.1 Correct usage.
   6.2 ID or AR encountered.
   6.3 Gas emergency procedure.

17.15 Heat Exchanger Safety Checks

It is extremely important that the heat exchanger is checked for damage during service visits. If not, the circulation air from the fan can enter the heat exchanger and disturb the flame picture causing incomplete combustion and the production of carbon monoxide, which can then be distributed around the premises via the duct system.

Damage of the stainless steel heat exchanger may be:

- Cracks or holes.
- Corrosion or metal fatigue.
- Faulty welds or split seams.

Overheating and heat stress caused by incorrectly set fan stat, blocked air filter, dirty fan blades, excessive gas rate and incorrect burner location are the most likely causes of these problems.

The most obvious sign of this condition is a normal flame picture until the fan comes on whereupon flame disturbance is evident, although it may not always be so obvious.

The heat exchanger shall be inspected both externally and internally from the bottom (when the burner has been removed) and from the top (when the fan unit and baffle has been removed) by using a mirror and torch.

17.15.1 Visual inspection of the heat exchanger

- Turn off and isolate the appliance.
- Remove the burner, any access panels/covers and the circulation fan as to allow access to the top sides and bottom of the heat exchanger.
- Using an inspection lamp or suitably bright torch inspect the outside of the heat exchanger looking for signs of damage such as cracking, holes, etc., especially around welds.
- Inspect the connection between the heat exchanger and flue system for integrity. In some instances mechanical fixings can become corroded or slacken over time as the heat exchanger and associated components expand and contract during the operation of the appliance.

- Remove and inspect any baffles and visually inspect the inside of the heat exchanger from both the top inspection aperture and at the bottom within the combustion chamber.

   An additional check is carried out which is used to supplement the internal inspection of the heat exchanger: Where possible darken the area in which the heater is installed and shine the light source across the outside of the heat exchanger from the fan aperture and inspection panel. Looking inside the heat exchanger at both points. Any cracks or holes will be evident as light will shine through into the inside of the heat exchanger.

- After inspection reassemble the heater, replacing any gaskets or seals using the manufacturer's approved components or materials, as appropriate.
- Check for gas tightness of any disturbed joints.
- Attach a pressure gauge to an appropriate point on the appliance, turn the appliance on and check the burner pressure and where necessary the gas rate. Adjust where required to the manufacturer's recommended setting.

NOTE: Where the manufacturer's specifies, combustion analysis may be required.

- Visually inspect the flame picture and check for any disturbance as the fan operates. If flame disturbance is noted check for air leakage from joints between the appliance and plenum, and on any ductwork. Check any flue seals for integrity. Rectify any defects.
- Turn the appliance back on and wait for it to heat up to its normal operating temperature.

NOTE: Some defects will not become apparent until the heat exchanger has reached its normal operating temperature (10 to 15 minutes). At this point the metals within the heat exchanger will expand resulting in any cracks or weld defects opening up.

- Re-check the flame picture making sure the fan does not cause any distortion.
- Where defects have been found and cannot be rectified there and then, the current Gas Industry Unsafe Situations Procedure (IGEM/G/11) shall be applied.

17.15.2 Checking the heat exchanger using a smoke pellet

- Light the appliance and allow to reach its normal operating temperature (10 to 15 minutes).
- Turn the appliance off both at the time clock and gas valve (extinguish the pilot).
- Close all warm air outlets with exception of the outlet closest to the heater.
- Introduce lighted smoke pellet into the combustion chamber (large 9 g smoke pellets may not be suitable for this purpose as introducing to much smoke into the combustion chamber at one time may cause smoke to spill out the front of the combustion chamber; 3 to 5 g pellets may be more appropriate). Remember the appliance has just been on and all surfaces around this area will be hot.
- Turn the fan on by using the summer/winter switch.
- Check for any traces of smoke coming out of the open warm air outlet. If traces of smoke are present, carry out a visual inspection of the heat exchanger as specified in sub-section 17.15.1 of this Chapter.
- Where the appliance passes the smoke test operate the appliance and check for flame distortion with the fan in operation. Again where distortion is evident carry out a visual inspection of the heat exchanger.

17.15.3 Checking the heat exchanger using an indoor air quality analyser

This method is not specified in BS 5864, but may be used to supplement any visual inspection. The type of analyser used shall conform to BS EN 50543 (supersedes BS 8494) directly measuring CO and CO_2 levels. The benefit of this type of analysers is their ability to measure down to a few parts per million CO_2.

- Turn the appliance off, both at the time clock and gas valve (extinguish the pilot).
- Close all warm air outlets with exception of the outlet closest to the heater.
- Measure outside ambient readings of CO and CO_2 to ensure the analyser is calibrated and purged prior to the test (depending on location the outdoor reading should be approximately 0 ppm CO and 350 ppm CO_2; readings close to main roads and in the centre of cities will be higher). With the heater off measure ambient indoor levels. These should not be significantly higher that those for outdoor.
- Turn on the circulating fan and take a measurement at the warm air outlet. There should be no change to the measured indoor levels as the heater is only re-circulating indoor air. Take a note of these readings.
- Turn the appliance on and allow the air heater to reach its normal operating temperature. Monitor the CO and CO_2 levels at the warm air outlet during this heat up period. An indication that combustion products may be entering the circulation air stream is a significant rise in the levels of CO and CO_2 above that of the original measurement. If this were to occur further investigation is required.
- It should be noted that this test is not a substitute for those procedures given in sub-sections 17.15.1 and 17.15.2 of this Chapter.

Chapter 18
Gas Fired Space Heaters

		Page No.
18.1	Introduction	18.1
18.2	Scope	18.2
18.3	Appliance Types	18.2
	18.3.1 Gas fires	18.2
	18.3.1.1 Construction of radiant convector gas fire	18.4
	18.3.2 Fires designed for use with a direct flue	18.6
	18.3.3 Flued convector	18.8
	18.3.3.1 Construction of flued convectors (natural and fan draught)	18.8
	18.3.4 Heating stoves	18.9
	18.3.5 Inset live fuel effect	18.10
	18.3.5.1 Construction of an ILFE	18.10
	18.3.6 Cassette fire	18.11
	18.3.7 Decorative fuel effect fires	18.13
	18.3.7.1 Construction of DFE fire	18.14
	18.3.8 Flueless space heaters	18.15
	18.3.8.1 Construction of flueless heater – wall mounted (hall heater)	18.15
	18.3.8.2 Construction of flueless heater – catalytic	18.16
18.4	Location	18.17

Chapter 18
Gas Fired Space Heaters

			Page No.
18.5	Ventilation		18.18
	18.5.1	Multi-appliance installations	18.18
	18.5.2	Open flue appliances – radiant, radiant convectors & ILFE	18.18
	18.5.3	Open flue appliances – DFE	18.19
	18.5.4	Flueless appliances	18.20
	18.5.5	Ventilation for flueless fires in rooms including conservatories	18.21
	18.5.6	Ventilation for an internal space including integral greenhouses	18.22
	18.5.7	Ventilation for independent greenhouses	18.23
18.6	Flueing		18.24
	18.6.1	General application	18.24
	18.6.2	Hearth plate	18.24
	18.6.3	Minimum chimney dimensions	18.25
	18.6.4	Types of flue system	18.26
		18.6.4.1 Masonry chimneys	18.26
		18.6.4.2 Masonry chimney - liners	18.27
		18.6.4.3 Masonry chimney – flexible liner installation	18.27
		18.6.4.4 Precast flue block	18.29
		18.6.4.5 Pre-fabricated flue systems	18.31
		18.6.4.6 Proprietary fan flue systems	18.32
		18.6.4.7 Manufacturer specific fan flue	18.34
		18.6.4.8 Room sealed	18.35

Chapter 18
Gas Fired Space Heaters

		Page No.
18.6.5	Natural draught – special requirements for DFE Fires	18.35
18.6.6	Builders openings, fireplaces and catchment spaces	18.37
18.6.6.1	Catchment space	18.37
18.6.6.2	Catchment space - minimum dimensions of outset fire	18.38
18.6.6.3	Catchment space – minimum dimensions for ILFE	18.39
18.6.7	Fireplace types for DFE	18.40
18.6.7.1	Fireplace openings – DFE	18.42
18.6.7.2	Fireplace openings – DFE – constraints for suspended canopy	18.44
18.6.8	Closure plate	18.46
18.6.9	Sealing builders opening	18.47
18.6.10	Spigot restrictor	18.48
18.6.11	Flue spigot extension	18.49
18.6.12	Fire precautions	18.50
18.6.12.1	Flooring – wall mounted fires conforming to BS 5871-1 - Gas Fires Convector Heaters and Heating Stoves	18.50
18.6.12.2	Hearths – gas fires, convectors and heating stove	18.51
18.6.12.3	Hearths – ILFE & DFE	18.51
18.6.12.4	Hearths – hole in the wall ILFE & DFE	18.53

Chapter 18
Gas Fired Space Heaters

		Page No.
18.6.12.5	Side wall	18.54
18.6.12.6	Canopies	18.54
18.6.12.7	Customers – user protection	18.55
18.6.13	Termination	18.56
18.6.13.1	Terminal bird guards	18.56
18.6.13.2	Flue terminals	18.56
18.6.13.3	Condensing appliances termination	18.57
18.7	Gas Supply	18.58
18.7.1	Surface connection	18.59
18.7.3	Concealed connection	18.61
8.8	Controls	18.62
18.8.1	Control Categories	18.62
18.8.2	Pressure controls	18.62
18.8.3	Flow controls	18.62
18.8.3.1	Flow controls – appliance isolation valve/gas cock	18.63
18.8.3.2	Flow controls – gas tap	18.63
18.8.3.3	Flow controls – solenoid	18.63

Chapter 18
Gas Fired Space Heaters

			Page No.
	18.8.4	System monitoring/safety	18.64
		18.8.4.1 System monitoring/safety – atmospheric sensing device	18.64
		18.8.4.2 System monitoring/safety – spillage monitoring	18.64
		18.8.4.3 System monitoring/safety – fan flow proving	18.65
	18.8.5	Ignition systems	18.66
	18.8.6	Flame monitoring	18.67
	18.8.7	Thermostats	18.67
18.9	Commissioning		18.68
18.10	Maintenance		18.71

References in this Chapter

[1] BS EN 1859: 2009 + A1: 2013 Chimneys. Metal chimneys. Test methods

Note: BS EN 1859 supersedes BS 4543

[2] BS EN 449: 2002 + A1: 2007 Specification for dedicated liquefied petroleum gas appliances. Domestic flueless space heaters (including diffusive catalytic combustion heaters).

[3] IGEM/UP/18 Gas installations for vehicle repair and body shops

[4] BS EN 1457: 2012 Chimneys. Clay/ceramic flue liners. (Parts 1 & 2).

[5] BS 65: 1991 Specification for vitrified clay pipes, fittings and ducts, also flexible mechanical joints for use solely with surface water pipes and fittings.

Chapter 18
Gas Fired Space Heaters

[6] BS EN 1806: 2006 Chimneys. Clay/ceramic flue blocks for single wall chimneys. Requirements and test methods.

[7] BS EN 1858: 2008 + A1: 2011 Chimneys. Components. Concrete flue blocks.

[8] BS 7977: 2009 + A1: 2013 Specification for safety and rational use of energy of domestic gas appliances. Radiant/convectors.

[9] BS 476-4: 1970 Fire tests on building materials and structures. Non-combustibility test for materials.

[10] BS 1945: 1971 - Standard withdrawn 31st July 2018.

[11] PD 6516: 1987 Guide to guarding fires and heating appliances

[12] BS 8423: 2010 + A1: 2016 Fireguards for fires and heating appliances for domestic use. Specification.

18.1 Introduction

Gas-fired space heaters are a quick and simple method of providing effective heating into internal spaces. They can be used to provide all or part of the heating requirements within a room or full dwelling. Initially used as a replacement for existing open coal fires, they were generally fitted in areas with existing chimneys. These were normally located within the main living area(s) such as living rooms, bedrooms, kitchens, etc.

With the introduction of the smaller convector heaters and flexible flueing methods, heaters could easily be installed in many different locations. With the increasing use of central heating systems (wet and dry) the use of space heaters as the primary heating source began to diminish. In most accounts the gas fire is used more for back ground heating or as a decorative addition to living areas.

Over the last few years we are seeing more and more "cassette" type fires which have a less intrusive modern design (some look very similar to a LCD television). With a very shallow plan area they suit today's modern build houses due to less intrusion into the living area.

The main restriction for the installation of most space heaters is the need for adequate flueing. To alleviate this problem more manufacturers are producing a greater selection of independent gas-fired flueless heaters.

First and foremost to ensure safe operation, gas systems must meet the requirements of the GS(I&U)R. This document states the legal requirements for the safe installation and use of all gas systems within domestic and commercial premises. Unfortunately the regulations only specify the legal safety requirements; they do not specify the method in which these requirements are achieved.

To find the information we require to safely meet the requirements of the GS(I&U)R we refer to BS 5871: "Specification for the installation and maintenance of gas fires, convector heaters, fire/back boilers and decorative fuel effect gas appliances". As with any other gas appliance, any new gas fires must bear a mark of conformity to comply with the Gas Appliance (Safety) Regulations. This mark is the CE mark.

Due to the extensive range of space heaters BS 5871 is split into four different parts - see section 18.2 in this Chapter

18.2 Scope

Each part of the British Standard covers the following appliances –

BS 5871 part 1:
- Gas fires.
- Convector heaters.
- Heating Stoves.
- Fire fronts for back boiler units – this refers to either circulators or central heating back boiler units.

BS 5871 part 2:
- Inset live fuel effects with heat input not exceeding 15 kW (ILFE).
- Fire fronts for back boiler units – see above.

BS 5871 part 3:
- Decorative fuel effect with a heat input not exceeding 20 kW (DFE)

BS 5871 part 4:
- Independent gas-fired flueless fires not exceeding 6 kW
- Flueless convector heaters including single installation greenhouse heaters not exceeding 4.2 kW.
- Flueless heating stoves not exceeding 6 kW.

18.3 Appliance Types

18.3.1 Gas fires

Radiant gas fires are generally available in two types, namely:

(i). Radiant, or

(ii). Radiant Convectors.

The difference between the two being the radiant convector has a heat exchanger. The radiant surface may be ceramic radiant, imitation fuel effect (logs or coals) or pebbles. They can be either an open flue (type B) or room sealed (type C) natural draught or fan flue.

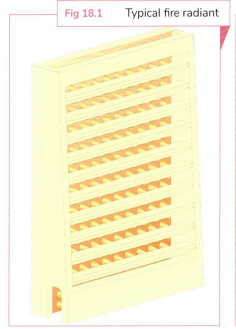

Fig 18.1 Typical fire radiant

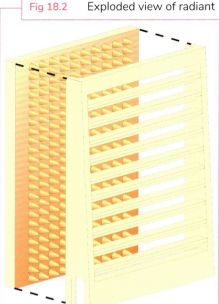

Fig 18.2 Exploded view of radiant

Figures 18.1 & 18.2 illustrates a typical radiant assembly. Radiants come in many shapes and sizes and are generally constructed of brittle fire clay (refractory). The rear dimples or thorns increase the surface area of the radiant and along with the wedge shape design allow for more efficient heat transfer from the products onto the radiant surface. When heated the radiant becomes incandescent with a temperature normally in excess of 850 °C.

The front slotted area is designed to allow additional secondary air to enter the refractory increasing combustion efficiency.

Open flue appliances are normally designed for installation into a normal masonry chimney however, they may be suitable for installation into flue block (precast), fabricated flue with flue collector/box or a proprietary fanned draught flue system such as a SE vent.

They may also be suitable for installation as a fire front for a back boiler unit. Appliances designed for use as a fire front for a central heating boiler cannot be installed without the BBU. An example of a fire front is shown in fig 18.3.

The fire is specific to the BBU – no other fire other than that specified by the manufacturer can be installed. Where a fire is used in conjunction with a circulator, the manufacturer shall be contacted to ensure suitability of installation.

As with any open flue appliance, where the heat input exceeds 7 kW purpose provided ventilation is required as per BS 5440 part 2. To remove the need for additional ventilation, most manufacturers keep the heat input of the gas fire to less than 7 kW.

Fig 18.3   Fire in front of BBU

18.3.1.1   Construction of radiant convector gas fire

Figure 18.4 shows a typical radiant convector fire installed onto an existing brick built chimney.

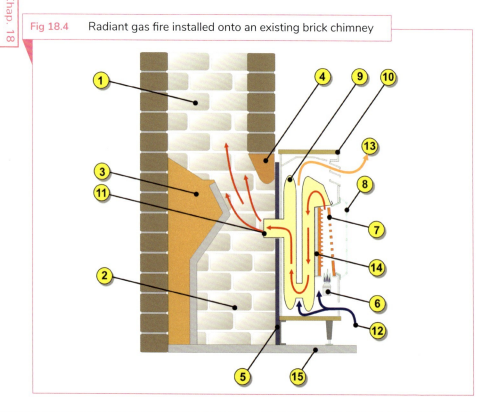

Fig 18.4   Radiant gas fire installed onto an existing brick chimney

Referring to fig 18.4, the main components of the fire installation are:

1. Chimney breast.
2. Builders opening.
3. Chair brick.
4. Lintel to support brickwork above builders opening. Normally a single cast concrete block.
5. Opening sealed with closure plate normally supplied with the fire, however this may be fabricated from a blank plate. Any fabricated closure plate shall meet manufacturer's specification.
6. Burner – may be of the simplex (single injector), duplex (multiple injectors) or manufacturer specific.
7. Radiant surface which may be ceramic radiant, pebbles or imitation fuel.
8. The dress guard is used to stop clothing, etc., coming in contact with radiant surface; this could also be in the form of a glass panel. Care should be taken with glass fronted fires since the surface of the glass becomes very hot there is a risk of severe burns. Do not touch the glass or use chemical cleaning agents as these can discolour the glass.
9. Heat exchanger and firebox. The firebox contains the radiants with the top formed to deflect the hot products of combustion through the heat exchanger.
10. Decorative casing normally constructed of wood and/or steel.
11. Flue spigot releases the PoC into the builders opening to allow evacuation through the chimney system direct to outside air.
12. Combustion and circulation air enters at the base of the appliance.
13. Heated air is dispersed into the room via louvres located at the top of the appliance with additional radiant heat emitted from the radiant surface and glass front (if applicable).
14. A firebrick is fitted behind the radiant to prevent heat loss and damage to the back of the firebox.
15. Hearth.

18.3.2 Fires designed for use with a direct flue

Where manufacturers permit, some fires are designed for connection direct onto a flue system. This installation method was not considered popular. With the advent of the "designer" space heater we are seeing more and more occurrences of this flueing method, especially with the expanding popularity of heating stoves and cassette type fires. These appliances are specifically designed by the manufacturer for a direct flue connection and cannot be installed using conventional methods. It should be noted conventional fires SHALL NOT be installed in this manner.

Classed as open flue appliances (type B_1), the draught diverter is normally located at the back of the appliance before the flue connection. The flue can be either top or rear outlet. Since we are not passing the products of combustion into a builders opening there is no requirement for a back plate.

Unless specified by the manufacturer these appliances can only be connected into a lined chimney by the following methods:

1. Metal twin wall flue system to BS EN 1856 part 2, or
2. A metallic flexible flue liner to BS EN 1856 part 2, or
3. A liner masonry chimney (for example lined with a clay liner), or
4. A factory made insulated chimney to BS EN 1859[1].

Any joints between the appliance and flue shall be mechanically held in position by the likes of a clamp or self-tapping screws and sealed using an appropriate sealant, for example high temperature silicone or fire cement. The flue shall have a continuous run from the appliance to the terminal. A flue terminal shall be installed in all accounts, irrespective of flue diameter.

Figures 18.5 & 18.6 show a direct connection fire fitted to a lined chimney system.

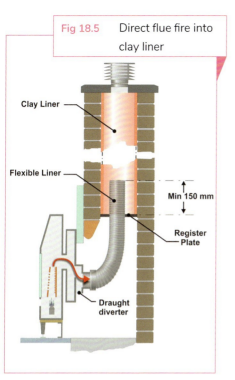

Fig 18.5 Direct flue fire into clay liner

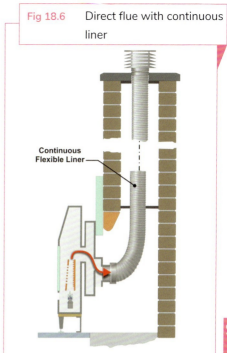

Fig 18.6 Direct flue with continuous liner

Figure 18.5 uses a flexible flue liner which partially enters a clay lined chimney – the flexible flue liner shall penetrate into the chimney by at least 150 mm. A register or clamp plate shall be installed within the throat of the chimney being appropriately supported and sealed to the brick work and liner (normally high temperature mastic is used for its flexibility and durability). Where a liner is used within an unlined masonry chimney, it shall be continuous throughout its length (fig 18.6).

18.3.3 Flued convector

Used as an alternative means of heating all or part of a dwelling. They are designed to heat the surrounding air by either natural or forced convection. Forced convection heaters have a circulation fan located underneath the appliance. Generally these appliances are type C room sealed, and normally wall mounted.

18.3.3.1 Construction of flued convectors (natural and fan draught)

Figures 18.7 & 18.8 shows a natural draught and a forced convection room sealed heater.

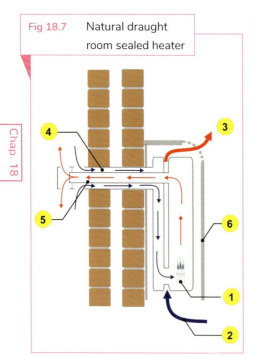

Fig 18.7 Natural draught room sealed heater

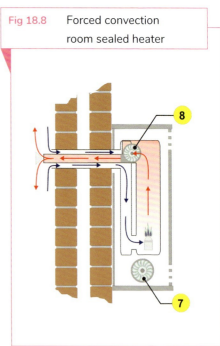

Fig 18.8 Forced convection room sealed heater

Referring to fig's 18.7 & 18.8:

1. Burner located within a sealed heat exchanger.
2. The cooler air enters at the bottom of the appliance where it obtains heat from the heat exchanger.
3. Warmed air is then passed into the room via louvres at the top of the appliance by natural convection.
4. Combustion air enters through the concentric flue system along the outer tube.

5. PoCs dispersed into atmosphere via the inner tube.
6. A decorative casing is placed over the heat exchanger.
7. For the fanned flue convector an additional convection fan which forces the heated air out at the top of the appliance.
8. The combustion fan sucks combustion air into the appliance through a concentric flue system, dispersing the PoC into atmosphere through the inner tube.

The main benefit of the fan convector is the forced convection air being dispersed into the room without the reliance of a convective air current. This heats the room quicker. In addition the flue system can be made smaller, hence less obtrusive and easier to install. Since these are room sealed appliances, the seals on the heat exchanger and flue are critical for the safe operation of the appliance. A safety interlock must be installed with the fan heater to ensure that the appliance will not operate if the combustion fan fails.

18 3 4   Heating stoves

Heating stoves are free standing appliances used to simulate a solid fuel or wood burning stove. They shall be installed as per the manufacturer's instructions into a normal fireplace opening via a closure plate, direct connection or installed with an independent flue system (normally vitreous enamel). They may be flueless (type A), open flue (type B) or room sealed (type C). Nominal heat input is between 3.6 kW to 6.3 kW net (as stated in BS 5871).

They are starting to become quite popular due to their rustic looks. They can be categorised as either traditional (fig 18.9A) or contemporary (fig 18.9B).

Fig 18.9A   Traditional stove

Fig 18.9B   Contemporary stove

18.3.5 Inset live fuel effect

As the name implies these space heaters are designed with simulation logs or coals to imitate a live fuel fire. They may be partially or fully recessed into an appropriate builders recess or opening.

The flue system is either open or room sealed.

Depending on the manufacturer, they may be suitable for installations into:

- A masonry chimney.
- Fabricated flue system.
- Appliance specific fanned draught flue system.
- Proprietary fanned draught flue system.
- Room sealed (natural draught or fan assisted) or
- Direct flue connection.

As with the radiant fire they can be installed as part of a fire/back boiler assembly if specified by the manufacturer.

18.3.5.1 Construction of an ILFE

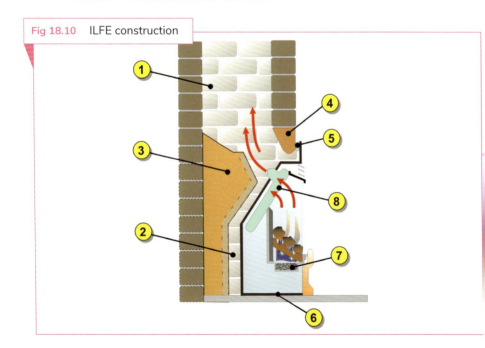

Fig 18.10   ILFE construction

Referring to fig 18.10, an ILFE installation consists of:

1. Chimney.
2. Builders opening showing debris collection void at back of appliance.
3. Chair brick which may have to be removed depending on fire construction. The appliance may be partially or fully recessed into the builders opening.
4. Lintel.
5. Since there is no closure plate, the opening is sealed on all sides against the wall/surround by means of a foam or fibrous seal around the appliance back box.
6. The back box is either secured to the back wall/surround by screwing the appliance to the wall using the raised lip at the front of the appliance or by using tie wires affixed through an eye bolt secured to the back of the catchment space. A decorative trim is placed in front of the back box.
7. The burner is normally situated within a box which may be open or filled with vermiculite or perlite. The radiant surface which can be imitation fuel or pebbles is placed above the burner and normally has no guard at the front.
8. The appliance may have a heat exchanger, this depends on the manufacturer. The flue spigot is generally located near the top of the appliance as a safety measure, to ensure that any build up of debris does not block the opening, it also offers up the PoC's to the throat of the chimney. Combustion and circulation air enters at the base of the appliance, heat is then released into the room via the heat exchanger (if applicable) and radiant heat from the radiant surface.

18.3.6 Cassette fire

The term "cassette" fire is normally applied to an appliance which slots into a fabricated firebox installed within a purpose built builders opening (see fig 18.11). They are normally installed in a raised builders opening (hole in the wall), fig 18.12.

Fig 18.11   Cassette fire

Fig 18.12 Debris collector

The flue connection is on the top of the firebox. In most accounts these fires are installed into a lined chimney but if the manufacturer permits, may be installed into an unlined chimney using optional flue kit. The flue kit is a specially designed device which prevents entry of debris into the firebox and/or appliance and shall only be used with the appliance for which it is intended. When installing these devices manufacturer's instructions shall be strictly adhered to.

The flue kit shall only be installed where the integrity of the chimney has been found satisfactory by means of inspection and satisfactory flue flow test. Where the chimney was previously used for solid fuel burning appliances the chimney shall be swept. A flue kit shall not be installed into a chimney where it is known or suspected that condensation will be a problem. Where the flue kit connects onto a short length of flexible liner, it shall conform to BS EN 1856 part 2.

In general BS 5871 requires a clearance of 50 mm between the flue outlet and any surface, however when using a flue kit this dimension is not applicable as the fire sits into its own purpose built housing directly connected to the kit.

When using a flue kit with a direct flue connection the chimney or flue shall be a minimum of 50 mm greater than the maximum cross-sectional area of the debris deflector. The deflector does not need to sit central within the flue or chimney.

Where an appliance has either a top outlet flue spigot, debris deflector device or fitted to an unlined chimney a label should be supplied with the flue kit, displayed in a prominent position, readily visible to an installer. The label should contain the following text:

> **WARNING – THIS APPLIANCE IS INSTALLED TO AN UNLINED CHIMNEY. FOR EXAMINATION OF THE DEBRIS VOID AND CONDITION OF THE CHIMNEY REFER TO THE APPLIANCE MANUFACTURERS INSTRUCTIONS OR REMOVE THE WHOLE FIREBOX**

The minimum catchment volume of the builders opening, measured from below the lowest point of the debris collector slots, should be maintained (12 dm^3). This may be achieved by the manufacturer incorporating spacer bars or distance pieces at the rear and/or sides of the firebox. Any oversized void may be reduced in size by means of lining with bricks, blocks or by inserting a metallic flue box. Light weight aerated concrete blocks should not be used since exposure to products of combustion could cause untimely failure of the blocks. Dense concrete blocks should be used.

When installed, any debris collection void shall be readily accessible for inspection and cleaning either by removal of the appliance or through purpose provided inspection panels on the appliance.

18.3.7   Decorative fuel effect fires

Decorative fuel effect fires are used more for their aesthetic appearance rather than actual heating ability (hence the name decorative fuel effect). The efficiency of a standard basket type fire can be as low as 20 %. The radiant surface can be imitation logs, coals or pebbles.

Installed as type B appliances (open flued) either natural or fan draught. They are designed to be installed into an appropriate builders opening, fireplace recess or under an associated independent canopy. Heat inputs can be as high as 20 kW net.

18.3.7.1 Construction of DFE fire

Fig 18.13 DFE construction

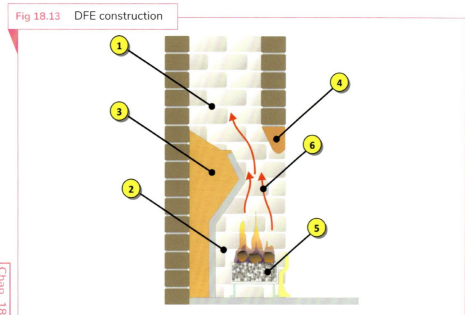

Referring to fig 18.13, an DFE installation consists of:

1. Chimney
2. Builders opening/recess constructed to suit appliance specification.
3. Chair brick, which may have to be removed depending on fire construction.
4. Lintel.
5. The burner, normally situated within a box which may be open or filled with vermiculite or perlite. The radiant surface is normally imitation fuel or pebbles with no guard at the front (risk of direct contact by persons or clothing). Combustion air enters at the base of the appliance, heat is then released into the room mainly by radiation.
6. The PoC are drawn into the chimney by the flue pull however, large quantities of air are also drawn into the flue from the room. This can result in draughts being generated causing discomfort to the customer. A blockage in the flue will result in flame displacement with large quantities of PoC entering the room. The appliance is not protected against falling debris from the flue which may result in poor combustion and damage to the imitation fuels.

18.3.8 Flueless space heaters

A flueless space heater is an appliance designed to operate without the need of a flue system or a means of evacuating the products of combustion.

BS 5871 part 4 does not cover:

1. Mobile or portable appliances conforming to BS EN 449[2] (LPG cabinet heaters), or
2. Appliances such as closed flue fires in motor and touring caravans, or
3. Appliances in boats.
4. Installations in horticultural premises, or
5. Installations in transportable accommodation units.

They may be installed into a purpose made builders recess, floor standing or mounted directly onto a wall.

As with any flueless appliance, the products of combustion are released directly into the room. This can result in problems with vitiation of the atmosphere and condensation within poorly ventilated rooms or internal spaces. Due to these operational problems the ventilation criteria for flueless fires is very specific in application. Due to their mode of operation, these appliances are normally restricted to a maximum heat input of 4.3 kW net.

18.3.8.1 Construction of flueless heater – wall mounted (hall heater)

Being an older style of appliance, many have been removed with the advent of central heating systems.

Generally, they were installed in hallways to keep the entrance to the building warm and reduce the heat losses from other rooms, hence they were commonly known as "hall heaters". The heat input was relatively low, but they were an effective form of heating.

The main problem with these heaters is condensation from the water vapour generated by the combustion process. Again, ventilation is paramount to reduce this problem and also to ensure the atmosphere does not become vitiated.

Figure 18.14 shows a typical wall mounted unit showing the burner within the appliance casing (metal with wood). The front of the appliance casing is protected against direct heat by a combustion box placed around the burner.

The air for combustion enters at the bottom or front of the appliance through louvres located on the casing. The warmed air and PoC are discharged into the room or space in which the appliance is installed from louvres at the top of the appliance.

18.3.8.2 Construction of flueless heater – catalytic

These appliances are the modern equivalent of the flueless hall heater as described previously. Again the greatest benefit is they do not require a flue system.

This becomes beneficial where a building does not have a purpose designed chimney or where the costs of repairing an existing chimney is prohibitive. In this diagram (fig 18.15) the appliance is installed against a non-combustible surface (brick wall), a false chimney breast is constructed to dress the front, similar to a normal chimney. This is one option, it can also be installed into a preconstructed opening or into the cavity void by removing the inner leaf of brick work. The appliance manufacturer's should be consulted at all times.

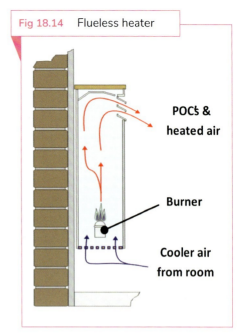

Fig 18.14   Flueless heater

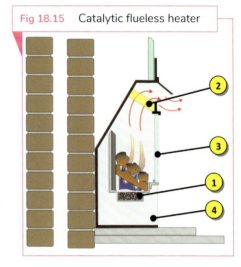

Fig 18.15   Catalytic flueless heater

1. Normally a ribbon type burner is used giving a small flickering yellow tinged flame. Gravel pits, radiants or imitation fuel effects may also be used.
2. The products of combustion pass through a catalyst which "cleans" any gases which pass through it. The catalyst works by breaking down any contaminants, such as carbon monoxide, ensuring the hot diluted PoC only contain carbon dioxide and water vapour as they are released into atmosphere.
3. To ensure all gases flow through the catalyst, the unit is sealed at the front with a glass panel. If the appliance is operated without this front or the glass is damaged, there is a risk of releasing products of incomplete combustion into atmosphere. It is imperative this glass front is intact and installed correctly. Additional radiated heat is generated by the incandescent radiant surface and hot glass front.
4. Air for combustion enters at the base of the appliance.

Manufacturers' claim these appliances are 100 % efficient due to no heat losses through a flue system. As with the "hall heater", the main problem with these heaters is condensation from the water vapour generated by the combustion process. Ventilation is paramount to reduce this problem.

18.4 Location

As per the GS(I&U)R; Regulation 30 and BS 5871, any open flued appliance must not be installed within a bathroom or shower room.

Where a room is used or intended to be used as sleeping accommodation all space heaters above 12.7 kW net (14 kW gross) must be room sealed. Where an appliance has a heat input less than 12.7 kW net, it is preferable that the appliance is room sealed, however if an open flue appliance is installed it must have an acceptable device for monitoring the atmosphere such that it will safely shut the appliance down if unacceptable levels of PoC are detected. Where doubt exists if the device is suitable or not, do not install the fire.

Space heaters may be installed in private garages unless otherwise stated by the manufacturer. For vehicle repair and body shops refer to IGEM/UP/18[3].

18.5 Ventilation

Ventilation shall be in accordance with BS 5440 part 2. In all accounts any ventilation opening shall not be installed within the builders opening. Where the presence of radon gas is known or suspected, the ventilation opening shall not communicate with the under floor space or disturb any preventative measures put in place to prevent radon entering the building.

18.5.1 Multi-appliance installations

Ventilation is not normally required where we have two open flue space heaters installed in interconnected rooms if the flue systems are of a similar construction and height. The total rated heat input of the installation shall not exceed 14 kW net. If any of these criteria is not met, additional ventilation will be required.

The permanent vent should, if practical, be located between the appliances. This does not apply to decorative fuel effect fires (see sub-section 18.5.3 in this Chapter) and fire/BBU as we apply the multi-appliance rule given in BS 5440-2.

18.5.2 Open flue appliances – radiant, radiant convectors & ILFE

In most accounts the adventitious ventilation provided by a dwelling should be adequate for the safe operation of the fire. Consideration should be given to dwellings which have been upgraded to include additional energy saving measures such as double glazing, cavity insulation, draught proofing, etc., and new building construction methods. These measures may reduce the availability of adventitious air.

If doubt exists on adventitious ventilation provision it is advisable to install purpose provided ventilation. In addition any means of extract such as kitchen fans, cooker hoods (especially ducted extract), paddle fans, etc. can create below atmospheric pressures or turbulent air which can affect the safe operation of the flue system. Where these effects are noted and could affect the safe operation of the appliance, additional purpose provided ventilation shall be installed.

As stated in BS 5440-2, where the heat input exceeds 7 kW net, an additional 5 cm^2 effective free area ventilation is required for every kW above 7 kW net.

18.5.3 Open flue appliances – DFE

For decorative fuel effect fires a minimum ventilation of 100 cm^2 is required per fire over and above any additional ventilation for other appliances, unless otherwise stated by the manufacturer. Any air vent shall not communicate directly with the builders opening or fireplace recess. Existing under floor air supplies into the builders opening or fireplace recess shall be blocked off to avoid draughts causing any adverse effect on the operation of the appliance burner or flue system.

Where two DFE fires are installed within the same room or internal space the total ventilation required is the sum of the ventilation for the two appliances e.g. 100 cm^2 + 100 cm^2 = 200 cm^2. The initial ventilation requirement of 100 cm^2 per appliance includes an allowance for adventitious ventilation, given that this allowance can only be used once, we need to add on a further 35 cm^2 ventilation to take into account the adventitious ventilation for the second appliance. Therefore in this case the total ventilation provision would not be 200 cm^2 but 235 cm^2.

It should be noted that this does not apply to a through room which has originally been two rooms with the interconnecting wall removed. In this case the total ventilation for two DFE fires would only be 200 cm^2 with no additional adventitious allowance of 35 cm^2 added.

When there are other appliances installed in the same room, internal space or through room as the DFE fire(s), the ventilation requirement is the total for the DFE fire(s) plus that as calculated using the multi-appliance rule given in BS 5440-2. However, where these appliances are open flue and installed in a room or internal space, there is no allowance applied for adventitious ventilation, e.g. the calculation would be 5 cm^2 per kW and not 5 cm^2 per kW above 7 kW. For through rooms this would only apply where there are two or more DFE's installed.

18.5.4 Flueless appliances

Where a flueless appliance is installed we need to ensure that the heated room or internal space has an openable window or other means of ventilation direct to outside.

Any ventilation route shall not communicate with the builders opening/recess or any other internal space (unless it is suitably ducted through that space direct to outside) including below floor areas. The appliance shall be sited at least 1 m from any vent opening for combustion and any other ventilator installed within the area.

In addition care shall be given to installing the appliance into an opening below an existing chimney, in front of a fireplace opening or close to an existing flue/chimney. The purpose of this is to ensure air movement does not disturb the flame picture creating incomplete combustion, overheating and sooting.

Unless stated otherwise by the appliance manufacturer, it is advisable to appropriately seal the base of any redundant chimney/flue. Two or more flueless appliances shall not be installed in the same room unless the total volume of the room is adequate for the individual need of each appliance.

Where the flueless heater is being installed in front of a redundant solid fuel back boiler it is preferable that the boiler be removed and the chimney opening sealed. Where the BBU is to be left in situ it shall not be left in such a condition that pressure could build up making it unsafe. It is advisable to leave the open vent intact to its termination point. Where the open vent is removed or cut the unit shall be drained with any waterway access covers removed or a hole of 6 mm minimum diameter drilled into the boiler.

The ventilation criteria for flueless heaters are based on whether the appliance is installed in a room or internal space. The difference between the two is:

- Room – an occupied (habitable) area such as a living room, lounge, kitchen, dining room, etc., including conservatories.
- Internal space – not an occupied space, i.e. hallway, cupboard, landing or for the purposes of calculating ventilation, an integral greenhouse (note that an integral green house forms part of a dwelling and is connected to that dwelling by means of a door or window. Whereas, an independent greenhouse is one which is completely detached from the dwelling and is not connected to the dwelling by any means).

18.5.5 Ventilation for flueless fires in rooms including conservatories

A room is normally an occupied space therefore in addition to the PoC from our appliances we have expelled air from the occupants. This expelled air is carbon dioxide and water vapour.

To accommodate this, the ventilation provision into the room is greater than that for an internal unoccupied space such as a hallway. The room in which the flueless appliance is installed needs to be large enough to allow the safe operation of the appliance.

We need to remember that these appliances release the products of combustion directly into the room space and as such require an adequate volume of air for dilution. The minimum room volume is calculated as 1 m³ for every 45 W (0.045 kW) of rated heat input. If this limit is exceeded we cannot install the appliance. An appliance with less heat input shall be selected.

Where the room is large enough an additional ventilation of 100 cm² plus a further 55 cm² for every kW net above 2.7 kW net is required. Where an appliance is 2.7 kW or less the fixed 100 cm² ventilation provision is required.

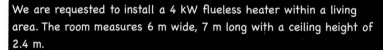

Example

We are requested to install a 4 kW flueless heater within a living area. The room measures 6 m wide, 7 m long with a ceiling height of 2.4 m.

Step 1: Calculate the room volume.

Room volume = 6 m x 7 m x 2.4 m = 100.8 m³

Step 2: Calculate the minimum room volume in which the appliance can be installed.

Heat input = 4 kW (convert to watts by multiplying heat input by 1000)

4 kW x 1000 = 4000 W

We are allowed 1 m³ for every 45 W therefore, if we divide the heat input in watts by 45 this will give our minimum room volume.

   4000 W ÷ 45 W = 88.9 m³

The room volume is larger than the minimum required by the standard; therefore we can install the appliance.

Step 3: Calculate ventilation provision required.

1. For the first 2.7 kW we need to provide 100 cm^2.
2. For the remainder we need to provide 55 cm^2 for every kW over and above 2.7 kW,

    4 kW − 2.7 kW = 1.3 kW
    1.3 kW × 55 cm^2 = 71.5 cm^2

The total minimum effective free air requirement for ventilation is;
    100 cm^2 + 71.5 cm^2 = 171.5 cm^2

18.5.6 Ventilation for an internal space including integral greenhouses

Since these areas are classified as unoccupied spaces the ventilation provision is different for that within a room. The minimum room size is calculated as 1 m^3 of room volume for every 90 W. The additional ventilation is 100 cm^2 plus a further 27.5 cm^2 for every kW above 5.4 kW.

Example

We are requested to install a 3.5 kW flueless heater within a hall area. The hall measures 3 m wide, 6 m long with a ceiling height of 2.4 m.

Step 1: Calculate the space volume.

Room volume = 3 m × 6 m × 2.4 m = 43.2 m^3

Step 2: Calculate the minimum room volume in which the appliance can be installed.

Heat input = 3.5 kW (convert to watts by multiplying heat input by 1000)

    3.5 kW × 1000 = 3500 W

We are allowed 1 m^3 for every 90 W therefore, if we divide the heat input in watts by 90 this will give our minimum room volume.

    3500 W ÷ 90 W = 38.9 m^3

The room volume is larger than the minimum required by the standard; therefore we can install the appliance.

> **Step 3: calculate ventilation provision required.**
>
> 1. For the first 5.4 kW we need to provide 100 cm².
>
> Since our appliance does not exceed 5.4 kW the total requirement for ventilation is 100 cm² minimum effective free area.

18.5.7 Ventilation for independent greenhouses

For heat inputs less than 2.7 kW, additional ventilation is not required. For inputs above 2.7 kW the ventilation provision shall included both high and low level ventilation. Each vent shall have an effective free area of 39 cm² per kW in excess of 2.7 kW.

> **Example**
>
> Calculate the ventilation requirement for a 3.7 kW heater installed within an independent greenhouse.
>
> Answer
>
> > 3.7 kW − 2.7 kW = 1 kW
> >
> > 1 kW × 39 cm² = 39 cm²
>
> We need to provide at least 39 cm² effective free area of ventilation at both high and low level.

18.6 Flueing

18.6.1 General application

Space heaters shall be flued in accordance with BS 5440 part 1. Every flue shall be verified as in a safe working condition and fit for purpose. This is detailed again in BS 5440-1 – for open flue appliances we require a visual inspection, flue flow test followed by a spillage test.

Any flue which has been previously used for an appliance burning oil or solid fuel shall be swept prior to installing the space heater. All flue systems shall be of the correct type and size as specified by the manufacturer. Special requirements are required for "cassette" type heaters.

18.6.2 Hearth plate

Where the specification of a flue system has been changed, for example a liner has been installed, the Building Regulations stipulate a label in permanent form must be fitted giving information on the correct application of the flue system. This label is commonly known as a hearth plate (fig 18.16). It is used to alert future tradespeople to the specification of the flue system. This is a Building Regulation and hence mandatory.

Fig 18.16 Hearth plate

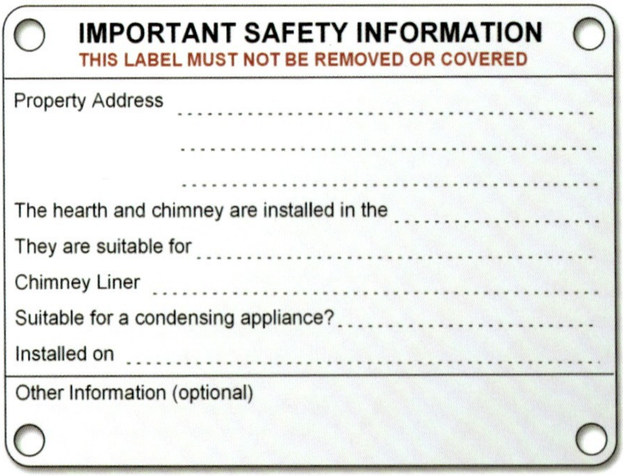

It needs to be posted within the premises in a position which is not easily obscured such as:

1. Gas or electricity meters.
2. Mains water stop cock.
3. The described chimney or hearth.

The following must be displayed on the hearth plate:

1. Location of the hearth, fireplace or beginning of the flue system.
2. Chimney designation i.e. British Standards pertaining to the system.
3. Category of flue system for example Class 1.
4. Generic appliance types which can be used in the flue system including if suitable for condensing appliances.
5. Type and size of flue.
6. Installation date.
7. Any other information such as European chimney product designation, installation and maintenance advice, limitations, warnings on performance etc. (see Chapter 11 Flueing and Chimney Standards).

18.6.3   Minimum chimney dimensions

BS 5871 specifies the minimum diameter for the installation of the gas fire:

- Gas fires and ILFE's 125 mm,
- DFE 175 mm.

These sizes may vary depending on manufacturers requirements and individual appliance needs. A standard brick chimney dimensions are normally 225 mm x 225 mm, which is adequate for most fire installations.

18.6.4 Types of flue system

Types of flue system are:

1. Masonry chimney – lined or unlined.
2. Precast flue blocks.
3. Prefabricated flue systems.
4. Proprietary fanned draught open flue systems.
5. Manufacturer specific fanned draught open flue systems.
6. Room sealed natural draught.
7. Room sealed fanned draught.

18.6.4.1 Masonry chimneys

Flue terminals are generally not required for flues with a diameter of greater than 170 mm.

However, above this size, depending on flue condition, termination, operation and operational requirements including manufacturer specification, an approved terminal may be required.

Dampers or restrictors within the existing chimney shall either be removed or permanently fixed in the open position (fig 18.17). Dampers or restrictor plates are generally used with solid fuel fires with in-built hot water boilers at the back of the fire place. They were used to direct the hot products of combustion from the fire up the back of the fire brick to heat the water contained in the copper or steel boiler.

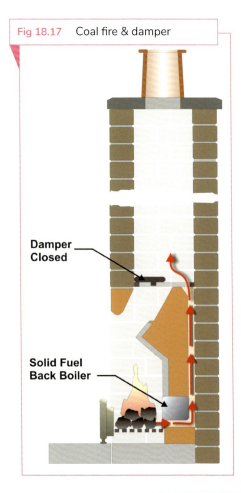

Fig 18.17 Coal fire & damper

The boiler used gravity to circulate the water into a direct cylinder usually located in a room directly above the fire. Most dampers were constructed of cast iron and could be readily removed by shattering the frame with a heavy hammer. Beware of flying debris & soot. PPE shall be worn at all times.

The catchment space shall be cleared of any debris such as soot, masonry, etc., prior to the installation of any space heater. Care needs to be taken to ensure the builders opening is suitable for installation, in some instances this may contain an air box which circulated warmed air into bedrooms directly above the fire. In this case, if the box was not intact we have a chance of PoC leaking into these rooms. This style of box should be removed prior to installation of the fire.

18.6.4.2   Masonry chimney - liners

Masonry chimneys can be lined with:

1. Flexible Flue liner conforming to BS 715 or BS EN 1856-2.
2. Clay Lined conforming to BS EN 1457[4] or BS 65[5].
3. Poured concrete to British Board of Agrément (BBA) Standard.

Clay liners are normally installed when the chimney is first constructed. Flexible liners and poured concrete are normally used to repair faulty existing flues or, where specified by the appliance manufacturer (for example with direct flues or back boiler units). Any liner shall not affect the safe operation of the flue and be of a minimum size as specified by the appliance manufacturer. Even though the chimney is being lined, structural defects shall be repaired prior to lining the chimney (see Chapter 11 of this Guide for more information).

18.6.4.3   Masonry chimney – flexible liner installation

1. Flexible liners should rise and be continuous from the point of connection to the termination point.
2. No part of the liner should form an angle of more than 45° from the vertical.
3. Liners shall be mechanically secured and sealed at top and bottom, a clamp plate is used on both top and bottom connections to support the flue liner.
4. Where mineral wool is used, it should be supported such that it does not fall back into the opening for example by the use of a debris or register plate.

5. For liners which terminate into the builders opening which are sealed with a register or debris plate, the liner should not protrude more than 25 mm into the opening. This will ensure the correct operation of the flue system and stop flue gases collecting at the top of the builders opening.

The following diagrams (fig's 18.18 to 18.21) give examples of the installation of flexible liners suitable for use with space heaters.

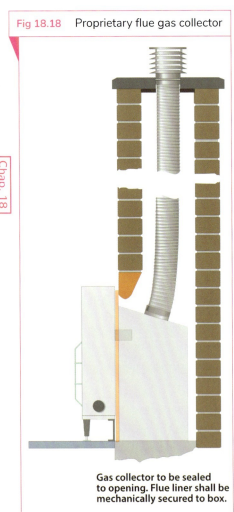

Fig 18.18 Proprietary flue gas collector

Gas collector to be sealed to opening. Flue liner shall be mechanically secured to box.

Fig 18.19 Gas flue box to BS 715

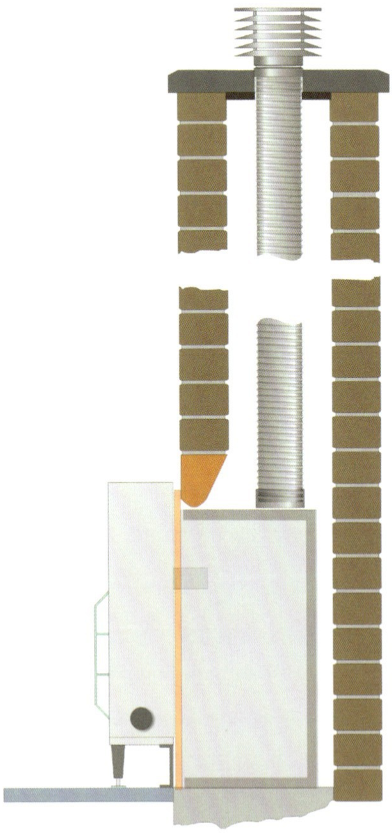

Gas flue box to be sealed to opening. Flue liner shall be mechanically secured to box.

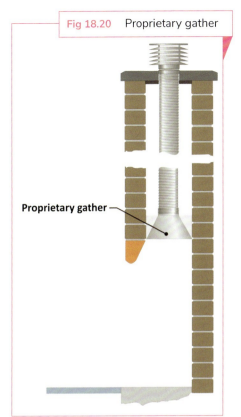

Fig 18.20 Proprietary gather

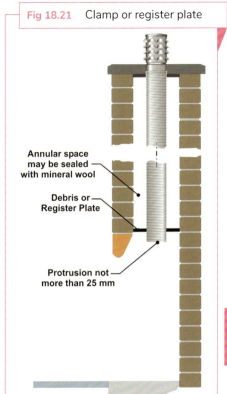

Fig 18.21 Clamp or register plate

18.6.4.4 Precast flue block

Special requirements:

- Blocks shall meet appropriate standards, for example BS EN 1806[6], BS EN 1858[7], etc.
- Blocks may be of light weight aerated or dense concrete depending on year of installation. Caution needs to be exercised with the older aerated blocks since they are more susceptible to deterioration when exposed to products of combustion. In addition, the cross sectional area is less than that of blocks of modern construction.
- Appliance shall be suitable for installation into a flue block system (manufacturer shall be consulted).
- The base of the flue shall be of an appropriate size suitable for the appliance.
- Special instructions shall be adhered to regarding installations, for example cooler plates, etc.

Precast flue systems shall be inspected thoroughly throughout their length, especially in the roof space where the flue transition block changes to twin wall flue. Flexible liner is not permitted in these areas. Signs of deterioration can be seen with staining on the walls along the length of the flue system.

Appliances shall not be installed or left operational where the integrity of the flue system is in question.

Older flue block construction created problems, generally with the reduced cross sectional area and block material. Many were not suitable for the installation of a space heater. Unsatisfactory flues can be inspected internally by the use of inspection cameras, however this can be costly.

Repairs to block systems can be cost prohibitive and hence its is more likely that an alternative means of space heating and/or flueing is advisable, for example electric heaters, room sealed appliances, proprietary fan assisted systems, etc.

Figure 18.22 shows a typical construction of a precast block flue system. Note the three starter blocks, with the lintel cover block reducing the flue way to the specified size of the bonding blocks. Construction shall be to BS 5440-1.

Fig 18.22 Catchment space – precast block chimney system

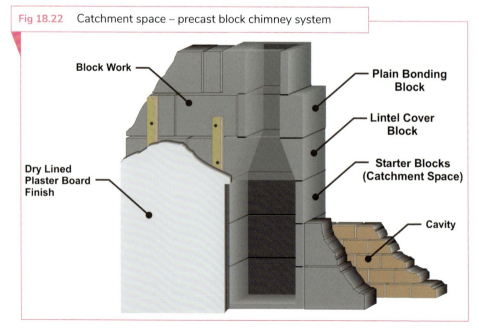

18.6.4.4.1 Cooler plate

Cooler plates are used by some manufacturers to stop the flue gases hitting directly off the precast blocks (fig 18.23). This stops discolouration and heat/moisture damage to the block and joints. As it's name implies, it cools the flue gases prior to entry into the flue system. This shall be fitted if specified by the manufacturer.

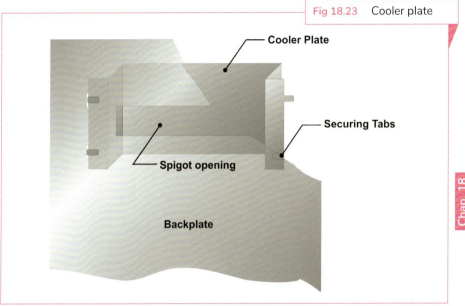

Fig 18.23 Cooler plate

18.6.4.5 Pre-fabricated flue systems

Used where:

1. A building has no chimney or other means of flueing, or
2. The existing builders opening or recess is over sized or unsuitable.

Prefabricated flue boxes are normally constructed from sheet metal with single or double skinned construction. Flue box and pipe shall conform to BS 4543, BS 715 or BS EN 1856 parts 1 & 2.

They shall be of a suitable construction as specified by the appliance manufacturer.

They are normally installed where the dwelling does not have an existing chimney. The box and connected flue system can be hidden behind a false chimney breast. When installed the flue box shall not protrude into a garage or out of an external wall. Care shall be taken when installing into a timber framed building, appropriate insulation and moisture prevention methods shall be employed.

Figure 18.24 shows the construction of a Selkirk flue system using a double skinned flue box.

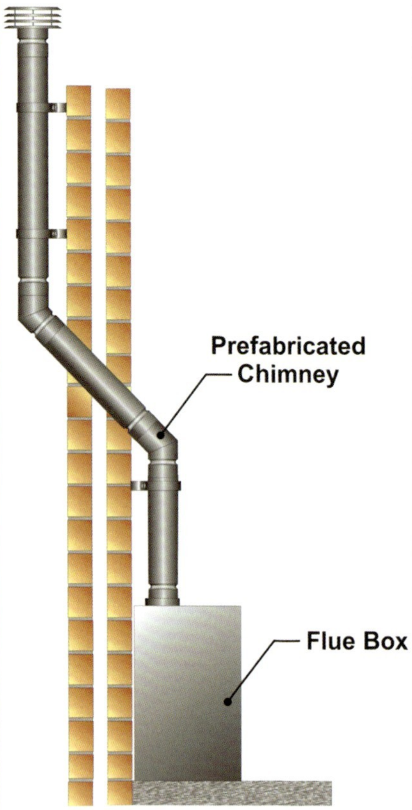

18.6.4.6 Proprietary fan flue systems

Proprietary fan flue systems were primarily designed as an alternative means for flueing open flue space heaters. This type of flue system was not manufacturer specific for the gas appliances. Due to its versatility, the customer could choose from a range of standard gas fires from different manufacturers, as long as they were suitable for normal open flue applications.

The draw back of this design, especially on the older systems, was the flue. The installation was quite obtrusive. Along with the additional complexity and cost of installation, electric's and fan noise these systems lost their popularity (fig 18.25).

Installation shall be in accordance with the manufacturer's instructions and flued to BS 5440-1. They can be rear or side flue exit. Any appliance used in these systems shall be approved by the manufacturer; the increased flue pull may affect the efficiency and safe operation of the appliance.

Fig 18.24 Pre-fabricated chimney

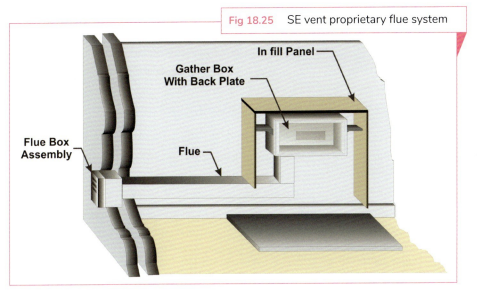

Fig 18.25 SE vent proprietary flue system

With advancements in appliance design, electrical technology and new building design most appliance manufacturers produce an extensive range of specifically designed space heaters removing the need for the proprietary systems.

The SE vent system in fig 18.25, consists of a small gather box which is attached to a prefabricated box flue system. The fan is incorporated in a weather proof flue box on the outside of the premises. Termination shall be as specified in BS 5440 -1. Access to the fan is achieved via a removable external panel.

The appliance manufacturer's back plate shall be cut to suit the gather box and appropriately sealed. Normally the manufacturer of the flue system supplies spring clips to hold the back plate in position. Any joints in the box flue system shall be sealed with an appropriate sealant as specified by the manufacturer.

Since the flue is maintained at a negative pressure, any poor jointing in the flue would not result in PoC leaking into the room. As with any fan assisted flue system, the gas supply must be interlocked such that the appliance cannot be operated if the fan were to fail. Normally the manufacturer of the flue system supplies a solenoid assembly and wiring centre to ensure this specification is met. An infill panel is used as a decorative finish around the gather box and can be adjusted to suit the fire dimensions.

As mentioned, the general problem with this type of system is noise generated from the fan unit plus the additional installation costs associated with the electric's.

18.6.4.7 Manufacturer specific fan flue

Manufacturer specific flue systems are specially designed as part of an appliance assembly. They shall not be used for any other appliances unless specified by the manufacturer. They shall always be installed as per the manufacturer's instructions. A fan flow proving device is supplied as part of the installation kit.

The fan assembly is normally located on the outside wall to ensure the flue system is maintained at a negative pressure, removing the hazard of PoC leaking into the room, this also reduces the noise intrusion from the fan unit. The fan system may be side or rear exit with the fire installed against or recessed into the inner leaf of an outside wall, or within a builders recess or opening. As with the proprietary systems there is the problem with fan noise coupled with the added electric's.

Figure 18.26 is a good illustration of the appliance construction, showing the back of the appliance with the flue system and external fan unit.

Fig 18.26　Gallery no chimney

18.6.4.8 Room sealed

Room sealed appliances can be either fan draught or natural draught. The benefit of this type of heater is safety. Since combustion air is not drawn from the room, no additional ventilation is required. The main drawback is the need for an outside wall. Casing and flue seals shall be checked prior to installation and during any routine maintenance. The appliance shall not be operated with damaged seals.

When installed into a cavity wall particular attention shall be given to any inner wooden construction and any damage to moisture prevention measures such as vapour barriers. Damage to any wall panel construction could cause structural problems or moisture penetration resulting in dampness. A drip ring or collar is installed around the flue, between the inner and outer leaves of the building to stop condensation tracking along the flue pipe. Adequate clearance shall be left around combustible material. Additional fire protection, such as fire resistant insulating barriers may be required. Manufacturer's instruction shall be strictly adhered to especially when it comes to wall preparation.

As stated previously any mechanically assisted flue must have a safety interlock. Termination and installation shall meet the requirements in BS 5440-1.

18.6.5 Natural draught – special requirements for DFE Fires

Figure 18.27 overleaf provides us with a means in which to determine minimum flue dimensions for DFE fires, ensuring the safe evacuation of the products of combustion.

To use this nomogram we need to firstly measure the height and width of the fireplace opening. This will then determine the fireplace opening area (this can simply be done with a calculator using w x h).

Using the estimated height of the chimney we can read off either the flue area for a rectangular flue or flue diameter for a circular flue.

Fig 18.27 Calculating flue dimensions

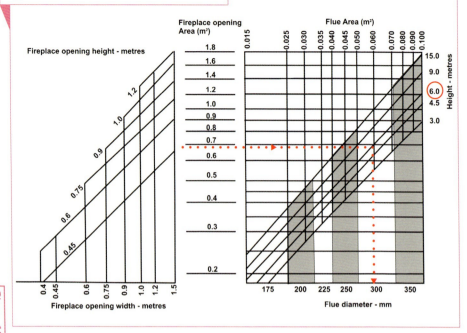

The example given in BS 5871 part 3 (bottom of nomogram) provides us with a fireplace opening of dimensions – 0.9 m wide by 0.75 m high resulting in a fireplace opening area of 0.68 m². Using this fireplace opening area, we can refer to the right-hand side of the graph (fig 18.27) where, given a flue height of 6 m, we can read off that the minimum flue diameter required is 300 mm (this is represented by the dotted line within the example & shown in fig 18.27).

When a canopy is used it becomes more difficult to determine the minimum flue dimensions. BS 5871 part 4 combats this by providing specific constraints which should be met if installing a canopy. Where these constraints are not met we can calculate a relative fireplace opening to allow us to use the nomogram for minimum flue dimensions.

18.6.6 Builders openings, fireplaces and catchment spaces

This section covers the specifications for builders openings, fireplaces and catchment spaces associated with all appliance types.

18.6.6.1 Catchment space

Excessively large catchment spaces can affect the safe operation of the appliances by creating "dead zones" therefore reducing the flue pull at the appliance. This could result in spillage. The maximum void dimensions for radiant/radiant convectors, stoves and ILFE's are shown in fig 18.28.

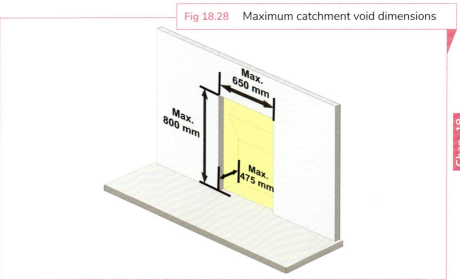

Fig 18.28 Maximum catchment void dimensions

If the fireplace maximum dimensions are exceeded we can reduce the size of the void by using one of the following options:

- installing infill panels constructed of a suitable non-combustible material,
- installing a suitable fire surround, sealing it completely to the builders opening with an appropriate non-combustible material,
- bricking up the opening to the required dimensions.

NOTE: Combustible material shall not be used within the builders opening, for example using a wooden frame to infill uneven surfaces.

18.6.6.2 Catchment space - minimum dimensions of outset fire

For gas fires we need to maintain a specified distance from any obstructions to allow the PoC to safely evacuate from the appliance and disperse into the flue system. In addition to this, an adequate void shall be left below the appliance to allow the accumulation of debris such that it will not build up and block the flue spigot.

For floor standing appliances the flue spigot outlet shall be at least 50 mm laterally from any obstruction and 250 mm from the base. To ensure the products do not return into the room through the back plate spigot opening, the spigot shall protrude at least 15 mm into the opening.

Where the appliance is wall mounted the 250 mm is measured from the inner wall brick level. All other dimensions are the same.

The flue throat shall be 110 mm ± 10 mm.

In some instances the chair brick will have to be removed to maintain these dimensions. In all accounts the manufacturers Instructions shall be adhered to.

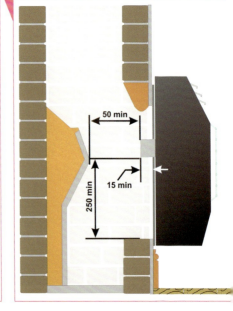

Fig 18.29 Void dimensions (mm) for floor standing gas fires

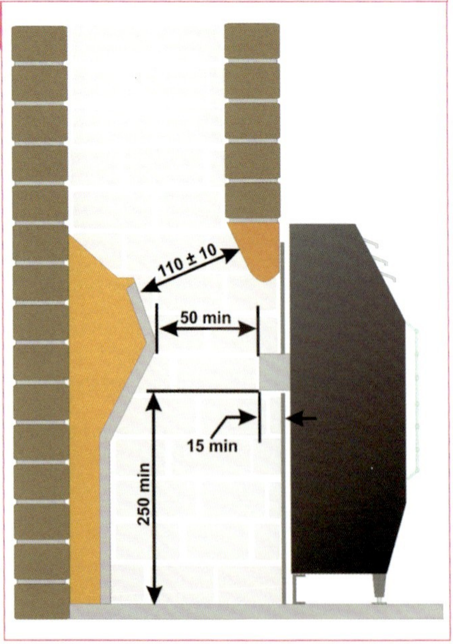

Fig 18.30 Void dimensions (mm) for wall mounted gas fires

18.6.6.3 Catchment space – minimum dimensions for ILFE

For inset fires the height of the flue spigot is determined by the construction of the fire since the base of the appliance sits on the base of the builders opening. Due to this constraint the standards only stipulate a minimum distance of 50 mm measured in an arc around the spigot.

In addition to this an adequate volume of free space shall be maintained around the appliance to allow the accumulation of debris such that it will not block or otherwise restrict the spigot, affecting the safe operation of the appliance. Again the installation shall meet the manufacturer's specifications.

Table 18.1 specifies the minimum void volumes and distances below the flue spigot to accommodate this. As we can see from this table, a flue system which has previously been used for a solid fuel or oil burning appliance requires a larger void below the spigot, this is due to the accumulation of soot and residue during the appliance operation. Higher levels of contamination and debris are expected, even after sweeping the chimney.

Table 18.1 Minimum void volumes

Debris Catchment	Masonry Chimneys			Block Chimneys & Flue Systems	
Minimum Void Volume (dm³)	Unlined	Lined		New or unused or previously used with gas	Previously used with solid fuel or oil
		New or unused or previously used with gas	Previously used with solid fuel or oil		
2		✓		✓	
12	✓		✓		✓
Depth (mm)					
75		✓		✓	
250	✓		✓		✓

✓ Indicates a requirement

Note: 1 dm³ = 1000000 mm³

18.6.7 Fireplace types for DFE

Typical fireplace types are shown in fig's 18.31 to 18.35:

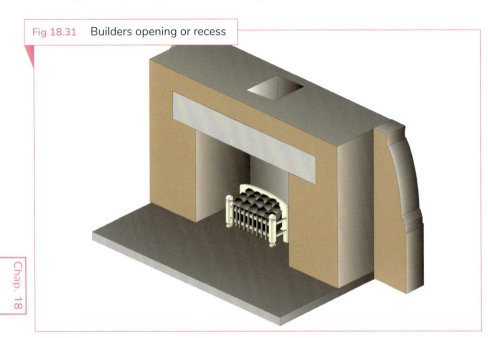

Fig 18.31 Builders opening or recess

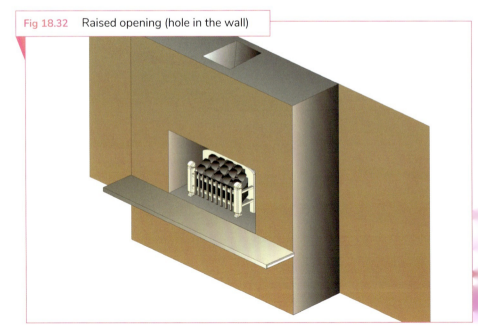

Fig 18.32 Raised opening (hole in the wall)

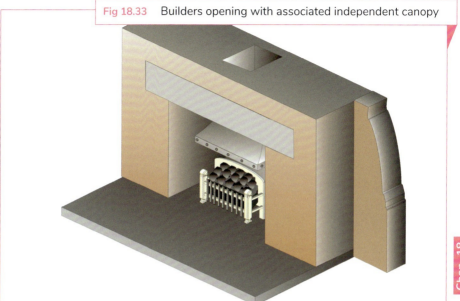

Fig 18.33   Builders opening with associated independent canopy

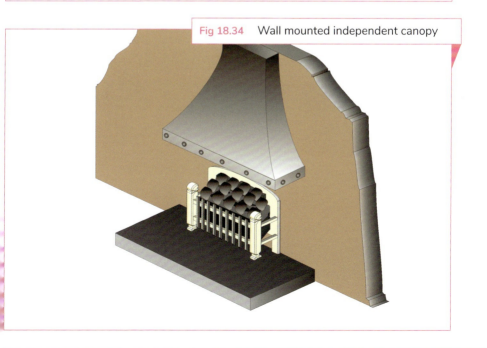

Fig 18.34   Wall mounted independent canopy

Fig 18.35 Associated independent canopy

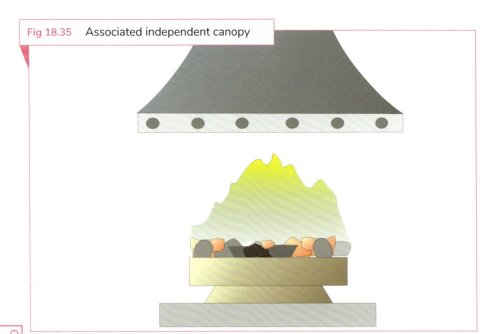

18.6.7.1 Fireplace openings – DFE

Constraints for wall mounted canopy

The following constraints – canopy construction and dimensions shown in fig 18.36 – determine the size of the fireplace opening:

1. The front elevation canopy taper angle shall not be more than 45°.
2. The canopy height above the fire-bed shall not exceed 400 mm.
3. The side of the flame or refractory bed shall not be less than 300 mm from the canopy edge.
4. The side elevation canopy angle shall not exceed 45°.
5. The front of the flame or refractory bed shall not be less than 100 mm from the front of the canopy.

The size of the canopy area is used with the graph in fig 18.27 to determine the minimum flue dimensions.

Fig 18.36 DFE canopy constraints

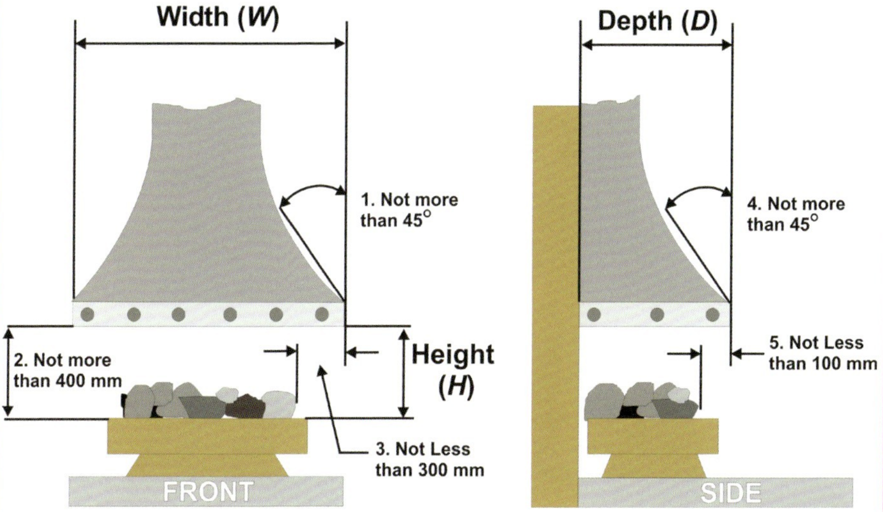

Front view:
- Width (W)
- 1. Not more than 45°
- 2. Not more than 400 mm
- Height (H)
- 3. Not Less than 300 mm

Side view:
- Depth (D)
- 4. Not more than 45°
- 5. Not Less than 100 mm

Where all constraints are met

Where all the constraints stated are met, the fireplace area is calculated using the following;

Fireplace area = Width(W) x Depth(D)

Example all constraints met

In this example we have a canopy which measures 0.9 m wide by 0.3 m deep. The height of the chimney is 6 m.

Fireplace area would be 0.9 x 0.3 = 0.27 m²

Using this with the graph (fig 18.27) we can determine the flue area or diameter. In this case the flue diameter would be 175 mm.

Some or all constraints not met

If <u>some or all</u> of the constraints were not met then the area of the fireplace opening would be calculated using the following equation:

Fireplace area = Height of canopy above firebed (H) X [Width + (2 x Depth)]

This increases the nominal size of the builders opening when used within the Nomogram (fig 18.27).

Example some or all constraints not met

In this example we will use the same dimensions as the previous example.

The canopy is 0.9 m wide by 0.3 m deep, located 0.3 m above the fire bed. The proposed chimney height is 6 m.

The fireplace area would be:

   = 0.3 m × [0.9 m + (2 × 0.3 m)]
   = 0.3 m × [0.9 m + 0.6 m]
   = 0.3 m × 1.5 m
   = 0.45 m^2

Using the nomogram an area of 0.45 m^2 with a flue height of 6 m would result in a flue dimension of 250 mm. This is considerably larger than when all the constraints have been met.

18.6.7.2 Fireplace openings – DFE – constraints for suspended canopy

Again the following constraints determine the size of the fireplace opening. This relates to canopy construction and dimensions for a suspended canopy (fig 18.37):

1. The canopy height above the fire bed shall not exceed 400 mm.
2. The front elevation canopy taper angle shall not be more than 45°.
3. The sides of the flame or refractory bed shall not be less than 300 mm from the canopy edges on all sides.
4. The side elevation canopy angle shall not exceed 45°.

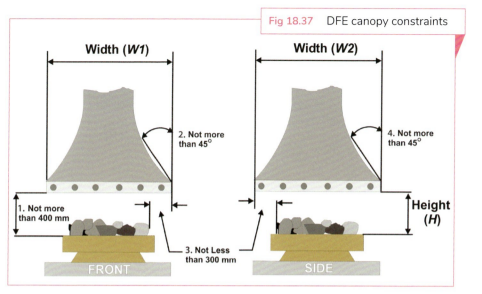

Fig 18.37 DFE canopy constraints

Example all constraints met

If all these constraints are met we use the following formula to determine the fireplace area:

Rectangular fireplace area = width W1 × width W2.

Circular canopy fireplace area = $\dfrac{\pi (W1)^2}{4}$

(arithmetic calculation for the area of a circle π = 3.142)

Fireplace openings – DFE – some or all constraints not met

If any of the constraints were not met then the area of the fireplace opening would be:

Rectangular = 2 × H × (W1 + W2)
Circular = π × (W1 × H)

18.6.8 Closure plate

Closure plates are used to seal the builders opening regulating the flow of air through the appliance and into the flue system. These are supplied by the manufacturer however, where a blank closure plate is used it shall be cut to the manufacturer's specifications to ensure the correct operation of the fire.

Tapes and sealing materials shall be able to withstand temperatures in excess of 100 °C without loosing their adhesive properties.

The closure plate shall be completely sealed to the opening on all sides (fig's 18.38 & 18.39). Air relief openings shall not be taped up unless specified by the manufacturer. Tapes to PRS10 are normally used on smooth surfaces such as finished walls or fireplace backs.

Where the surface is uneven tapes may not create an adequate seal, therefore alternative sealing methods shall be used, for example a non-setting fire resistant mastic. It is advisable when using mastics to mechanically affix the closure plate to the opening. Do not use nylon or plastic rawl plugs next to the fire because the heat can melt the rawl plug.

The seal shall be renewed at every service.

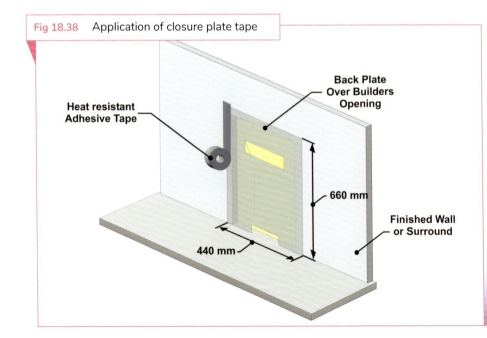

Fig 18.38   Application of closure plate tape

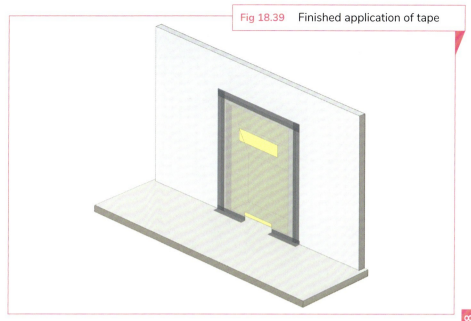

Fig 18.39 Finished application of tape

18.6.9 Sealing builders opening

To ensure the safe operation of the appliance(s) all openings into the builders opening or recess shall be appropriately sealed (other than the manufacturer's defined front openings and flue exit). Inadequately sealed openings not only provide a route for products of combustion to migrate to other parts of the building, but may also cause excessive air movement within the builders opening resulting in poor chimney/flue performance and/or flame distortion (especially where a BBU or circulator is fitted).

Figure 18.40 illustrates the sealing of the builders opening for an ILFE fire and BBU.

The main areas to be sealed are:

1. Fire surround to opening.
2. Holes where pipes or electrical cables exit or enter the catchment area.
3. Existing chimney where the flexible liner enters the chimney. Seal with clamp plate, rock wool, etc.
4. Any other visible exit or entry points where not specified by the manufacturer such as under floor air supplies.
5. Fires may require to be sealed to the surround (ILFE fires mainly).

Fig 18.40 Sealing builders opening - ILFE fire and BBU

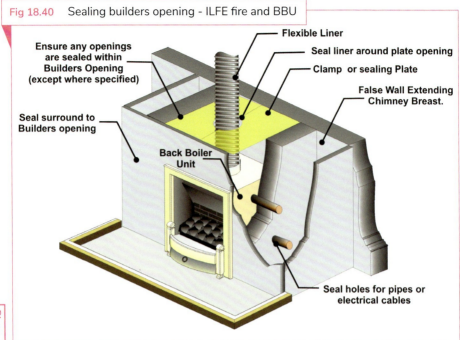

18.6.10 Spigot restrictor

Installed normally on radiant or radiant convectors and heating stoves. They are supplied by the manufacturer where the performance of the appliance may be effected by excessive flue pull. This is generally the case with high chimneys.

Since the builders opening is sealed using a closure plate, excessive flue pull could lead to flame lift and decreased efficiency. It shall be installed where specified by the manufacturer.

Due to poor flue performance they should never be installed with a precast block flue unless otherwise specified by the manufacturer; this could lead to spillage.

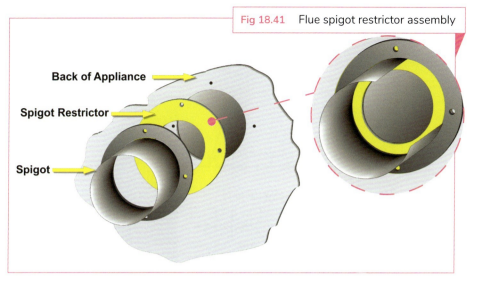

Fig 18.41 Flue spigot restrictor assembly

18.6.11 Flue spigot extension

A spigot extension is used where a low obstruction such as a mantle piece does not allow the appliance to sit flush with the back plate (fig 18.42). The manufacturer's extension shall be used as a retrofit is not allowed.

Maximum length it can extend from back of appliance is 150 mm or as per manufacturer's recommendations. It shall protrude into the back plate by a minimum of 15 mm with a space of 50 mm from the outlet of the spigot extension to any obstruction.

In-fill panels may be used to extend the fireplace forward to allow flush fittings. Remembering any infill panel shall be of a fire resistant material.

Fig 18.42 Flue spigot extension

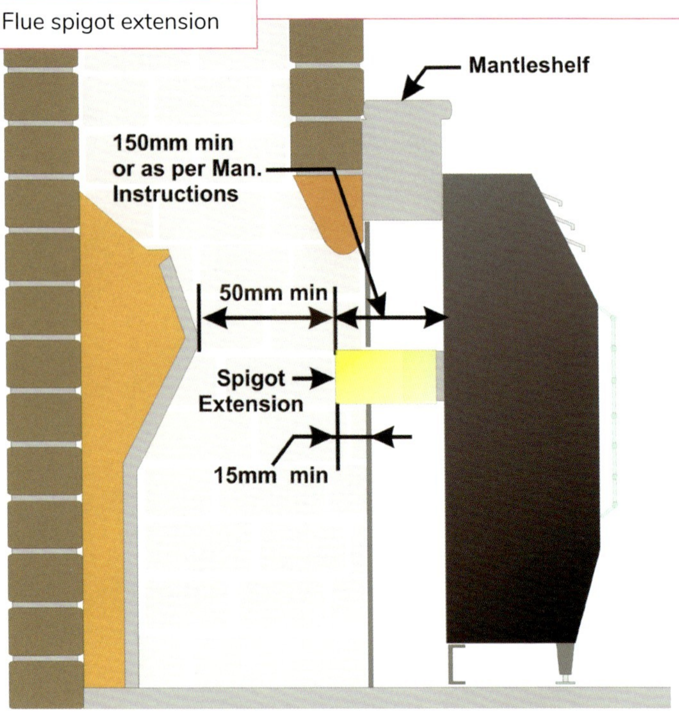

Labels in figure: Mantleshelf; 150mm min or as per Man. Instructions; 50mm min; Spigot Extension; 15mm min

18.6.12 Fire precautions

18.6.12.1 Flooring – wall mounted fires conforming to BS 5871-1 – Gas Fires Convector Heaters and Heating Stoves

A hearth needs to be provided unless the fire conforms to BS 7977[8] part 1 for installation without a hearth. If the fire is wall mounted the flame or any incandescent surface shall be at least 225 mm above any combustible floor covering (carpets, etc.), fig 18.43.

Where no floor covering is present, it shall be at least 300 mm (fig 18.44) from the finished floor to make allowances for any carpet or combustible floor covering which may be fitted at a later date.

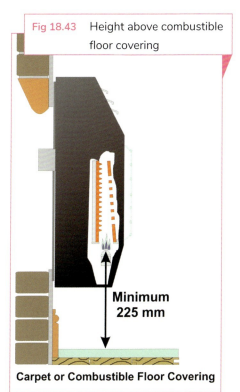

Fig 18.43 Height above combustible floor covering

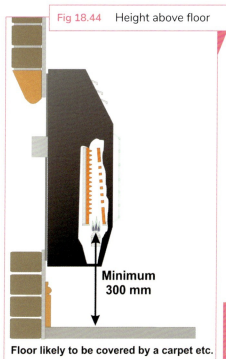

Fig 18.44 Height above floor

18.6.12.2 Hearths – gas fires, convectors and heating stove

Hearths shall be constructed of a non-combustible material conforming to BS 476[9] part 4, or Class O as specified in the Building Regulations. The minimum hearth thickness is 12 mm. It shall project forward from the back plane of fire at least 300 mm and extend at least 150 mm from the edge of any naked flame or incandescent material (radiants, etc.). The height a shelf can be mounted above the appliance will be specified by the appliance manufacturer.

18.6.12.3 Hearths – ILFE & DFE

These dimensions are generally the same as BS 5871-1 however, the hearth shall extend into the builders opening to support the appliance. The hearth shall be constructed of a non-combustible material to BS 476-4, or Class O as specified in the Building Regulations. The minimum hearth thickness is 12 mm (may require a thicker hearth to ensure the surface below the hearth does not exceed 80 °C).

Referring to fig 18.45, it shall project forward from naked flame or incandescent material at least 300 mm and extend at least 150 mm from the edge of any naked flame or incandescent material (radiants, etc.). If a non-combustible wall is within 150 mm, the hearth is required to extend up to that surface. A fender or similar up-stand of a minimum height of 50 mm shall be installed along the front and sides of the hearth, this requirement is to:

- discourage carpets or rugs from being placed or riding on to the hearth; and
- provide a means of warning to prevent persons impinging into the fire area (tactile warning).

The height a shelf can be mounted above the appliance will be specified by the appliance manufacturer.

NOTE: This may not apply to DFE fires with a canopy as the canopy would cover the appliance with no facility to install any shelf near the appliance.

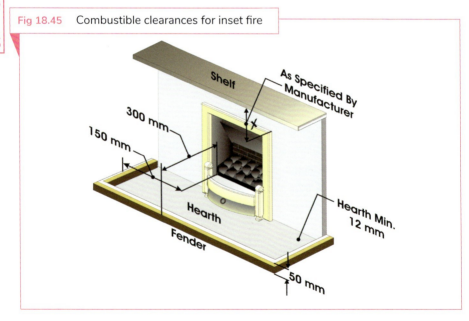

Fig 18.45   Combustible clearances for inset fire

18.6.12.4 Hearths – hole in the wall ILFE & DFE

For hole in the wall installations (fig 18.46) the minimum distance from floor level without the need of a hearth is the same as normal wall mounted gas fires, however additional criteria is specified for ILFE and DFE fires:

1. The hearth may not be required where the appliance manufacturer specifies.
2. The flame or incandescent refractory shall not be within 225 mm from any floor covering (as per gas fires), 300 mm with no floor covering (allowance for carpets, etc.).
3. The hearth beneath the appliance is such that the sum of the height from the floor "Y" plus the hearth depth X is a minimum of 225 mm. This concludes that if the appliance is of a height greater than 225 mm no hearth is required, alternatively if the height is less than 225 mm the nearer the appliance is to the floor the greater the depth of the hearth.

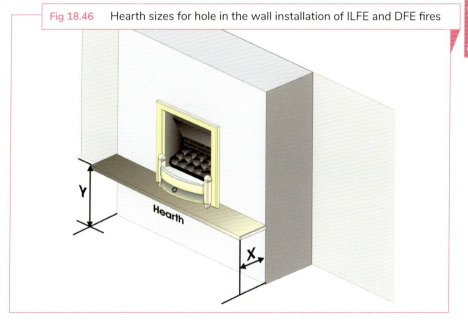

Fig 18.46   Hearth sizes for hole in the wall installation of ILFE and DFE fires

18.6.12.5 Side wall

Any combustible side wall shall be at least 500 mm from the flame or incandescent refractory surface (fig 18.47). For convector heaters any combustible side wall shall not be less than 150 mm from the warm air outlet or as specified by the manufacturer.

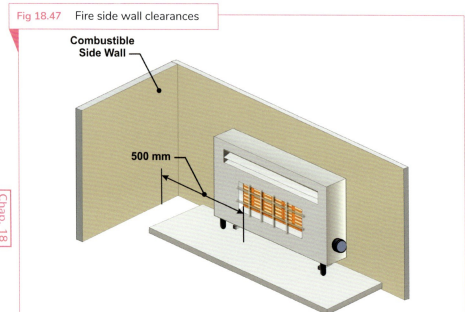

Fig 18.47 Fire side wall clearances

18.6.12.6 Canopies

Consideration shall be given where any part of a canopy may be subjected to high temperatures. Where the canopy is below 1 metre above the flame or incandescent fire-bed it may be subjected to these higher temperatures. BS 5871-3 takes this into consideration and recommends a separation distance of 300 mm from any combustible surface where the canopy is below the 1 metre distance. Above this figure the canopy or uninsulated flue pipe only requires a separation distance of 50 mm from combustible materials (as stated in BS 5440-1 with single skinned flue pipes).

An additional hazard is with hot metals on the canopy and flue which may be inadvertently touched by the customer resulting in the risk of burns. To reduce this risk it is advisable to install either insulated or double skinned units to reduce the surface temperatures.

18.6.12.7 Customers – user protection

Protection shall be provided, as far as reasonably practical, to safe guard customers from touching a naked flame or incandescent surface. The highest risk customers are young children, elderly and infirm. Contact with these hot surfaces can result in burns and/or possible ignition of clothing. Due to the construction of space heaters this protection is applied in different ways.

18.6.12.7.1 Customers protection - gas fires, convectors and heating stoves

For space heaters to BS 5871-1, user protection for radiant heaters, radiant convectors, heating stoves, etc., is offered by one of the following:

1. A dress guard conforming to BS 1945[10] which is part of the appliance assembly a glass front is considered as a dress guard (see also BS 7977-1 & PD 6516[11]).
2. Where the fire has an open front and no dress guard, a fireguard to BS 8423[12] shall be permanently fixed as part of the installation.

Reference to instruction and use of fireguards is given in clause 20 of BS 5871, indicating any manufacturer's instructions be left with the customer (as required by GS(I&U)R) giving particular attention to the young, elderly and infirm.

18.6.12.7.2 Customers protection – ILFE & DFE

ILFE and DFE fires normally are not supplied with a suitable dress guard or integral guard conforming to BS 7977-1 however, no additional safety requirements are required if a guard is fitted. Where no integral guard is present additional measures need to be employed if the appliance is installed at floor level, namely:

1. Ensuring any hearth meets the minimum dimensions as specified in BS 5871 parts 1 and 2
2. Installing a suitable barrier such as a fender, kerb or horizontal bar which shall meet the following criteria:
- Be not less than 50 mm but not more than 1000 mm (1 metre) from floor level.
- Positioned at least 300 mm in front of and 150 mm beyond the edge of any naked flame or incandescent refractory.

18.6.13 Termination

18.6.13.1 Terminal bird guards

In areas where nesting birds are known to be a problem, consideration should be given to the installation of an appropriate bird guard. Any bird guard needs to be constructed of a corrosion resistant material such as stainless steel, galvanised mesh and securely affixed in position.

To ensure birds do not gain access to the chimney, any opening on the mesh should not exceed 20 mm. Bird guards shall not impair the performance of the flue system. Bird guards range from simple wire structures to more complex design. An example is shown in fig 18.48.

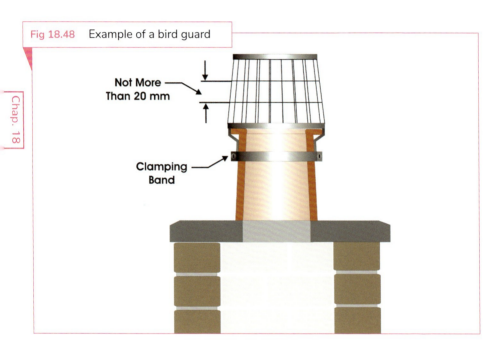

Fig 18.48 Example of a bird guard

18.6.13.2 Flue terminals

Flue termination and terminals should meet the requirements of the manufacturer and/or those specified in BS 5440 part 1. Where a flue has a diameter of 170 mm or less, an approved terminal needs to be installed. An exception is with all direct flue connection fires; these types of fire shall have a terminal guard, irrespective of flue size.

18.6.13.3 Condensing appliances termination

The specific design of these appliances is such that we can extract the heat out of the flue gases to such an extent that the water vapour within the flue gases starts to condense. This is normally achieved around 55 °C. Appliances operating in condensing mode can raise the efficiency of the appliance from approximately 65 – 75 % to above 90 %. To achieve this they require specially designed combustion chambers, burners and combustion fans normally operating by means of electrical/electronic control.

Due to the low flue gas temperatures we can evacuate the products of combustion through a small bore Glass Reinforced Plastic (GRP) flue pipe, the maximum length of which is specified by the individual manufacturer.

As with any condensing appliance we have to take into consideration the removal of any condensate, which should be allowed to drain freely from the flue into a suitable drain or soak away, similar to the specifications for condensing boilers.

Since the flue is fan assisted, the flue termination normally meets BS 5440-1 for a room sealed appliance. Always refer to the manufacturer's instructions to ensure compliance. As the flue gas temperatures are so low, we need to give consideration when terminating these appliances to ensure that the exhaust plume does not create a nuisance with neighbouring properties. Figure 18.49 shows a typical condensing flue terminal.

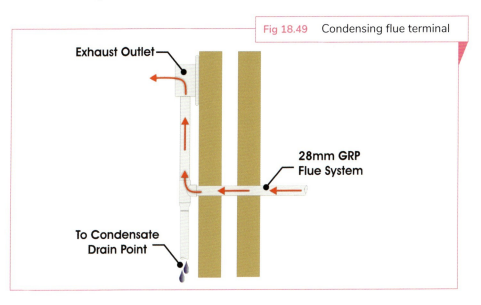

Fig 18.49 Condensing flue terminal

18.7 Gas Supply

Pipework shall be installed to meet either BS 6891 or IGEM/UP/2, as appropriate. Pipe materials may be of malleable iron, mild steel, copper or stainless steel. Fittings can be of any of the materials listed or brass. As stated in the GS(I&U)R (Regulation 26(2)), flexible pipework is strictly forbidden for flued domestic appliances - the only exception being a gas tumble dryer which can be classified as either type A or type B (dependent on appliance heat input) and which utilises a flexible gas connection to negate the effects of vibration.

Pipework must not be installed into a cavity wall unless that pipework is supplying a living flame effect fire which is installed into the cavity (Regulation 19(4)). If this is the case the pipework must be:

- As short as possible.
- Enclosed in a gas tight sleeve.
- Sealed at the joint at which the pipework enters the fire.

Unless it is not reasonably practicable a means of isolation shall be provided for the appliance with a means of disconnection downstream. This is to allow service and maintenance of the appliance. The means of disconnection may be part of the appliance installation, for example the appliance elbow.

Where the connection to a space heater is concealed, any part of the pipework which is buried or runs within the chimney recess shall be suitably protected against corrosion, e.g. use coated soft copper or wrapping the pipe in a suitable PVC tape (soot and cement has a detrimental effect on metallic pipework).

Where the pipe passes through a solid floor or wall it shall be enclosed in a suitable gas tight sleeve sealed at one end with a fire resistant non-setting mastic. Where the pipe enters the flue box, the point of entry shall be suitably sealed.

18.7.1 Surface connection

Figure 18.50 illustrates a typical surface installation of a gas fire. All fittings needed to install the fire are normally supplied as a fire fitting kit. The appliance elbow is specific to the appliance and only the manufacturer's recommended fitting shall be used.

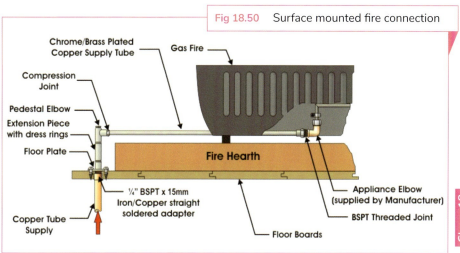

Fig 18.50 Surface mounted fire connection

Care needs to be given to the size of hole drilled for the gas pipe in the flooring. To large a hole will not allow for the floor plate screws to be affixed to the flooring; it is essential that these screws are fitted to avoid future damage to the connecting pipework by the likes of vacuum cleaners etc.

An extension piece is supplied to raise the pedestal elbow up over the lip of the hearth, where required. The joints on the pedestal elbow are made as per a normal screwed fitting however, dress rings are used to hide the joint. They are not used to seal the gas fitting.

Figures 18.51 & 18.52 show different types of surface isolation valve.

Fig 18.51 Drop lever valve

Fig 18.52 Pedestal elbow

The construction of the drop lever valve in fig 18.51 is similar to that of a normal taper plug valve with a niting washer and nut. Due to the metal to metal face, this valve needs to be lubricated using suitable grease. If the valve is not suitably lubricated it may seize increasing the potential of a gas escape. The handle for the valve is connected to the plug by a pin joint, this allows the lever to drop into a recess when closed. This is a safety measure so the valve cannot be accidentally operated unless the lever is raised.

The more common pedestal elbow uses a concealed disc on seat type valve. The valve body has a screw slot cut into it to allow the valve to be operated by means of a screw driver inserted into the top of the fitting. A sealing cap is used to hide the valve and also create a gas tight seal. Since the thread of the valve is not sealed to the body of the fitting, gas will pass through the threaded joint when the valve is open. It is imperative that the sealing cap is adequately sealed to the top of the elbow to ensure gas does not escape into the room. This is a common problem with this type of fitting.

18.7.3 Concealed connection

Figure 18.53 shows an ILFE fire with three possible concealed connection routes, including any additional requirements such as sleeving, corrosion protection and sealing.

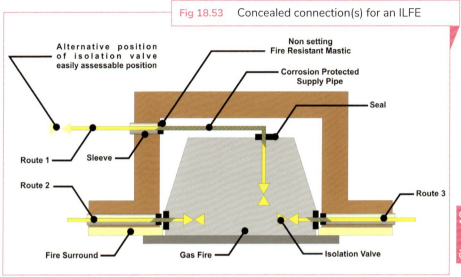

Fig 18.53 Concealed connection(s) for an ILFE

8.8 Controls

18.8.1 Control Categories

Controls can be split into 7 different categories depending on their purpose. Namely:

1. Pressure controls.
2. Flow controls.
3. System monitoring/safety controls.
4. Ignition systems.
5. Flame monitoring systems.
6. Temperature controls.
7. Multifunctional control.

18.8.2 Pressure controls

Pressure controls are used to control the pressure in all or part of a gas installation or on an individual appliance. The main pressure control used within a space heater is the appliance regulator. These are normally simple type regulators relying on a constant pressure from our primary regulator installed upstream of the appliance.

The appliance regulator is used to adjust the burner pressure to that specified by the manufacturer. There is normally no requirement for an appliance regulator on modern appliances. Manufacturers' rely on appliance design and constant inlet pressures to achieve their stated burner pressure and gas rate. An example of an appliance regulator is shown in fig 18.54.

Fig 18.54 Appliance regulator on a fire

18.8.3 Flow controls

The three main types of flow control are:

1. Appliance isolation valve or gas cock.
2. Gas Tap, and
3. Solenoid.

18.8.3.1   Flow controls – appliance isolation valve/gas cock

Appliance isolation valves or gas cocks were discussed previously. If the valve is a plug type valve it needs to be checked for operation and greased if required.

18.8.3.2   Flow controls – gas tap

A gas tap is the manual control used by the customer to control the appliance as required. As with the gas cock this is normally a taper plug however, some older style fires used push button valves. Gas taps may incorporate an ignition microswitch or piezo igniter (fig 18.55) and a thermoelectric flame supervision device.

Fig 18.55   Example of a fire gas tap

It is essential that these valves are checked during a service.

Stiff gas taps can lead to broken gas taps or more dangerously, they may seize when the appliance is on not allowing the customer to switch the fire off. Should this happen, isolate the gas supply at either the appliance isolation valve or at the ECV (**do not use** the screw down valve on the pedestal elbow as gas escapes when closing the valve, which may be ignited by the fire). Allow the valve to cool then strip and lubricate.

18.8.3.3   Flow controls – solenoid

Solenoids are used with electrical control systems. They will only open with an electrical signal which may be AC or DC (fig 18.56).

Fig 18.56   Gas solenoid

These are normally non-serviceable items and should not be stripped down; damage may occur to the control, especially any gas seals. They shall be tested for positive closure by means of a mini tightness test or let-by test. A damaged valve seating will lead to the valve passing unburnt gas into the appliance.

18.8.4 System monitoring/safety

The three main types of system monitoring/safety controls are:

1. Atmospheric Sensing Devices.
2. Spillage Monitoring Devices or TTB
3. Fan flow proving device.

18.8.4.1 System monitoring/safety – atmospheric sensing device

Used in conjunction with the thermoelectric valve, it consists of a two port burner which reacts to increasing levels of PoC. The pilot flame which heats the thermocouple progressively lifts off as the atmosphere vitiates.

Full safety shut down occurs at approximately 1.5 to 2 % CO_2 or 200 ppm CO. These are a non-serviceable items. The ASD normally trips where spillage occurs due to an unsatisfactory flue. There is no industry prescribed test for this type of control.

18.8.4.2 System monitoring/safety – spillage monitoring

Spillage Monitoring Device or TTB (a Dutch acronym for Thermische Terrugslag Beveiling, which translates to 'thermal blowback protection'), as with the ASD, is used in conjunction with a thermoelectric valve normally via an interrupter type thermocouple. The sensor is normally a disc type thermostat, but some variations use a liquid expansion type thermostat. They are normally located on a bracket at or near the edge of the draught diverter.

Again they are factory set and non-serviceable.

If extensive spillage occurs, it heats the sensor which in turn interrupts the current to the thermoelectric valve shutting off the valve. If this device has been tampered with, for example bridged out, it is classed as an ID situation under GIUSP (IGEM/G/11) and is RIDDOR reportable.

18.8.4.3 System monitoring/safety – fan flow proving

Fan flow proving devices are used as a safety interlock which ensures the combustion and/or flue fan are operational prior to burner ignition. They may be in the form of a differential switch (fig 18.57) or paddle switch connected to an electrical control system.

Fig 18.57 Pressure switch

NOTE: Current monitoring of the fan motor (for direct drive units) is now recognised as an approved method of fan flow proving. This uses the motor stall, run and no load current to determine if the fan is operating correctly.

18.8.5 Ignition systems

Ignition systems for appliances come in many shapes and forms namely:

1. Manual ignition by taper or match.
2. Permanent pilot (fig 18.58).
3. Filament igniters (fig 18.59) –
   - glow coil,
   - hot surface ignition.
4. Spark ignition (fig's 18.60 & 18.61) –
   - piezo – electric,
   - capacitor discharge,
   - electronic pulse,
   - direct spark (DSI),
   - intermittent pilot (IP).

Ignition systems are affected by the normal faults such as spark gap, electrode lead damage, poor battery performance, damaged electrode, blocked injector (pilot), etc.

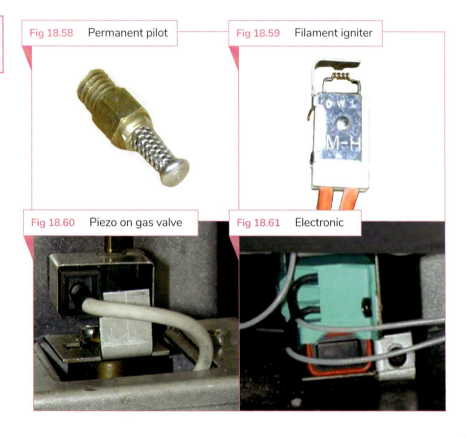

Fig 18.58 Permanent pilot

Fig 18.59 Filament igniter

Fig 18.60 Piezo on gas valve

Fig 18.61 Electronic

18.8.6 Flame monitoring

The most common flame monitoring systems are thermoelectric and flame rectification. Thermoelectric valves and flame rectification shall be tested to industry standards.

Figures 18.62 & 18.63 show a thermoelectric valve as part of a tap assembly and a thermocouple in a pilot assembly.

Fig 18.62 Thermoelectric valve

Fig 18.63 Thermocouple in pilot flame

18.8.7 Thermostats

Thermostats are more commonly used on fan assisted unit heaters such as warmplan, drugisars, etc.

Older style gas fires may also have a thermostat.

The most common types of thermostat are:

- Mechanical.
- Electrical, which may be liquid expansion, bimetallic disc or thermistors.

18.9 Commissioning

Commissioning of any gas appliance shall be carried out as per manufacturer's instructions.

The GS(I&U)R; Regulation 33(1) specifies the minimum checks which must be carried out to ensure the safe operation of the appliance.

1. The effectiveness of the flue.
2. Adequate supply of combustion air.
3. Operating pressure is as per manufacturer's recommendations.
4. Verify that the gas supply is gastight.
5. Appliance is installed as per the GS(I&U)R and manufacturer's Instructions.
6. Safe operation of all gas safety controls.

Where any of these checks indicate the appliance cannot be used safely, it must be left disconnected from the gas supply until all faults are rectified. The appliance shall be labelled accordingly.

Before we commission the appliance we shall first check the suitability of the site, this includes:

1. Location as per manufacturer's instructions and BS 5871 parts 1 to 4, as appropriate.
2. Clearances from obstacles and combustible materials.
3. Hearth dimensions or wall mounting height.
4. Visual Inspection of flue to check that it conforms to BS 5440 taking into consideration its route, construction, termination, etc.
5. Visual inspection of catchment area, where applicable.
6. Ventilation requirements.
7. Appliance assembly, fixings and stability - check for damage on appliance.
8. All packaging has been removed especially inside the flueways.
9. Adequate supplies of gas and electricity.
10. Check fuse rating at electrical fused spur – remember a plug is not permitted for fixed appliances as per BS 7671.

- Before installing an open flue appliance into position in front of a fireplace opening and before permanently fitting any closure plate, carry out a flue flow test.
- Install the appliance then test the gas supply for tightness.
- Purge the installation.
- Before we turn on the electric's, inspect the installation and carry out the relevant electrical safety checks.
- Test the operation and performance of all controls.
- Check burner pressure and/or heat input against manufacturer's instructions or data plate. Adjust where necessary (note that this is especially important for a flueless fire as over-gassing can severely affect the safe operation of the appliance even with a catalytic insert(s) installed).
- Check the flame picture is as specified by the appliance manufacturer; remember to also check any pilots.
- Test for spillage. The manufacturer's instruction shall be adhered to for the positioning of any smoke match. Care needs to be taken when performing a spillage test on the appliance as the radiated heat around the area in which the spillage test is carried out may be excessive and lead to burns. Figure 18.64 illustrates the specific spillage test requirements for a Valor contour fire.

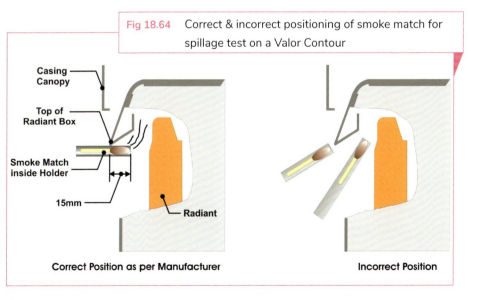

Fig 18.64   Correct & incorrect positioning of smoke match for spillage test on a Valor Contour

- A combustion analysis of any flueless fire is required when commissioning the appliance after installation. This shall be carried out in accordance with the manufacturer's instruction or, where there is no specific information given, in accordance with BS 7967. The result of any combustion test shall be recorded along with the results of any other tests etc.
- Finally clear the work area, instruct the customer on the use, maintenance, service requirements and gas emergency procedures.
- Where a flueless appliance is installed additional advice on the safe use of the appliance should be given. This advice includes making the customer aware of condensation if the appliance is used for any long period of time as these appliances are normally designed as a secondary heat source.

  Inform them of the operation of the atmosphere monitoring system, making them aware that these react to fault conditions and will shut the appliance down when activated; repeat shut down needs to be reported and investigated.

  Finally, advise on the safety benefits of the installation of an approved carbon monoxide alarm. These may be regarded as a "back-up precaution" and not a substitute for correct installation and servicing/maintenance of the appliance and ventilation.
- Hand over the manufacturer's instructions (Regulation 29 of the GS(I&U)R) and any other relevant information such as commissioning sheets, results of tests, etc.
- If required record the flue details on a hearth plate and install in the relevant position.

18.10 Maintenance

For servicing and maintenance we shall always refer to the manufacturer's instructions. This will give us information on how to safely dismantle and clean the appliance.

- check the effectiveness of the flue,
- check the ventilation,
- check the operating pressure or heat input or, where necessary, both,
- check the safe operation of the appliance,
- instruct the customer of any defects.

Where the manufacturer's instructions are not available, endeavour to obtain a copy from the manufacturer (phone or web site). Where there are none available refer to the information contained in industry documents such as BS 5871.

A readable data plate must be affixed to the appliance; an appliance cannot be proved safe if no readable data plate is available. We cannot prove the actual type of appliance even in the presence of the manufacturer's instructions as there may be different model types with different operational characteristics. We need to ensure the appliance is suitable for the gas type, it is approved to the appropriate safety standards, its supply and operating pressures, etc. all of which is contained on the data plate.

- Firstly, ask the customer if there are any problems with operation – take note.
- Before you strip the appliance, test its operation and visually inspect for obvious defects, note same.
- Check suitability of site.

1. Location as per manufacturer's instructions and BS 5871 parts 1 to 4, as applicable.
2. Clearances from obstacles and combustible materials.
3. Hearth dimensions or wall mounting height.
4. Visual inspection of flue such that it conforms to BS 5440 part 1, taking into consideration its route, construction, termination, etc.
5. Visual inspection of catchment area, where applicable
6. Ventilation requirements.

7. Appliance assembly, fixings and stability - check for damage on appliance.
8. All packaging has been removed especially inside the flueways.
9. Adequate supplies of gas and electricity.
10. Check fuse rating at electrical fused spur; remember a plug is not permitted for fixed appliances as per BS 7671.

- Check correct positioning and condition of radiants or ceramics before removal. Make sure they are cool before handling. Do not place on customer's carpet.
- Test gas installation for tightness prior to disconnection.

Dismantle and clean procedure:

1. Remove casing, panels and tap handle (clean as required).
2. Isolate appliance from gas and electrical supplies.
3. Disconnect fire and remove closure plate (if applicable).
4. Clean and inspect catchment space (if applicable).
5. Inspect any seals on appliance and flue system.
6. Remove radiants/ceramics and clean with a soft brush.
7. Inspect radiant carrier, firebox and heat exchanger for damage such as cracks, distortion, damaged seals, etc.
8. Remove and clean main and/or pilot burners and injectors.
9. Clean burner primary air ports.
10. Brush, clean and inspect ASD, TTB, etc.
11. Clean and inspect ignition system.
12. Clean and inspect flame supervision devices.
13. Re-install back plate and seal with appropriate tape or sealing material.
14. Re-assemble appliance and associated components.
15. Re-connect and establish gas and electric supplies.
16. Test gas supply for tightness.
17. Carry out flue flow test (where necessary).

- Test for gas supply for tightness.
- Purge gas supply.
- Check electrical supply (conforms with BS 7671: electrical safety checks, etc).
- Test operation and performance of :
    - pressure control devices (primary & appliance regulators),
    - flow control devices (isolation valves and gas taps, etc.).
    - system monitoring/safety devices (OSD, ASD, TTB, etc.),
    - flame supervision device (thermoelectric, rectification, etc.),
    - ignition system,
    - temperature controls (if applicable).
- Check burner pressure and/or heat input.
- Check flame picture (pilot and main burner).
- Carry out spillage test (where necessary).
- A combustion analysis of any flueless fire shall be carried out during any maintenance or safety checks. This shall be carried out in accordance with the manufacturer's instruction or, where there is no specific information given, in accordance with BS 7967. The result of any combustion test shall be recorded along with the results of any other tests, etc.
- Clear work area.
- Instruct customer (on correct use, service and maintenance requirements, gas emergency procedures). For flueless fires it is prudent to advise the customer to install an approved carbon monoxide detector where one is not installed.
- Check if a hearth plate is fitted.

Chapter 19
Water Heaters

		Page No.
19.1	Introduction	19.1
19.2	Scope	19.1
19.3	Design Considerations	19.2
19.4	Appliance Types	19.3
	19.4.1 Flueless instantaneous sink water heater	19.4
	19.4.2 Instantaneous multipoint water heater	19.5
	19.4.3 Storage water heaters (circulators)	19.5
19.5	Location	19.6
	19.5.1 Flueless water heaters - specific requirements	19.6
	19.5.2 Flued water heaters - specific requirements	19.8
	19.5.3 Basement areas	19.8
	19.5.4 Living rooms, kitchens, utility rooms, halls and passageways	19.8
	19.5.5 Compartments	19.8
	19.5.6 Cylinder/airing cupboards and roof space installations	19.9
	19.5.7 External installations	19.9
19.6	Flue system	19.10
	19.6.1 Specific installation requirements for condensing appliances	19.10
19.7	Ventilation	19.11

Chapter 19
Water Heaters

		Page No.
19.8	Water Supply	19.11
	19.8.1. Dead legs	19.12
	19.8.1.1 Passive dead leg	19.13
	19.8.1.2 Active dead leg	19.14
19.9	Gas Supply	19.15
	19.9.1 Storage water heaters	19.15
	19.9.2 Instantaneous water heaters	19.15
19.10	Electrical Supply	19.15
19.11	Measuring Water Heater Performance	19.16
19.12	Controls for Instantaneous Water Heaters	19.18
	19.12.1 User controls	19.18
	19.12.1.1 Gas tap	19.18
	19.12.1.2 Temperature control	19.19
	19.12.1.3 Thermostat	19.19
	19.12.2 Safety controls & components	19.19
	19.12.2.1 Isolation valves	19.19
	19.12.2.2 The gas section	19.20
	19.12.2.3 Burner restrictor	19.20
	19.12.2.4 Flame supervision device	19.20
	19.12.2.5 Atmospheric sensing device	19.21
	19.12.2.6 Interrupted thermocouple circuits	19.21
	19.12.2.7 Main gas valve	19.22
	19.12.2.8 Water section	19.23

Chapter 19
Water Heaters

		Page No.
19.12.2.9	Water throttle or water governor	**19.23**
19.12.2.10	Venturi	**19.23**
19.12.2.11	Slow ignition device	**19.24**
19.12.2.12	Diaphragm	**19.24**
19.12.2.13	Filters	**19.25**
19.12.2.14	Fanned flue and pressure/flow sensing	**19.25**
19.12.2.15	Multifunctional control unit	**19.26**
19.12.2.16	Flow switch	**19.26**

19.13 Controls for Storage Water Heaters — **19.27**

- 19.13.1 User controls — **19.27**
- 19.13.2 Safety controls & components — **19.27**
  - 19.13.2.1 Isolation valve — **19.27**
  - 19.13.2.2 Liquid expansion thermostat — **19.27**
  - 19.13.2.3 Atmospheric sensing device — **19.28**
  - 19.13.2.4 Multifunctional unit — **19.28**

19.14 Commissioning — **19.30**

- 19.14.1 Commissioning procedure for flueless instantaneous sink water heaters — **19.30**
- 19.14.2 Commissioning procedure for room sealed instantaneous multipoint water heaters — **19.32**

Chapter 19
Water Heaters

	Page No.
19.15 Maintenance	**19.34**
19.15.1 Servicing procedure for flueless instantaneous sink water heaters	19.34
19.15.2 Servicing procedure for room sealed instantaneous multipoint water heaters	19.36

References in this Chapter

[1] BS 5546: 2010 Specification for installation and maintenance of gas-fired water-heating appliances of rated input not exceeding 70 kW net

[2] BS EN 806: Specification for installations inside buildings conveying water for human consumption. (Parts 1 to 5).

[3] BS 8558: 2015 Guide to the design, installation, testing and maintenance of services supplying water for domestic use within buildings and their curtilages.

Note: BS 8558 compliments BS EN 806 and replaces the previous standard of BS 6700.

19.1 Introduction

This section has been prepared in relation to domestic, natural gas and LPG instantaneous and storage water heating appliances (flue types A, B and C), which may operate in either condensing or non-condensing modes. It may also apply, in part, to spa and pool water heating appliances.

The supply of hot water from a central source for multi-occupancy dwellings is not covered within this document. The installation will be in accordance with BS 5546[1] and the GS(I&U)R. Reference shall also be made to local building legislation, water bylaws, etc. to ensure full compliance.

19.2 Scope

Work activities will include installation, commissioning, repair and maintenance of both new and previously used appliances, with a heat input not exceeding 70 kW net.

Normally, work will be performed in domestic premises including permanently sited leisure accommodation vehicles (LAV), residential park homes (RPH) and permanently moored boats (B).

BS 5546 also applies to domestic type installations in commercial or industrial premises. There may be additional requirements in these situations outside the scope of domestic activities, therefore gas engineers shall be appropriately qualified for the scope of work that they perform. Examples include staff kitchens, temporary installations at shows, events and construction sites, small scale catering facilities, etc.

19.3 Design Considerations

The customer will have to be advised of the advantages of instantaneous (hot water on demand) versus storage (preheated water) in order that they can make an informed choice. The general advantages/disadvantages of each system are listed in table 19.1. It is essential that installers are aware of the room types and clearances specified by the appliance manufacturer prior to installation.

Table 19.1 Advantages/disadvantages of instantaneous hot water compared to storage hot water systems

Instantaneous Hot water		Storage Hot Water	
Advantages	Disadvantages	Advantages	Disadvantages
"Dry" loft space	Poor flow rate	Thermostatically controlled temperature	Flow rate dependent on "head of water"
Space savings, no cistern or cylinder	Minimum water pressure and flow rate necessary - can be aggravated during summer months	Cylinder can be heated by alternative fuel (electricity, including solar thermal or PV systems)	May require ventilation provision, most appliances are flue type B
Running costs are reduced	Lower hot water temperature during winter	Can supply more than one tap simultaneously	Adequate space required for storage vessel, controls, etc.
Most units are available as flue type C	High gas rate, larger supply pipe	Large quantity of preheated water with good flow rates	Additional capital and running costs

19.4 Appliance Types

New appliances shall be CE marked. Where a previously used appliance is being installed the installer shall ensure that the appliance is in a safe and serviceable condition. Where the appliance does not have a CE mark it should be fitted as per the manufacturer's instructions. Where these instructions are not available a copy shall be obtained from the manufacturer or their agent prior to installation.

All appliances must be suitable for the gas type and pressure supplied. If a conversion is required this shall be performed in accordance with the manufacturer's instructions using an approved conversion kit, ad hoc conversion is not permitted.

All appliances shall have a readable data plate (fig's 19.1 & 19.2) which provides important information in relation to:

- Gas type and supply pressure.
    - G20 is nat. gas @ 20 mbar.
    - G30 is butane @ 29 mbar.
    - G31 is propane @ 37 mbar.
- Intended country of use (GB).
- Operating pressure (burner).

The appliance serial number (along with the make, model and colour) is required if spare parts have to be ordered. The appliance and part GC number (Gas Council number) may also be required.

Fig 19.1   Circulator data badge

Fig 19.2   Instantaneous appliance data badge

19.4.1 Flueless instantaneous sink water heater

This type of appliance is fitted adjacent to the point of use (fig 19.3).

Fig 19.3 Flueless Sink Water Heater

They have a relatively low heat input and hot water flow rate and are designed for small hot water demands such as sinks and not for the connection to multiple outlets. Hot water delivery is normally by means of a swivel spout, which is part of the appliance assembly. However, some models can facilitate direct connection to a draw-off point.

The water heater may be connected to either mains or storage cold water supplies depending on model.

Reference shall be made to the manufacturer's specification to ensure suitability. Since these appliances are flueless, the size of room in which they are located, proximity of the products outlet to combustible materials and adequate ventilation provision are paramount to their safe operation. Most appliances now have an atmospheric sensing device fitted as standard to shut the appliance down before the dangerous build up of products of combustion which can vitiate the atmosphere. It should be noted that older appliances may not have this facility and therefore may not be suitable for their application.

19.4.2 Instantaneous multipoint water heater

This type of appliance may be open flue (type B) or room sealed (type C). They are designed to provide instantaneous hot water on demand and are normally connected to multiple hot water outlets such as kitchens, bath rooms, shower rooms, etc (fig 19.4). However, as with the combination boiler they have a limited hot water flow rate (approximately 5 to 10 litres per minute) and may not be suitable for full house demand.

The water heater may be connected to either mains or stored cold water supplies depending on model. Again reference shall be made to the manufacturer's specification to ensure suitability of the connection methods.

Fig 19.4   Multipoint Water Heater

19.4.3   Storage water heaters (circulators)

Circulators may be flueless (type A) or flued (type B or C) and be either a stand alone appliance or incorporated as part of another appliance such as an air heater (fig 19.5). Flueless circulators are seldom encountered nowadays.

They are used to either directly or indirectly heat a storage vessel by means of gravity or pumped circulation.

Fig 19.5 Open Flued Circulator

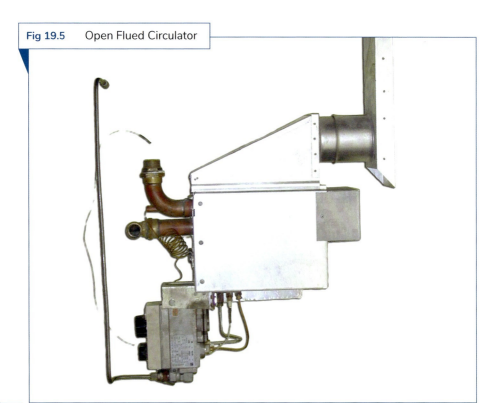

19.5 Location

19.5.1 Flueless water heaters - specific requirements

Flueless (flue type A) water heaters must not be installed in bathrooms or shower rooms. In all other cases the appliance can only be installed if the room volume is in excess of 5 m^3.

Flueless water heaters with a rated input of 12 kW gross (10.8 kW net) or less installed in rooms used or intended to be used as sleeping accommodation shall incorporate a safety control designed to shut down the appliance before there is a build up of a dangerous quantity of the products of combustion in the room concerned (ASD). The room shall have an openable window and permanent ventilation direct to outside.

This type of water heater may be installed within a cloakroom or toilet provided the room volume meets the criteria stated above with the ventilation provision direct to outside.

Flueless instantaneous water heaters shall not supply any taps or outlets in any rooms other than the room which contains the water heater.

Unless specified by the manufacturer, flueless storage and flueless instantaneous water heaters shall have a minimum clearance of 300 mm between the products outlet and any ceiling.

If fitted beneath a shelf, there shall be at least 150 mm clearance and the underside of the shelf shall be protected by a sheet of non-combustible material. Where the shelf protection is made of a material which is non-insulating, such as a metal plate, an air gap of at least 5 mm shall be maintained between the material and the shelf to stop excessive heat transfer onto the shelf material. If the clearance between the products outlet and the underside of the shelf is 300 mm or greater, the sheet of non-combustible material does not required to be fitted.

Flueless water heaters should have a label attached in a prominent position stating that the maximum period of continuous use is five minutes fig 19.6).

Fig 19.6 5-minute label

The draw-off for a small flueless water heating appliance should be as short as possible and not exceed 3 m in length to minimise the delay in providing hot water to the outlet and thereby reducing the overall time of operation.

The swivel spout of a water heater shall terminate with a minimum clearance above the spillover level of the sink as detailed below:

- Up to ½ inch spout – 20 mm clearance,
- Greater than ½ inch and not exceeding ¾ inch – 25 mm clearance,
- Greater than ¾ inch – 70 mm clearance.

19.5.2 Flued water heaters - specific requirements

As with flueless water heaters, open flue (type B) appliances must not be installed in bathrooms or shower rooms. The installation of room sealed appliances is permitted, but only if no other alternative is available. Open flue and room sealed appliances may be installed within a cloakroom or toilet provided the ventilation provision is direct to outside.

Water heaters with a heat input exceeding 14 kW gross (12.6 kW net) installed in rooms used or intended to be used for sleeping accommodation shall only be room sealed. For open flued water heaters 14 kW gross (12.6 kW net) or less installed within these areas shall incorporate a safety control designed to shut down the appliance before there is a build up of a dangerous quantity of the products of combustion in the room concerned (ASD). Only room sealed water heaters shall be installed in bedsitting rooms of less than 20 m^3.

The installation of back boiler units and back circulator units shall comply with the manufacturer's instructions and BS 5871-1. Installation of flues through timber frame properties is detailed in the Institution of Gas Engineers and Managers document IGE/UP/7.

19.5.3 Basement areas

LPG gas appliances **must not be installed** in any room or internal space which is located below ground level, for example basements or cellars, unless that part of the building has at least one side which opens to ground level.

19.5.4 Living rooms, kitchens, utility rooms, halls and passageways

All types of water heating appliance are allowed to be installed within these areas, however further guidance shall be obtained with respect to compliance with the current fire regulations. Consideration shall be given to aesthetic appearance, noise and water vapour resulting in condensation from flueless appliances.

19.5.5 Compartments

Installation of flueless appliances within compartments or cupboards **is not permitted**.

Any compartment used for the installation of a water heating appliance shall be a fixed rigid structure where construction materials, clearances from combustible materials and servicing/inspection access dimensions shall be in accordance with the manufacturer's instructions.

Where the manufacturer does not provide specific information, a minimum clearance of 75 mm should be maintained between the appliance and any combustible materials. Further information can be obtained from the relevant building regulations.

No vents from the compartment or cupboard shall communicate with a bathroom or shower room if the appliance is flue type A or B. In addition, vents shall not communicate with a room used or intended to be used as sleeping accommodation if the appliance is flue type A or B unless the appliance could be properly installed in such a room.

Further generic information with regards to compartments used to house gas appliances (including understair installations) can be referenced in Chapter 14 of this Guide.

19.5.6 Cylinder/airing cupboards and roof space installations

There are no specific requirements over and above that of the industry generic information as given in Chapter 14 for these types of installation. However, as stated previously, flueless appliances are not permitted to be installed in a cylinder or airing cupboard.

19.5.7 External installations

Instantaneous water heaters are not permitted to be installed in any external location. For any other type of water heating appliance they may be installed externally provided the appliance manufacturer permits such an installation without the need for additional protection or, where this is not the case, the appliance must incorporate suitable frost protection and be installed in a weather proof enclosure. The construction of the enclosure shall meet the same constraints as detailed for that of a normal compartment. The enclosure should have a facility to prevent unauthorised access, normally a door lock or hasp and padlock would suffice.

A waterproof fused electrical isolation switch shall be located at an accessible position within the enclosure to positively isolate the appliance and any associated electrical controls.

Ventilation provision into the enclosure shall be in accordance with BS 5440-2 and be installed direct to outside at both high and low level. The low level ventilator should be located at least 300 mm above ground level.

Any permanent openings, including those to facilitate water pipes, gaps around doors and the enclosure structure, ventilation, etc., should not have any minor dimension greater than 10 mm to prevent entry of birds and vermin into the enclosure. These openings should not be less than 5 mm where necessary to prevent blockages. All pipework located externally shall be suitably protected against corrosion, damage and, for water pipes, freezing.

19.6 Flue system

The flue/chimney system shall comply with the manufacturer's instructions and BS 5440-1.

19.6.1 Specific installation requirements for condensing appliances

Any water heater, which operates in a condensing mode shall be installed as per the manufacturer's instruction or, where there is no specific information, to BS 5546. Chimney/flue installation, condensate disposal, setting up combustion (air/gas ratio control adjustment) etc., shall be done in strict accordance with the manufacturer (see appropriate Chapters within this Guide).

The chimney outlet shall be positioned such that the plume does not cause a nuisance either to the user or neighbouring properties. Where this may be a problem the manufacturer will provide additional information including any adaptation which may be available for the chimney outlet to redirect the plume. This can be achieved by, for example:

- rotation of the chimney outlet,
- installation of a deflector elbow,
- use of a plume kit for high level termination of the exhaust outlet.

The termination point needs to allow free dispersal of any plume. It shall not be located within car ports or where any flue gases will be directed towards openings, doorways or windows or close to adjacent structures such as walls, boundary fences and buildings.

The condensate pipe shall be constructed of a material which is resistant to the slightly acidic condensate such as PVC, PVC-U, ABS, etc. The condensate pipe shall be sized and installed in accordance with the manufacturer's instruction. See Chapter 14. for further guidance on the installation and termination of condensate drainage pipe.

19.7 Ventilation

The ventilation provision will be dictated by the appliance type and it's location. It shall comply with the manufacturer's instructions and BS 5440-2 (see Chapter 4 of this Guide).

19.8 Water Supply

Installations must comply with the Water Supply (Water Fittings) Regulations (England and Wales), water byelaws (Scotland), and BS EN 806[2] and BS 8558[3].

Solder shall be "soft" and lead free. Sufficient working pressure at the prescribed flow rate is necessary for mains fed, instantaneous water heaters.

The use of "loose jumper" isolation valves on the water inlet connection may lead to pressure damage with instantaneous water heaters, especially if there are dead legs present.

Adequate filtration is necessary in order to avoid blockage of the small orifice found within the water section of instantaneous water heaters. Storage hot water systems shall also comply with the relevant Building Regulations.

The formation of scale within appliance heat exchangers can cause restricted flow rate, lower temperature increase of water and localised overheating which can lead to premature failure of the heat exchanger (fig 19.7). Any water fittings need to be resistant to corrosion and dezincification, where required.

Fig 19.7 Scaled heat exchange

Other types of corrosion may need to be considered for example:

- the use of ferrous pipe and fittings,
- electrolytic corrosion,
- the presence of solid, foreign matter in contact with galvanised vessels.

Never put corrosion inhibiter into direct cylinders or systems!

If the storage hot water cylinder is to be left empty, any electric immersion water heater shall be permanently disconnected from the electrical supply.

If the water supply for an instantaneous water heater is suspected of being inadequate then the WORKING pressure can be measured with a cold tap operating at the flow rate which will be delivered by the heater – connect the water pressure gauge (fig 19.8) to a convenient point such as a washing machine service valve, turn on a cold tap to the required flow rate (fig 19.9) and read the pressure gauge. Compare the reading with the water heater manufacturer's specification. Typically, 1 bar is specified.

Fig 19.8   Suitable pressure gauge

Fig 19.9   Flow at tap

19.8.1. Dead legs

There are two types of dead leg which could have an adverse affect on instantaneous water heating systems - passive and active.

19.8.1.1 Passive dead leg

This is a redundant section of pipe which serves no useful purpose (fig 19.10). It is usually caused when a storage system is replaced with an instantaneous system. The symptoms will be that the appliance burner stays on for a period of time, usually a matter of seconds after the taps have been turned off; the longer the dead leg, the longer the period. The symptoms will be worse if the pipe contains air instead of water. The remedy is to cut and cap the pipework close to the active pipework to remove the dead leg.

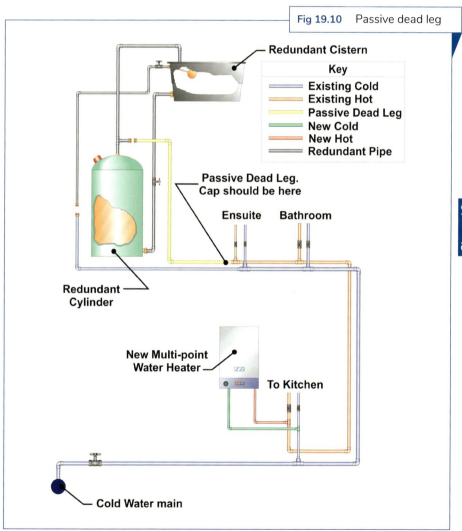

Fig 19.10 Passive dead leg

19.8.1.2 Active dead leg

This is created when two taps are opened simultaneously; only one tap provides hot water (usually the downstairs tap). However, air enters the pipework supplying the upstairs tap and is the trapped when this tap is turned off so forming a dead leg with the symptoms previously explained being evident (fig 19.11). In order to prevent this a non-return valve can be fitted.

Under certain circumstances, dead legs can result in previously heated water being re-heated which can result in a steam rupture of the appliance heat exchanger.

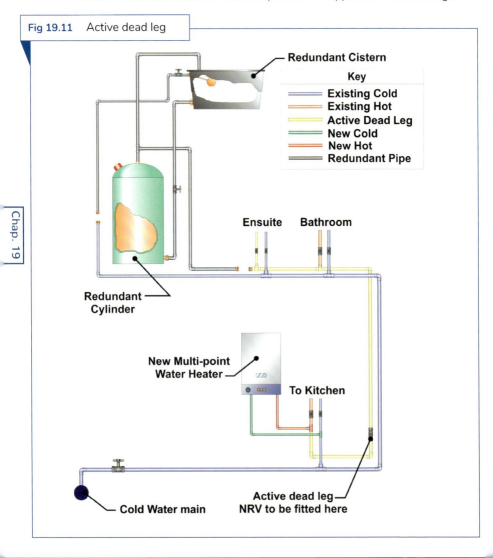

Fig 19.11 Active dead leg

For this reason, most modern appliances have an overheat stat and a pressure relief valve fitted.

19.9 Gas Supply

Gas pipework should be installed in accordance with the GS(I&U)R and BS 6891 or IGEM/UP/2, as appropriate. A suitable isolation valve shall be installed adjacent to the appliance.

19.9.1 Storage water heaters

Generally speaking, the heat input (and gas rate) of storage water heaters is relatively low, in the order of 4 kW net. The gas supply pipe can be as small as 6 mm although it is normal practice to run 15 mm pipe (sometimes the last metre or so will be 8 mm).

19.9.2 Instantaneous water heaters

Multipoint water heaters have by comparison, a relatively high heat input (and gas rate), in the order of 27.3 kW net. The gas supply pipe usually has to be 22 mm. Most instantaneous water heaters are not fitted with an appliance regulator; they need to be supplied with a working pressure of 20 mbar in order to achieve the correct operating pressure (burner pressure). If the gas supply pressure is low the heater will not perform to specification.

19.10 Electrical Supply

Water heating appliances which require an electrical supply shall be installed in accordance with BS 7671. The cable size and fuse rating shall be in accordance with the manufacturer's instructions; normally protection is by a fuse rated at 3 amperes. The means of isolation may be by:

- a three pin plug and an unswitched socket (in order to encourage physical disconnection when work is performed),
- a fused, double pole, switched connection unit (spur box).

Generally speaking it is only multipoint water heaters with fanned flue systems that need an electrical supply. If the appliance is located in a bathroom or shower room all electrical equipment will require to be positioned in accordance with the clearance zones specified by BS 7671. See also Chapter 14; section 14.9.2 for detailed guidance on safe isolation of gas appliances, as applicable.

19.11 Measuring Water Heater Performance

The performance of an instantaneous water heater is defined by the rate of water delivered and by what temperature rise has been achieved.

Typically, a manufacturer will specify the performance, for example 9 l/min at 30 °C temperature rise.

Proceed as follows

Step 1
Prior to measuring these, the burner pressure or preferably the heat input should be checked and corrected, if necessary.

Step 2
A simple alcohol in glass thermometer (fig 19.12) or digital thermometer (fig's 19.13 & 19.14) can be used to measure the temperature of the cold water supply and then that of the hot water, the difference being the rise. Adjust the flow rate at the appliance temperature selector until the temperature rise is as specified (38 °C in this case).

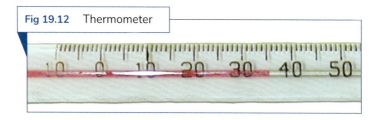

Fig 19.12   Thermometer

Fig 19.13   Cold water temperature

Fig 19.14   Hot water temperature

Step 3

Without altering the hot water flow setting, measure the flow rate; it should be approximately 9 litres per minute.

Various equipment is available to measure the flow rate:

Weir gauge
Water flows through this simple piece of equipment and the level reached in the spill slot indicates the flow rate (fig 19.15).

Fig 19.15　Weir gauge

Combi cup
A variation on the weir gauge. The engineer adjusts the slider which alters the variable orifice in the base of the cup (fig 19.16). When the level in the cup remains constant, the reading is taken from the slider.

Fig 19.16　Combi cup

First principles
Perhaps the most cost effective and accurate method. The time taken to fill a container of a known capacity (usually 1 litre) is measured using a stop watch and the flow rate can then be calculated (fig 19.17).

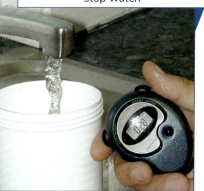

Fig 19.17　1 ltr container & stop watch

Example:

If the temperature rise has been set to 30 °C and the time taken to fill a 1 L vessel is measured as 6.8 seconds then the actual flow rate is;

60 ÷ 6.8 = 8.8 L/min (slightly low).

19.12 Controls for Instantaneous Water Heaters

19.12.1 User controls

There is very little in the way of user controls. Once the pilot light is lit the appliance is fully automatic other than any manual adjustment of water temperature.

19.12.1.1 Gas tap

On some models there is a gas tap (fig's 19.18 & 19.19) which allows the user to select the functions of OFF, IGNITION and MAIN FLAME.

Other models may have push buttons (fig 19.20) which allow the user to select ON, IGNITION and an OFF button.

Flueless; open flued; natural draught, room sealed; and some fanned flue, room sealed instantaneous water heaters have a permanent pilot which ignites the main burner and energises the thermoelectric FSD. The ignition of the permanent pilot is either piezo or electronic, battery powered.

More modern fanned flue, room sealed instantaneous water heaters will have automatic, electronic ignition, mains powered from the printed circuit control board.

Fig 19.18 Control tap

Fig 19.19 Control knob

Fig 19.20 Push button control

19.12.1.2 Temperature control

Throttle

This device throttles the water flow rate (increases or decreases) and is manually operated. It is provided so that the user can alter the water temperature; reducing the water flow rate results in an increased water temperature (fig's 19.21A & 19.21B). This is useful in winter when the incoming cold water temperature is lower than normal.

Fig 19.21A Temp. control

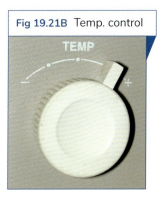

Fig 19.21B Temp. control

19.12.1.3 Thermostat

This is a liquid expansion thermostat with its phial located in the heat exchanger, but it does not control the gas flow. Instead it automatically alters the water flow (like the throttle).

19.12.2 Safety controls & components

19.12.2.1 Isolation valves

These valves are provided for the servicing engineer (fig 19.22). These are usually a manually operated ball valve (screwdriver or lever operation) and are often provided with a test or drain point.

Fig 19.22 Isolation valves

19.12.2.2 The gas section

The housing comprises the gas controls listed in sub-sections 19.12.2.3 to 19.12.2.7.

19.12.2.3 Burner restrictor

This device is either a fixed or adjustable orifice (fig 19.23) or an adjustable butterfly valve. **IT IS SET BY THE MANUFACTURER AND SHALL NOT BE ALTERED**. There is often paint or varnish applied to seal the cap screw.

Fig 19.23   Burner restrictor

19.12.2.4 Flame supervision device

Flueless; open flued; natural draught, room sealed; and some fanned flue room sealed instantaneous water heaters are fitted with a thermoelectric FSD (fig's 19.24, 19.25 & 19.26). More recently, fanned flue, room sealed instantaneous water heaters are fitted with a flame rectification FSD.

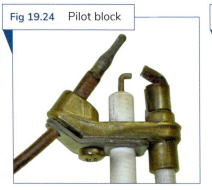

Fig 19.24   Pilot block

Fig 19.25   Electrode

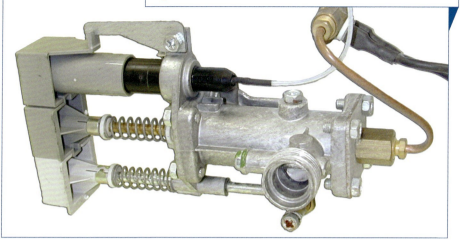

Fig 19.26   Gas control section with thermoelectric valve

19.12.2.5   Atmospheric sensing device

All flueless and open flued instantaneous water heaters will be fitted with an ASD (fig 19.27).

19.12.2.6   Interrupted thermocouple circuits

In order to protect the appliance against overheating or heat exchanger blockage (flueless heaters), a high limit or overheat thermo-disc stat is attached to the heat exchanger and wired so as to interrupt the current flow generated by the thermocouple which will result in pilot and main burner shutdown (fig's 19.28, 19.29 & 19.30).

Instead of an overheat stat, a spillage sensor may be fitted in the draught diverter of open flue heaters.

Fig 19.27   ASD

Fig 19.28 Thermo-disc Interrupter

Fig 19.29 Interrupter connections

Fig 19.30 Thermo-disc interrupter secured to heat exchanger

19.12.2.7 Main gas valve

This is a disc on seat type valve which is operated by the difference in water pressure created when the hot water tap is operated. Its closure is effected by a spring when the tap is turned off (fig 19.31).

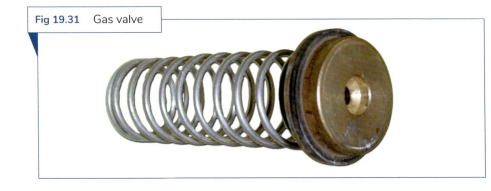

Fig 19.31 Gas valve

19.12.2.8 Water section

The housing comprises the water controls listed in sub-sections 19.12.2.9 to 19.12.2.13.

19.12.2.9 Water throttle or water governor

One or other of these will be fitted to the appliance in order to deliver the correct water flow rate (fig's 19.32 & 19.33).

Fig 19.32   Throttle screw

Fig 19.33   Throttle assembly

19.12.2.10 Venturi

This device is necessary in order to create low water pressure when the hot water tap is operated. It also restricts the water flow through the appliance and different sizes are specified for mains or cistern-fed appliance models (fig's 19.34 & 19.35).

Fig 19.34   Venturi

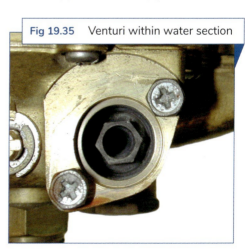

Fig 19.35   Venturi within water section

19.12.2.11 Slow ignition device

The purpose of the slow ignition device is to prevent explosive ignition; instantaneous water heaters have a relatively large heat input. It can be water operated (fig 19.36 & 19.37) or gas operated (fig 19.38).

Fig 19.36 Slow ignition device

Fig 19.37 Slow ignition device in water section

Fig 19.38 Gas operated slow ignition device

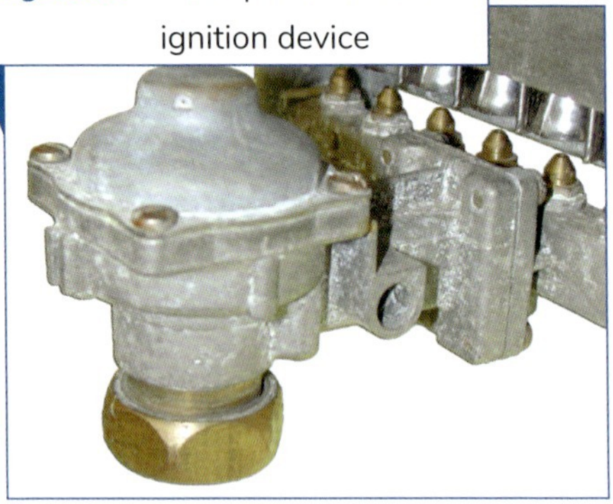

19.12.2.12 Diaphragm

The diaphragm separates the water section into two chambers and is normally clamped between two plates (fig's 19.39 & 19.40). When subjected to high pressure below and low pressure above, it flexes and the push rod opens the main gas valve.

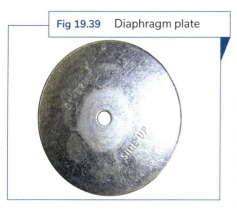

Fig 19.39 Diaphragm plate

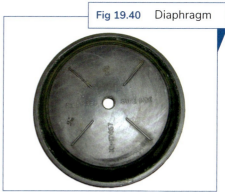

Fig 19.40 Diaphragm

19.12.2.13 Filters

Not really classed as controls but essential. The quality of water can vary (especially with private water supplies) and impurities can cause blockages with the water section.

19.12.2.14 Fanned flue and pressure/flow sensing

Fanned assisted flues require a pressure switch (sometimes used in conjunction with a venturi) in order to prevent appliance operation in the event of flue fan failure (fig's 19.42 & 19.43).

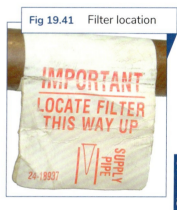

Fig 19.41 Filter location

Fig 19.42 Fan venturi

Fig 19.43 Fan assembly

19.12.2.15 Multifunctional control unit

These will differ in the way that they control the gas flow to the burner. The model shown (fig 19.44) is from a Vokera Aqua Nova water Heater and gives a modulating gas rate depending on the water temperature which is measured by a thermister.

Fig 19.44   Multifunction valve

19.12.2.16 Flow switch

Used to detect the demand for hot water (fig 19.45). Used instead of the differential valve found on non-electric appliances. Often utilises a magnetically operated switch.

Fig 19.45   Flow switch

19.13 Controls for Storage Water Heaters

19.13.1 User controls

Like its instantaneous counterpart, there is very little in the way of user controls on these appliances; once lit they tend to be left on 24 hours per day. A permanent pilot with piezo ignition is normally encountered.

The only user control is the thermostat. This is a liquid expansion operated gas valve (either a separate control or part of a multifunctional unit) with its phial located in the heat exchanger.

Older appliance thermostats were clamped directly onto the heat exchanger, there was no capillary tube or phial required. Once the temperature is reached the valve will close and the burner flame will reduce to by-pass rate.

Some stats are not user adjustable but can be altered by the commissioning engineer depending on whether the water cylinder is direct or indirect. As most water circulation is by gravity (as opposed to pumped) it is important to ensure a constant rise of the flow pipe otherwise, if there is poor circulation, the stat will operate before the circulation is established due to the hot water not escaping from the heat exchanger.

19.13.2 Safety controls & components

19.13.2.1 Isolation valve

This valve is provided for the servicing engineer. It is usually a manually operated ball valve (screwdriver or lever) or taper plug valve.

19.13.2.2 Liquid expansion thermostat

This device may be fixed by the engineer during commissioning or the temperature setting can be adjusted by the user depending on the appliance model (fig's 19.46 & 19.47).

Fig 19.46 Thermostat

Fig 19.47 Thermostat control

19.13.2.3 Atmospheric sensing device

Open flued storage water heaters 14 kW gross or less installed in bedrooms shall be fitted with an ASD.

19.13.2.4 Multifunctional unit

The multifunctional unit (fig's 19.48 & 19.49) comprises the controls listed as follows (and also the stat detailed above).

Pressure regulator or adjustable orifice

This allows for adjustment of the operating pressure in accordance with the manufacturer's instructions.

Flame supervision device

Open flued, storage water heaters are fitted with a thermoelectric FSD.

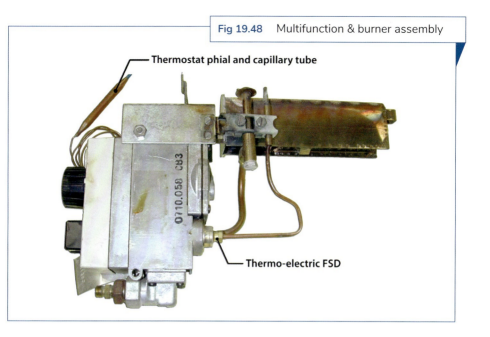

Fig 19.48   Multifunction & burner assembly

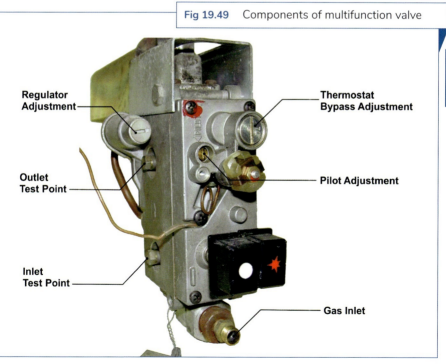

Fig 19.49   Components of multifunction valve

19.14 Commissioning

In all cases the manufacturer's commissioning procedure shall be complied with.

A generic procedure is detailed below:

19.14.1 Commissioning procedure for flueless instantaneous sink water heaters

1. Check site –
    1.1 Suitability of location (BS 5546)
    1.2 Clearances from obstacles.
    1.3 Proximity to combustibles.
    1.4 Room volume/ventilation requirements (direct to outside).
    1.5 Openable window.
    1.6 Five minute warning label.
    1.7 Packaging removal/assembly and fixing.
    1.8 Adequate supplies:
        1.8.1 gas,
        1.8.2 water.
2. Test for tightness –
    2.1 Gas.
    2.2 Water.
3. Purge supplies –
    3.1 Gas.
    3.2 Water.
4. Test operation and performance –
    4.1 Control devices:
        4.1.1 isolation valves:
            4.1.1.1 gas,
            4.1.1.2 water.
        4.1.2 control knob.
        4.1.3 ignition system.
        4.1.4 temperature adjustment throttle.

- 4.1.5 water taps:
  - 4.1.5.1 cold,
  - 4.1.5.2 hot.
- 4.2 Safety devices:
  - 4.2.1 flame safety device,
  - 4.2.2 spillage device,
  - 4.2.3 atmosphere sensing device (visual only),
  - 4.2.4 gas escapes,
  - 4.2.5 burner is extinguished when hot tap is turned off.
- 4.3 Check burner pressure and heat input.
- 4.4 Check flame picture:
  - 4.4.1 pilot,
  - 4.4.2 main,
  - 4.4.3 if required by manufacturer, perform combustion analysis.
- 4.5 Check water flow rate and temperature rise.
- 4.6 Check the safe operation of appliance is not affected by extract fans or re-circulatory fans.

5. Instruct the customer –
   - 5.1 Correct usage (leave all instructions with customer).
   - 5.2 Maintenance requirements (owner of appliance advised in writing).
   - 5.3 Advise user on the benefits and limitations of a CO detector. Indicate that it is not a substitute for proper installation and maintenance of the appliance.
   - 5.4 Gas emergency procedure.
   - 5.5 Frost protection.

19.14.2 Commissioning procedure for room sealed instantaneous multipoint water heaters

1. Check site –
    1.1 Clearances from obstacles.
    1.2 Proximity to combustibles.
    1.3 Suitability of flue:
        1.3.1 adequate flue length (wall thickness, bends, etc.),
        1.3.2 terminal position,
        1.3.3 masonry reinstatement.
    1.4 Ventilation requirements (compartment).
    1.5 Assembly and fixing (casing seal, dead legs, etc.).
    1.6 Packaging removal.
    1.7 Adequate supplies:
        1.7.1 gas,
        1.7.2 water.
2. Test for tightness –
    2.1 Gas.
    2.2 Water.
3. Purge supplies –
    3.1 gas,
    3.2 water.
4. Test operation and performance –
    4.1 Control devices.
        4.1.1 isolation valves:
            4.1.1.1 gas,
            4.1.1.2 water.
        4.1.2 control knob.
        4.1.3 ignition system.
        4.1.4 temperature adjustment throttle.
        4.1.5 water taps:
            4.1.5.1 cold,
            4.1.5.2 hot.

4.2 Safety.
- 4.2.1 flame safety device,
- 4.2.2 gas escape,
- 4.2.3 burner is extinguished when hot tap is turned off.

4.3 Check burner pressure and heat input.

4.4 Check flame picture.
- 4.4.1 pilot,
- 4.4.2 main,
- 4.4.3 if required by the manufacturer, perform a combustion analysis.

4.5 Check water flow rate and temperature rise.

5. Electrical checks –

These will be dependent on what alterations/installations have been carried out. Basically the water heating circuits shall be checked for;

5.1 Conformity with BS 7671:
- 5.1.1 supplementary bonding,
- 5.1.2 provision of safe isolation of appliance from single point,
- 5.1.3 fuse/mcb/cable sizes,
- 5.1.4 jointing/securing/colour coding.

5.2 Earth continuity (<1 Ohm).

5.3 Resistance to earth (L-E, N-E).

5.4 Polarity.

5.5 Correct operation of circuits.

Engineers shall be suitably qualified and have adequate test equipment.

6. Instruct customer –
- 6.1 Correct usage (leave manufacturer's instructions).
- 6.2 Maintenance requirements (owner of appliance advised in writing).
- 6.3 Gas emergency procedure.
- 6.4 Frost protection requirements.

19.15 Maintenance

In all cases the manufacturer's maintenance and servicing procedures shall be complied with.

A generic procedure is detailed below:

19.15.1 Servicing procedure for flueless instantaneous sink water heaters

1. Check site –
   1.1 Ask customer regarding operation/performance of appliance.
   1.2 Test operation and visually check for obvious defects.
   1.3 Suitability of location (BS 5546).
   1.4 Clearances from obstacles.
   1.5 Proximity to combustibles.
   1.6 Room volume/ventilation requirements (direct to outside).
   1.7 Openable window.
   1.8 Five minute warning label.
   1.9 Adequate supplies:
       1.9.1 gas,
       1.9.2 water.
2. Test for tightness –
   2.1 Gas.
   2.2 Water.
3. Dismantle and clean –
   3.1 Remove tap handles and casing.
   3.2 Remove and clean:
       3.2.1 pilot (ASD) and main burners,
       3.2.2 gas and water sections,
       3.2.3 examine/replace washers, "O" rings and diaphragm,
       3.2.4 grease (silicone) push rod and water governor,
       3.2.5 check and clean venturi and slow ignition device.
   3.3 Clean heating body (combustion chamber and heat exchanger), descale if hard water as required.

4. Test operation and performance –
   4.1 Control devices:
      4.1.1 isolation valves,
         4.1.1.1 gas,
         4.1.1.2 water.
      4.1.2 control knob.
      4.1.3 ignition system.
      4.1.4 temperature adjustment throttle.
      4.1.5 water taps;
         4.1.5.1 cold,
         4.1.5.2 hot.
   4.2 Safety devices:
      4.2.1 flame safety device,
      4.2.2 spillage device (metal plate),
      4.2.3 atmosphere sensing device (visual only),
      4.2.4 gas escapes,
      4.2.5 burner is extinguished when hot tap is turned off,
      4.2.6 where required perform a combustion analysis.
   4.3 Check burner pressure and heat input.
   4.4 Check flame picture:
      4.4.1 pilot,
      4.4.2 main.
   4.5 Check water flow rate and temperature rise.
   4.6 Check the safe operation of appliance is not affected by extract fans or re-circulatory fans.
5. Advise the customer –
   5.1 Correct usage.
   5.2 Maintenance requirements.
   5.3 Advise user on the benefits and limitations of a CO detector. Indicate that it is not a substitute for proper installation and maintenance of the appliance.
   5.4 Gas emergency procedure.
   5.5 Frost protection.

19.15.2 Servicing procedure for room sealed instantaneous multipoint water heaters

1. Check site –
    1.1 Ask customer regarding operation/performance of appliance.
    1.2 Test operation and visually check for obvious defects.
    1.3 Suitability of location (BS 5546).
    1.4 Clearances from obstacles.
    1.5 Proximity to combustibles.
    1.6 Ventilation requirements (compartment).
    1.7 Suitability of flue:
        1.7.1 adequate flue length (wall thickness, bends, etc.),
        1.7.2 terminal position,
        1.7.3 masonry reinstatement.
    1.8 Adequate supplies:
        1.8.1 gas,
        1.8.2 water.
2. Test for tightness –
    2.1 Gas.
    2.2 Water.
3. Dismantle and clean –
    3.1 Remove casing and examine seal (including flue seals).
    3.2 Remove and clean:
        3.2.1 pilot and main burners,
        3.2.2 gas and water sections,
        3.2.3 examine/replace washers, "O" rings and diaphragm,
        3.2.4 grease (silicone) push rod and water governor,
        3.2.5 venturi and slow ignition device.
    3.3 Clean heating body (combustion chamber and heat exchanger), descale if hard water.
4. Test operation and performance –
    4.1 Control devices.
        4.1.1 isolation valves;
            4.1.1.1 gas,
            4.1.1.2 water.
        4.1.2 control knob.
        4.1.3 ignition system.

- 4.1.4 temperature adjustment throttle (Summer/Winter) or thermostat.
- 4.1.5 water taps;
  - 4.1.5.1 cold,
  - 4.1.5.2 hot.
- 4.2 Safety devices.
  - 4.2.1 flame safety device.
  - 4.2.2 gas escapes.
  - 4.2.3 burner is extinguished when hot tap is turned off (dead legs and push rod).
  - 4.2.4 pressure switch (if fanned flue).
- 4.3 Check burner pressure and heat input.
- 4.4 Check flame picture:
  - 4.4.1 pilot,
  - 4.4.2 main,
  - 4.4.3 if required by the manufacturer, perform a combustion analysis.
- 4.5 Check water flow rate and temperature rise (adjust water throttle if applicable).

5. Electrical checks –

Inspect and test as follows.

- 5.1 Conformity with BS 7671:
  - 5.1.1 supplementary bonding.
  - 5.1.2 provision of safe isolation of whole system from single point.
  - 5.1.3 fuse/mcb/cable sizes.
- 5.2 Earth continuity (<1 Ohm).
- 5.3 Resistance to earth (L-E, N-E).
- 5.4 Polarity.
- 5.5 Correct operation of circuits.

Operatives shall be suitably qualified and have adequate test equipment.

6. Instruct the customer –
   - 6.1 Correct usage (leave manufacturer's instructions).
   - 6.2 Maintenance requirements (owner of appliance advised in writing).
   - 6.3 Gas emergency procedure.

Chapter 20
Gas Meters

		Page No.
20.1	Introduction	20.1
20.2	Acronyms, Terms and Definitions	20.2
20.3	Planning and Exchange of Information	20.4
20.4	Competency	20.5
	20.4.1 Working on existing gas meter installations	20.5
20.5	Gas Meters	20.9
	20.5.1 Determining the size of a meter	20.11
20.6	Gas Meter Housing	20.13
20.7	Low Pressure Gas Meter Installation	20.16
	20.7.1 Scope	20.16
	20.7.2 Low pressure meter installation design	20.16
	20.7.3 Location	20.17
	20.7.4 Multiple meter installations	20.18
	20.7.5 Installation of low pressure meters	20.19
	20.7.5.2 Pre-installation	20.19
	20.7.5.3 Electrical	20.21
	20.7.5.4 Fixing	20.21

Chapter 20
Gas Meters

			Page No.
	20.7.6	Commissioning low pressure meters	20.22
		20.7.6.1 Operating pressure	20.22
		20.7.6.2 Standing pressure	20.23
		20.7.6.3 Regulator	20.23
		20.7.6.4 Meter	20.24
		20.7.6.5 Notices	20.24
	20.7.7	Meter relocation	20.25
20.8	Medium Pressure Fed Meter Installations		20.27
	20.8.1	Scope	20.27
	20.8.2	Medium pressure fed meter installation design	20.28
	20.8.3	MP primary regulator including the protection system	20.30
	20.8.4	Meter inlet valve	20.31
	20.8.5	Vent pipe	20.32
	20.8.6	Meter box	20.33
	20.8.7	Relocation of medium pressure fed meters	20.34
		20.8.7.1 Risk assessment	20.34
	20.8.8	Medium pressure metering labels	20.35
	20.8.9	Routine inspection and maintenance of the MP meter installation	20.36
20.9	Meter Removal		20.37
20.10	Secondary Meters		20.38

Chapter 20
Gas Meters

Page No.

References in this Chapter

[1] BS 6400-1: 2016 Specification for installation, exchange, relocation, maintenance and removal of gas meters with a maximum capacity not exceeding 6 m^3/h. Low pressure (2nd family gases).

[2] BS 6400-2: 2018 Specification for installation, exchange, relocation, maintenance and removal of gas meters with a maximum capacity not exceeding 6 m^3/h. Medium pressure (2nd family gases).

[3] BS EN 1359: 2017 Gas meters. Diaphragm gas meters.

[4] BS EN 14236: 2018 Ultrasonic domestic gas meters.

[5] BS 476-7: 1997 Fire tests on building materials and structures. Method of test to determine the classification of the surface spread of flame of products.

[6] IGE/TD/4 Edition 4 +A: 2013 PE and steel gas services and service pipework

Chapter 20
Gas Meters

20.1 Introduction

The Office of the Gas and Electricity Markets (Ofgem) is an organisation who's primary interests are to existing and future gas customers. Its powers and duties include security of gas supplies, ensure competition, price control, reduction of greenhouse gases (smart metering and feed in tariffs, etc.) and enforcement of legislation as for example under the Gas Act 1986 with control over the utility suppliers. Ofgem is governed by the Gas and Electricity Markets Authority (GEMA).

Any supplier of gas must be licensed and approved by Ofgem. In addition, any company or organisation which installs primary meters must be registered as a SPAA* Approved Meter Installer (AMI).

Ofgem has transferred the role of approving meter installers to SPAA - Supply Point Administration Agreement – on 29th March 2017. Ofgem Approved Meter Installers (OAMI) will now be known as SPAA Approved Meter Installer (AMI).

Approved meter installers, under the terms of registration must operate to set approved Codes of Practice. These are:

- CoP 1a - Installation of low pressure meter installations with badged capacities not exceeding 6 m^3/h.
- CoP 1b - Installation of low pressure meter installations with badged capacities exceeding 6 m^3/h but not exceeding 1076 m^3/h.
- CoP 1c - Installation of higher pressure installations and low pressure installations not covered by COP 1a or COP 1b.

The appropriate British and Industry Standards are used to supplement these procedures. In the case of this guide reference will be made to BS 6400[1] part 1 (low pressure natural gas meter installations) and BS 6400[2] part 2 (medium pressure natural gas meter installations).

20.2 Acronyms, Terms and Definitions

To promote commonality of terminology throughout the gas industry specific acronyms and terms are used to describe different pressures within the installation (both design and operational), supply types, gas fittings, locations and sections within a gas network or installation.

The correct interpretation of industry documents relies on the engineer being familiar with these. A full list of acronyms and terms can be found in the standard, some of which are listed in this Chapter:

- **AECV - Additional Emergency Control Valve**. A valve which is not the emergency control valve but is intended to be used by the customer to shut off the gas in an emergency. This may be located either at the meter within the installation pipework. Depending on it's location it may only isolate part of the customers gas installation.
- **DMIP - Design Maximum Incidental Pressure.** This is the maximum pressure an installation is allowed to experience under fault conditions (limited by safety devices) when the installation is operated at design pressure. The DMIP of the British low pressure network is 200 mbar and 2.7 bar for medium pressure.
- **DMP - Design Minimum Pressure.** The minimum pressure at the end of the gas service when the system is operating at its design flow rate under extreme gas supply conditions. This can be as low as 19 mbar for low pressure supplies.
- **DP - Design Pressure.** The pressure used in the calculation methods to design a gas system. For low pressure networks this is 75 mbar and 2 bar for medium pressure.
- **ECV - Emergency Control Valve.** A valve installed at the end of a service pipe which is designed for use by the consumer to isolate the gas supply in an emergency.
- **Interconnecting Pipework.** Pipework assembled within the meter installation.

- **LP - Low Pressure.** A gas supply with a maximum operating pressure not exceeding 75 mbar.
- **LOP - Lowest Operating Pressure.** The lowest pressure a gas system can be operated at under normal operating conditions. The LOP of the gas supply is provided by the gas transporter.
- **MOP - Maximum Operating Pressure.** This is the maximum pressure a gas system can operate at continuously without causing damage under normal operating conditions. For a LP network this is 75 mbar and 2 bar for MP.
- **MIEFV - Metering Installation Excess Flow Valve.** This device is normally incorporated as part of the primary regulator assembly. Its main purpose is to automatically shut off or restrict the gas supply when the flow of gas exceeds a predetermined level.
- **MIV - Meter Inlet Valve.** Located upstream and adjacent to the primary meter this valve is used to isolate the supply of gas to the meter. It is normally fitted down stream of the primary regulator.
- **MP - Medium Pressure.** A gas supply where the pressure is greater than 75 mbar, but does not exceed 2 bar.
- **Meter Box.** Purpose made compartment designed and prefabricated to accommodate a meter installation.
- **Meter Compound.** Area or room designed and constructed to contain one or more meters with their associated gas fittings.
- **Meter Housing.** Meter box or meter compound external to the building.
- **Pliable Connector (Semi-rigid Connector).** Stainless steel tube formed with annular corrugations and having factory fitted ends connections.

20.3 Planning and Exchange of Information

At the initial design stage of a building there shall be consultation between those responsible for the design and planning of the development and the relevant gas transporter or supplier to ensure that the district supply is of a suitable pressure and capacity to meet the load requirements of the proposed gas installation.

Dissemination of information between both parties is important to ensure that the proposed metering installation is fit for purpose and installed in a timely manner. The following information shall be made available:

- Proposed gas load including any additional requirements for future expansion.
- Gas service supply pressures (DMP, LOP, MOP, DP & DMIP) and proposed installation (size and route).
- Location to building plan and boundary, internal or external location, meter housing type (surface/recessed/semi-concealed, purpose constructed enclosure) and ventilation requirements.
- Timescale - initial proposed time frame for the installation including service installation. Actual installation dates should be agreed.
- Any special appliance requirements (compressor, non-return valve, etc.).

20.4 Competency

Where a new primary meter (a meter used for measuring the quantity of gas used) is being installed or exchanged, the gas engineer undertaking that work on behalf of the Gas Supplier must be competent as well as registered as an Approved Meter Installer (AMI) for the business – known as the Meter Asset Manager (MAM) – under the Supply Point Administration Agreement (SPAA). The MAM operates under the guidelines of the Meter Asset Manager Code of Practice (MAMCoP).

Work (as defined under the GS(I&U)R) on existing gas meter installations involving competent Gas Safe registered engineers however, may not require registration as an AMI and this is discussed in more detail within sub-section 20.4.1.

Guidance on working on primary meter installations is provided by Gas Safe Register TB 127 'Gas industry guidance on work on meter installations', developed by IGEM on behalf of the MAMCoP management board, and what follows draws on elements of this guidance. The full TB can be accessed at **www.gassaferegister.co.uk**

20.4.1 Working on existing gas meter installations

The scope of the guidance in TB 127 applies to Great Britain* and to:

- predominately primary meters for measuring the quantity of gas used, but may also apply to some secondary meters,
- maximum capacity not exceeding 16 m^3/h,
- low-pressure Natural gas service, i.e. not exceeding 75 mbar; and
- installations covered by the GS(I&U)R – domestic and non-domestic (excluding an industrial process).

Before working on an existing meter installation it is important to define the work activity, as this will instruct us on the minimum competency requirements. Simply and for the maximum meter capacity covered by the above scope, work is broken into three distinct categories, which are shown in table 20.1.

* *Great Britain is defined as England, Scotland and Wales. It does not include Northern Ireland, Channel Islands or Isle of Man, which form the political union of the United Kingdom.*

Table 20.1 Three categories of work in relation to existing gas meter installations having a maximum capacity not exceeding 16 m³/h

Category	Description	Notes
A	Temporarily removing and refitting a meter – disconnection of an existing meter at the inlet and/or outlet connections and subsequent reconnection WITHOUT changing the meter position.	1. Minor unintentional shifts in the position of meter may be treated as Category A work. 2. Disconnection/reconnection would occur, for example to enable hot working. IT DOES NOT include refitting involving adding or taking away any component within the meter installation, for example a length of pipe.
B	Repositioning an existing meter using the existing fittings.	1. The new position will be within the same location, i.e. within the same cupboard/compartment, as the original meter position. 2. IT DOES NOT include repositioning involving adding or taking away any component within the meter installation, for example a length of pipe.
C	Relocating or repositioning an existing meter – using different or additional fittings, or when fittings are removed.	1. This means the length of pipework between the outlet of the ECV to the inlet of the meter will change. This may affect pressure drop, which in turn could affect performance of the whole gas installation; it is not permitted to make such alterations that would adversely affect the pressure delivered to appliances.

Having defined the categories of work (A, B or C) tables 20.2a, b & c can be used to identify the minimum competency requirements for engineers, including the applicable standards relevant to working on an existing gas meter installation.

Table 20.2a Category A – Temporarily removing and refitting an existing meter with a maximum capacity not exceeding 16 m³/h

Who can do the work?	Minimum ACS competencies required		Applicable Standards
	Domestic	Non-Domestic	
Gas Safe registered engineers	• Installation – CCN1 or CMA1 • Tightness testing & purging – CCN1	• Installation – CCN1 or CESP1 or CMA1 • Tightness testing & purging – TPCP1 or TPCP1A	BS 6400-1 IGEM/GM/6 IGEM/GM/8 IGE/UP/1 IGE/UP/1A IGEM/UP/1B IGEM/UP/1C

Note: There is no requirement to have the work pre-authorised by the MAM

Table 20.2b Category B – Repositioning an existing meter with a maximum capacity not exceeding 16 m³/h using the same fittings

Who can do the work?	Minimum ACS competencies required		Applicable Standards
	Domestic	Non-Domestic	
Gas Safe registered engineers	• Installation – CCN1 or CMA1 + MET1 or MET2, as appropriate • Tightness testing & purging – CCN1	• Installation – CCN1 or CESP1 or CMA1 + MET1 or MET2, as appropriate • Tightness testing & purging – TPCP1 or TPCP1A	BS 6400-1 IGEM/GM/6 IGEM/GM/8 IGE/UP/1 IGE/UP/1A IGEM/UP/1B IGEM/UP/1C

Note: There is no requirement to have the work pre-authorised by the MAM

Table 20.2c Category C – Relocating a meter, or repositioning a meter with a maximum capacity not exceeding 16 m^3/h using different fittings

Who can do the work?	Minimum ACS competencies required		Applicable Standards
	Domestic	Non-Domestic	
Gas Safe registered engineers + Approved Meter Installers	• Installation – CCN1 or CMA1 + MET1 or MET2, as appropriate • Tightness testing & purging – CCN1	• Installation – CCN1 or CESP1 or CMA1 + MET1 or MET2 or MET4, as appropriate • Tightness testing & purging – TPCP1 or TPCP1A	BS 6400-1 IGEM/GM/6 IGEM/GM/8 IGE/UP/1 IGEM/UP/1B IGE/UP/1A IGEM/UP/1C

Note: Pre-authorisation of the MAM will be required before work starts and the MAM should be notified after the work is complete (although the MAM may wavier this requirement during pre-authorisation).

NOTE 1: For category B or C work, it is recommended that on completion of works a permanent record in the form of a tag or label be left on the meter installation providing details of your name, contact details and brief description of works undertaken.

NOTE 2: Work on existing gas meters DOES NOT include adjusting the meter regulator.

Where the work you are undertaking doesn't directly involve the gas meter installation, i.e. you are working around the location of the meter, you must be mindful that such work doesn't diminish any existing provisions relating to access to the meter installation and the ECV (including reading the meter index), ventilation provisions, electrical safety, associated labelling including safety advice and contact details, etc.

ACS Codes

CCN1 – Core domestic natural gas safety	MET4 – Emergency service provider & gas meter installer
CMA1 – Domestic gas meter installer	TPCP1A – Non-domestic natural gas testing & purging
CESP1 – Emergency service provider	TPCP1 – Non-domestic natural gas; LPG; other gases testing & purging.
MET1 & 2 – Domestic natural gas meters	

20.5 Gas Meters

Domestic gas meters may be either diaphragm or electronic. Their designation, depending on design, may be U6 or G4 for diaphragm meters and E6 for electronic (ultrasonic) meters. Their standard maximum designed flow rate (Q_{max}) is 6 m^3/h. The meter casing may be constructed from pressed steel or plastics such as GRP. Plastic cased meters are normally intended for semi-concealed installations.

Any meter used in an internal location must be fire resistant. Meters marked with a 'T' or have no 'SJ' mark can be considered as fire resistant. New steel cased diaphragm meters shall be designed to conform with BS EN 1359[3] whereas new electronic (ultrasonic) meters shall conform to BS EN 14236[4]. Smart meters which measure the gas consumption and remotely transmit this "real time" data to the gas supplier are normally of the electronic type.

Meters may be either credit or prepayment and will incorporate a test point at its outlet, either on the boss or liner. Prepayment primary meters must not be used to supply secondary meter(s). Where a secondary meter is installed it shall have a MIV located as close as practical to the meter inlet connection.

The pressure absorption through any primary meter should not exceed 4 mbar at a flow rate of 6 m^3/h with a DMP of 19 mbar at the outlet of the ECV.

Common types of domestic gas meter are shown in fig's 20.1 to 20.7.

Fig 20.1 Ultrasonic meter

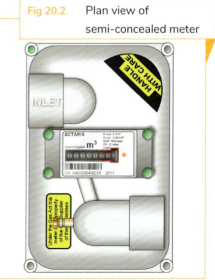

Fig 20.2 Plan view of semi-concealed meter

Fig 20.3 Steel cased diaphragm meter

Fig 20.4 Coin operated prepayment meter

Fig 20.5 Diaphragm electronic token meter (quantum meter)

Fig 20.6 Ultrasonic electronic token meter (quantum meter)

Fig 20.7 Ultrasonic smart meter

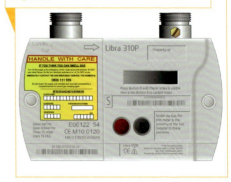

Meters shall be kept secure during transit with the Inlet and outlet connections appropriately capped to prevent the entry of debris. Diaphragm meters shall be kept in the upright position at all times.

20.5.1   Determining the size of a meter

The capacity of the gas meter shall be such that it can pass a sufficient quantity of gas to meet the demands of the gas installation with minimal pressure loss across the metering installation. When considering the installation of a new appliance or exchanging an existing appliance for one with a higher heat input, the meter should be checked to ensure it is capable of meeting the additional gas demand.

To determine the size of the gas meter we require to know the maximum gas flow rate of the installation. This can be calculated by using the manufacturer's stated heat input (gross) for each appliance. Note that in this account we use the GROSS heat input, therefore where the manufacturer states a net figure we require to multiply this by 1.11 (conversion factor for natural gas).

Since it is unlikely that all appliances will be on at any one time, a diversity factor is applied where there is more than two appliances, depending on each appliances level of use (table 20.3). Where there is only one or two appliances installed no diversity factor is applied with the gas consumption calculated on the total heat input of the installation.

Table 20.3   Appliance diversity factors used for meter sizing

Appliance Type	Diversity Factor
Central Heating Appliance (except combi boiler)	1
Unit Heater	1
Circulator	1
Combination Boiler	0.8
Instantaneous Water Heater	0.8
Sink Water Heater	0.6
Room Heaters	0.6
Tumble Dryer	0.6
Hotplate	0.6
Ovens	0.6
Cookers	0.4
Refrigerators	0

Example of meter sizing calculation:

The following shows the calculation methods used when sizing a meter, remember to convert any net heat input to gross.

Appliance	Max. Heat Input (kW Gross)		Diversity Factor		Load (kW)
Combination boiler	40.0	X	0.8	=	32.0
Gas fire	6.43	X	0.6	=	3.858
Oven	19.40	X	0.6	=	11.64
6 burner hob	12.60	X	0.6	=	7.56
			Total gas load	=	55.058 kW

Total gas rate (m³/h) = $\dfrac{\text{Gas Load (kW)} \times 3.6}{\text{Calorific value (MJ/m}^3\text{)}}$

$= \dfrac{55.058 \text{ kW} \times 3.6}{38.76 \text{ MJ/m}^3}$

$= 5.11 \text{ m}^3/\text{h}$

A U6, G4 or E6 meter would have adequate capacity for this installation (6 m³/h).

20.6 Gas Meter Housing

Domestic gas meter boxes come in a variety of different shapes and sizes to suit different applications. They are normally constructed of GRP and designed to allow ease of access for both customer and gas engineer using a common style meter key. They are sized to allow adequate space for installation, maintenance, exchange and adjustment of both the meter and its associated fittings.

All meter housings must be approved by the gas transporter as fit for purpose. In general terms they shall:

- Protect the meter and associated fittings against the weather and any acts of vandalism.
- Be manufactured of a material which is resistant to the effects of being exposed to gas and as such shall not allow any gas escape within the box to enter into a wall cavity or the premises.
- Be fire resistant by preventing the surface spread of flames in accordance with BS 476[5] part 7, Class 2.
- Allow ease of access by the customer using a special key (generally the industry designed common meter box key with a triangular key way is supplied with most meter boxes). The ECV must be readily accessible with ease of operation.
- Be appropriately identified for use as a gas meter box by being permanently marked with a letter 'G' (letter to be 24 mm high).

All meter housings shall be appropriately ventilated with purpose designed non-closeable ventilation. This may be via ventilators in the housing door or through the design of the housing, i.e. gaps around the access door, loose fitting box on the wall plate, etc. The free area of the ventilation shall be a minimum of 2 % of the plan area split evenly between high and low level.

For semi-concealed meter boxes the ventilation can only be at high level hence the ventilation is increased to a free area not less than 6 % of the plan area.

The different types of meter housing are:

- **Surface mounted** - a purpose made compartment designed to be attached to the external wall of a dwelling with no alteration to the building structure. This type of box accepts a variety of different meters and their associated fittings such as steel cased diaphragm, ultrasonic, etc.

Fig 20.8   Surface mounted meter box

- **Built-in** - a purpose made compartment which is designed to be inset into the external wall of a building (normally during construction) for a less intrusive finish than a surface mounted box. Due to the depth of the box it intrudes into the wall cavity. No fixings are normally required for this box as it is normally securely bedded in mortar during construction. As with the surface mounted box a variety of meters and their associated fittings can be installed.

Fig 20.9   Built in meter box

- **Semi-concealed** - this purpose made compartment is partially buried into the ground. It is normally coloured brown to allow it to "blend" into it's surroundings. Only corrosion resistant plastic cased meters specifically designed and manufactured for installation into a semi-concealed box can be installed.

Fig 20.10   Semi-concealed meter box

- **Semi-buried** - very similar to the semi-concealed box however, it is not buried as deep. It is specifically designed and manufactured to allow the installation of a steel cased diaphragm meter in a low level position.
- **Purpose built housing** - this type of housing may be prefabricated or constructed by the customer in line with the transporters recommendations. They are generally free standing structures located away from the building.

Fig 20.11   Semi-buried meter box

Damage to the meter box or housing may be repaired using appropriate materials. Where the meter box is built in, any minor repair to the box needs to ensure a gas tight seal. It should be noted that in some occasions hammer screws through each side of a built in meter box may have been used to secure the box. This is normally due to it not being installed at the time of construction or a damaged box has been replaced. This is only acceptable for low pressure installations only (this method is strictly forbidden for medium pressure fed installations) and where the screw heads have been sealed to ensure a gas tight seal.

For **low pressure** installations any main equipotential bonds within the box may exit a built-in meter box via the rear pipe spigot or bottom exit. The box shall not be pierced or drilled.

For **medium pressure** fed meter installations pipework and cables shall not enter directly into the meter housing from the building. The pipe or cable shall exit the housing before entering the premises. The rear spigot knock out SHALL NEVER be used.

20.7 Low Pressure Gas Meter Installation

20.7.1 Scope

Low pressure meter installations are installed in accordance with BS 6400 part 1: Specification for installation, exchange, relocation and removal of meters with a maximum capacity not exceeding 6 m^3/h - Low pressure 2nd family gases.

The scope of BS 6400 part 1 is:

- Primary and secondary meter installations.
- 2nd family gases supplied through a low pressure distribution system where the pressures are:
    - DMIP - 200 mbar,
    - MOP - not exceeding 75 mbar,
    - DMP - 19 mbar,
    - OP - 21 mbar at outlet of meter.
- Only meter installations which are fitted with a primary regulator downstream of an ECV.

The specification for installation of pipework is covered in BS 6891 and for gas services, IGE/TD/4[6].

20.7.2 Low pressure meter installation design

The meter installation components shall be arranged as shown in fig 20.12.

Fig 20.12   Typical metering layout

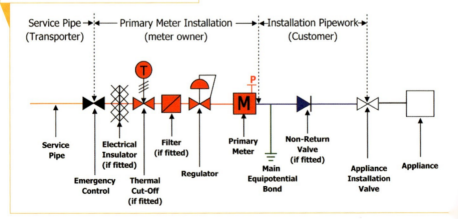

20.7.3 Location

Meters shall be sited such that it will allow ease of installation, adjustment and maintenance of the meter or meter components such as the regulator. The index should be positioned to allow ease of reading.

The meter should be installed in either:

- an external meter box, or
- internally within a garage, premises or outbuilding, or
- at the property boundary in a purpose built housing.

The meter shall be installed externally form any mobile dwelling. Permanently moored boats shall have the meter installed on the banking above the normal flood level.

Meters **shall NOT** be sited:

- In unusually hot or cold environments or in close proximity to any source of heat.
- Where food is stored.
- Where they may be subject to accidental damage (e.g. wheelie bins).
- So as to cause an obstruction (e.g. vehicular).
- In damp or corrosive situations (semi-concealed excepted) such as floors which may become wet, in contact with cement/cement compositions or brick.
- Where it will constitute a danger to persons.
- Within 150 mm of electrical meter/apparatus or within 25 mm of electrical supply or distribution cables unless an electrical insulating separating barrier is fitted.
- In low lying areas subject to flooding.
- In any unventilated space.
- Where the premises has two or more floors above ground floor (see Note overleaf), on or under the stairway or any other part of the premises which forms the sole means of escape from the premises in the event of a fire. Internal meters shall be sited as close as practicable to the service pipe entry point.

> **NOTE:** For premises with less than two or more floors above ground floor, and where there is no practical alternative, it is acceptable to Regulation 12(1)-(2) of the GS(I&U)R (see Guidance 166) to locate a meter on or under the sole means of escape from the premises provided that:
>
> a). the meter is fire-resistant; **or**
>
> b). the meter is housed in a fire-resistant compartment having automatic self-closing doors; **or**
>
> c). the service pipework (i.e. upstream and before the meter or regulator, if fitted) is fitted with a thermal cut-off device, which will automatically cut off the gas supply where the device temperature exceeds 95 °C.

20.7.4 Multiple meter installations

Multiple meters grouped together shall be installed such that:

- Internal meters are sited as close as practicable to the service pipe entry point.
- The meters are located in an area which has reasonable access at all times.
- The meters are either enclosed in a single lockable housing or in individual lockable meter boxes.
- A suitably labelled key is available to all occupants to allow access into the meter housing.
- Each meter and meter housing or meter box is clearly marked indicating the premises it serves.
- Each individual premise has an appropriately sited AECV.

20.7.5 Installation of low pressure meters

A typical low pressure, surface mounted meter installation is shown in fig 20.13.

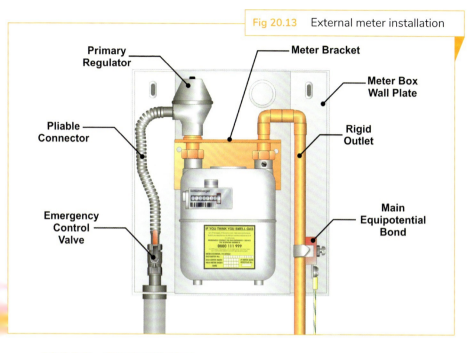

Fig 20.13 External meter installation

20.7.5.2 Pre-installation

Before installing a meter the following points should be checked and confirmed as satisfactory, if not the meter shall not be installed until all deficiencies have been rectified.

○ Confirm all necessary fittings for the meter installation are present and correct ensuring compatibility with the ECV outlet connection, gas type and pressure supplied. See figure 20.14 for meter kit components

○ Check that gas is present at the ECV and is supplied from a low pressure network.

NOTE: LP fire safe ball valve handles are normally coloured red whereas MP valves are orange with a bevelled ground face outlet connection.

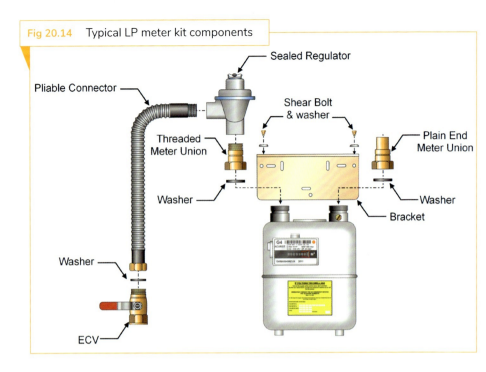

Fig 20.14   Typical LP meter kit components

- ◯ Check that the ECV and meter installation are easily accessible.
- ◯ Confirm that adequate ventilation is provided either in the meter housing or internal space.
- ◯ Confirm that the site is complete and ready to accept the completed installation. Check the housing is not damaged and securely fixed in position. Repair any damaged meter box if practicable, where this cannot be done, do not fit the meter until a replacement has been installed.
- ◯ Visually check that the regulator is sealed and in a sealed package before using on site. Never use a regulator which has not been packaged as debris may enter the fitting and damage the diaphragm, valve and/or valve seating. Only remove packaging on-site and check for any materials or debris in the gasways before assembly.
- ◯ Ensure all necessary labels and notices are available.

20.7.5.3 Electrical

A temporary earth continuity bond shall be attached to the installation prior to undertaking work, where appropriate, to protect the engineer from any potential electrical shock.

The installer of installation pipework shall either install PEB (protective equipotential bonding) to the pipework in accordance with BS 7671, if competent to do so, or advise the responsible person that such bonding is required. When relocating a meter the existing PEB may be satisfactory as found or may need to be re-located or replaced – depending on the view of the electrically competent individual.

20.7.5.4 Fixing

When assembling the main meter components - pliable connector, regulator and meter unions - and connecting them to the meter bracket and ECV, check the regulator manufacturer's installation instructions as to the recommended sealing of the connections (PTFE tape or jointing paste). The accompanying security shear bolts and washers have to be fitted to the bracket upon completion of the installation.

An internal meter may be floor mounted (on its plastic covered feet) or suspended from a floor mounted bracket.

The Emergency Control Valve must be installed in accordance with the GS(I&U)R (see Chapter 5 of this Guide for further information). The regulator shall be sealed and connected as near as practical to the ECV and meter inlet.

Corrugations of the pliable connector shall not be closed when the connector is bent as this could trap moisture leading to corrosion and premature failure. Only one pliable connector per installation is permitted, unless the installation is within a semi-concealed meter box (see section 20.6 in this Chapter) that either restrains the meter or the meter is connected to a bracket, in which case two pliable connectors can be used where an outlet adapter is fitted and the pressure absorption does not exceed 4 mbar across the meter installation.

The installation shall be tested for tightness after installation then subsequently purged in accordance with IGEM/UP/1B.

Where the meter is not being connected to the installation pipework it must be sealed after commissioning using an appropriate fitting. The ECV should be left in the on position after all works have been completed (this is used to signify that the meter has been commissioned and is ready for use).

Methods of sealing the outlet connection are shown in fig's 20.15 to 20.18.

Fig 20.15 Sealing disc (preferred)

Fig 20.16 BSP cap

Fig 20.17 Capillary cap

Fig 20.18 Compression (not recommended)

20.7.6   Commissioning low pressure meters

20.7.6.1   Operating pressure

The operating pressure shall be checked at the meter outlet test point to confirm that it is within the range of 19 to 23 mbar when the flow rate is between 0.5 m^3/h and 6m^3/h. Ideally, the OP should be 21 mbar at a flow rate of 3 m^3/h. At low flow rates the OP rises towards 23 mbar and at high flow rates, falls towards 19 mbar (see Chapter 7; section 7.3 Pressure profile of regulator).

20.7.6.2 Standing pressure

When the flow rate is zero i.e. no gas is flowing and any appliances are completely turned off, the pressure shall not exceed 30 mbar.

20.7.6.3 Regulator

The regulator shall be sealed to indicate unauthorised tampering. If an AMI alters the setting it shall be re-sealed after setting. The seal shall be marked with the AIM's number (fig 20.19 shows the superseded OAMI mark).

Fig 20.19 Regulator seal

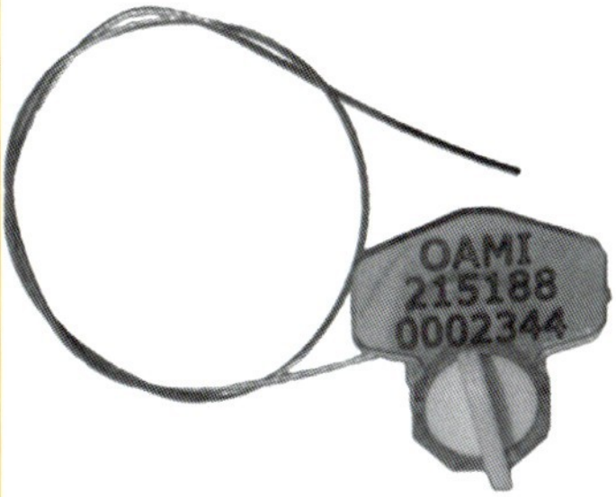

When using the industry meter regulator check device (orifice), great care should be taken to ensure that any released gas is vented to atmosphere (see purging procedure in Chapter 6 of this Guide). The meter disc will give a flow rate of approximately $3 \text{ m}^3\text{h}^{-1}$.

Fig 20.20 Industry check device on meter

Fig 20.21 Drilled meter disc & flame arrestor

NOTE: The industry meter regulator check device is used when the gas operative is not connecting the meter to installation pipework. Since there are no gas appliances to confirm the safe operation of the regulator the set orifice in the check device provides an adequate flow rate for this purpose. It is normally prudent to attach a pressure gauge to the meter outlet connection with the check device fitted. The meter can then be safely purged through the check device (a flame arrestor is incorporated) with the operating pressure confirmed during the purge process. This will reduce the amount of gas released into atmosphere during the commissioning process.

20.7.6.4   Meter

The meter shall be confirmed as operating satisfactory. This will involve the operative checking that:

1. Any prepayment system is operating correctly and confirmed as registering the correct amount of gas per unit of cost.
2. The index is incrementing smoothly
3. Tamper indications are re-set after installation. (New E6 meter index to read 99997.000 and 99999.999)
4. Meter details are read and recorded on job documentation.

20.7.6.5   Notices

Ensure all necessary labels and notices are firmly attached and are legible. Ensure any additional information required is filled in using permanent markings (see Chapter 13 for appropriate meter labels).

20.7.7 Meter relocation

A gas meter may be relocated to a different position due to a number of circumstances, which may have been instigated by either the meter owner (MAM, see subsection 20.4 regarding competencies), the owner of the premises or the gas supplier/transporter. Permission for relocation must be obtained with all parties involved agreeing with the work being carried out.

The MAM should be identified by the presence of required labelling on the meter installation, but where this is either missing or out-of-date, it should be possible to identify the MAM by calling the gas supplier (customer's fuel bill should identify the supplier), or alternatively, the Meter Number Enquiry Line on Tel: 0870 608 1524. This service is used to ascertain the Meter Point Reference Number (MPRN), the gas supplier (who can identify the MAM) and the gas transporter.

Before calling, ensure you have the authority form the gas user, the house number/name and its postcode.

The meter or meter installation shall be relocated by:

❍ relocating the meter only (fig 20.22), or
❍ relocating the meter and regulator (fig 20.23), or
❍ alteration of the service pipe.

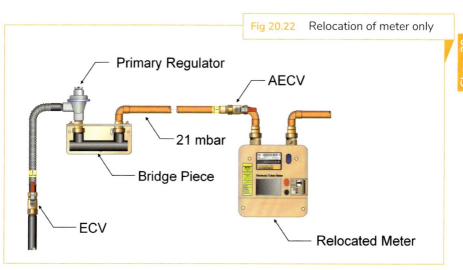

Fig 20.22   Relocation of meter only

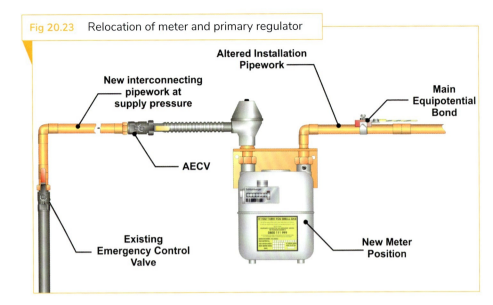

Fig 20.23   Relocation of meter and primary regulator

When the meter and, where applicable, regulator are moved this would normally result in additional pipework and fittings being installed. This has to be taken into account such that the pressure absorption through the primary meter installation at maximum capacity does not exceed the stated 4 mbar even after alteration.

The length of any interconnecting pipework between the ECV and meter installation which is within the building and is subject to the service pressure (the regulator has been relocated with the meter) shall be kept as short as possible and not exceed 2 m in length.

An AECV is required where:

- The meter has been moved more than 2 m from the existing ECV.
- The meter has been moved less than 2 m but is out of the line of sight of the existing ECV, for example in another room or housing.

When the meter only is relocated, the primary regulator shall be left connect in its original position next to the ECV.

20.8 Medium Pressure Fed Meter Installations

20.8.1 Scope

Medium pressure (MP) fed meter installations shall be installed in accordance with BS 6400 part 2: Specification for installation, exchange, relocation, maintenance and removal of gas meters with a maximum capacity not exceeding 6 m^3/h - Medium pressure 2nd family gases.

The scope of BS 6400-2 is:

- Primary meter installations only (secondary meters covered in BS 6400-1).
- 2nd family gases supplied through a medium pressure distribution system where the pressures are:
    - DMIP - 2.7 bar,
    - MOP - exceeding 75 mbar but not exceeding 2 bar,
    - DP - 2 bar,
    - OP - 21 mbar at outlet of meter.
- Only meter installations which are fitted with a primary regulator downstream of an ECV. The pressure control and protection systems must be part of the regulator assembly (PRV, meter installation excess flow valve, slam shut, etc.).

The specification for installation of pipework is covered in BS 6891 and for gas services, IGE/TD/4.

All fittings subjected to MP shall be preassembled with a strength and tightness test carried out by the manufacturer at the factory. All metering installations shall be fitted with a MIV.

No pipework or fittings subjected to MP shall be installed inside the premises.

Multi-occupancy dwellings and multiple meter installations shall only be supplied with low pressure up to the ECV; MP fed installations are not permitted.

20.8.2 Medium pressure fed meter installation design

The arrangement of components within a medium pressure fed metering installation are given in fig's 20.24 to 20.27.

Point X (as indicated in fig's 20.24 to 20.27) relates to the point in the installation at which the supply pressure changes to the outlet pressure of the regulator.

Any gas fitting installed upstream of this point shall be manufactured to withstand pressures as high as DMIP (2.7 bar). MP regulator assemblies come as a complete assembly which has been strength tested and tightness tested at the factory. An appropriate test certificate shall be supplied with the regulator kit to ensure conformance.

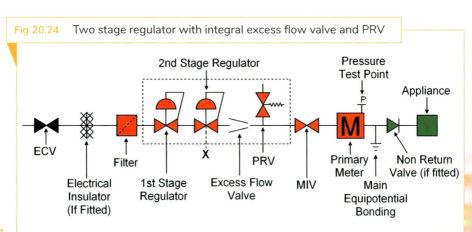

Fig 20.24 Two stage regulator with integral excess flow valve and PRV

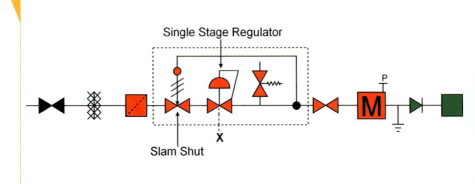

Fig 20.25 Single stage regulator with slam shut and PRV

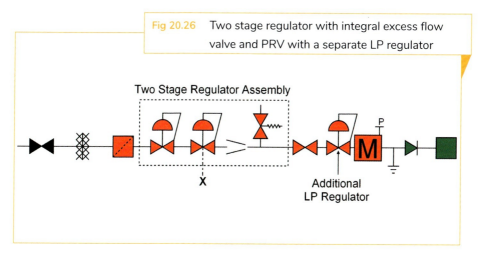

Fig 20.26 Two stage regulator with integral excess flow valve and PRV with a separate LP regulator

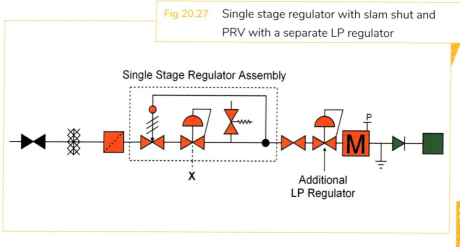

Fig 20.27 Single stage regulator with slam shut and PRV with a separate LP regulator

Any union connection exposed to the incoming supply pressure upstream of point X shall conform to BS EN ISO 10806 or have tapered threads which conform to BS EN 10226 parts 1 and 2 (formally BS 21). Normal meter washered fittings to BS 746 shall not be used on the MP side of the regulator.

Fittings downstream of point X up to the outlet of the MIV shall be factory tested and able to withstand the limiting pressure of the last safety device. The LP unions shall conform to BS 746 or threads which conform with BS EN 10266-1 (see Chapter 5; section 5.4 for acceptable material standards).

20.8.3 MP primary regulator including the protection system

The primary regulator shall be capable of supplying a pressure to the inlet of the meter between 19.25 mbar and 24 mbar at a gas flow rate between 0.5 m^3/h and the maximum capacity of the installation over varying supply pressures. The nominal operating pressure at the outlet of the meter should be maintained at 21 mbar under normal operating conditions.

The maximum lock-up pressure of a medium pressure regulator at the outlet of the meter is:

- at MOP, 27.5 mbar;
- at DMIP, 30 mbar.

The pressure control and protection system shall conform to IGEM/GM/PRS/28 (single stage regulator) or IGEM/GM/PRS/29 (two stage regulator).

All parameters of the regulator shall be factory set, any adjustment (where permitted by the manufacturers) shall be carried out by a suitably competent person. Do not try and adjust any MP regulator unless suitably qualified and authorised to do so.

Due to it's specialist nature commissioning will not be covered in this section. For ESP operatives and meter installers refer to Chapter 23 of this Guide.

20.8.4 Meter inlet valve

Figure 20.28 shows the location of the MIV, which is to be factory fitted between regulator outlet and meter inlet. Handle shall be removed, but only when the presence of an MIV is confirmed. It is used as a pressure break to allow a low pressure tightness test to be performed.

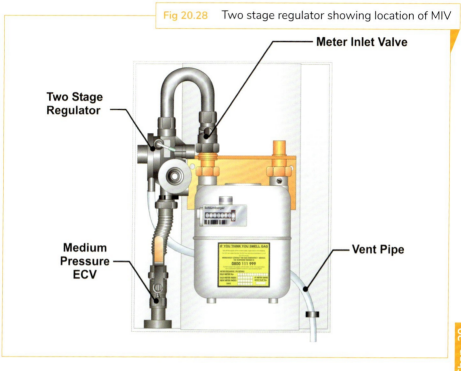

Fig 20.28 Two stage regulator showing location of MIV

20.8.5 Vent pipe

A vent pipe of clear flexible PVC shall be permanently connected to the regulator. The pipe shall be suitable for gaseous applications, having a MOP of at least 1 bar and an operating temperature range of -25 °C to 60 °C.

The vent pipe shall terminate outside the meter box (enclosure), facing downward and be positioned away from any sources of ignition, and not subjected to fouling, water ingress or blockage (see fig 20.29).

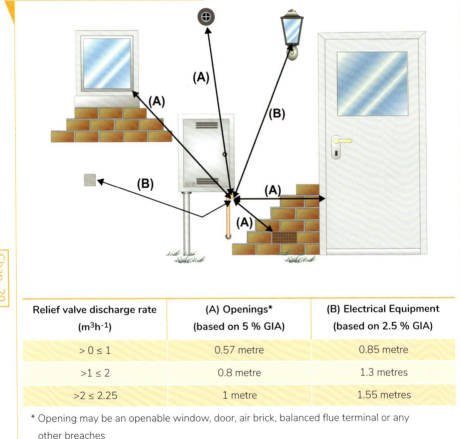

Fig 20.29 Vent pipe terminations

Relief valve discharge rate (m^3h^{-1})	(A) Openings* (based on 5 % GIA)	(B) Electrical Equipment (based on 2.5 % GIA)
> 0 ≤ 1	0.57 metre	0.85 metre
>1 ≤ 2	0.8 metre	1.3 metres
>2 ≤ 2.25	1 metre	1.55 metres

* Opening may be an openable window, door, air brick, balanced flue terminal or any other breaches

If it terminates less than 200 mm from ground level then it shall be fitted with a mesh filter. The vent pipe shall be fixed to structure of the meter box with at least two fixings spaced no more than 300 mm apart. The vent pipe shall protrude a minimum of 25 mm from the meter box. If the PVC pipe protrudes more than 75 mm then that part shall be of metallic material, i.e. stainless steel or copper pipe.

The internal diameter of the vent pipe shall not be less than 6 mm; where the vent pipe needs to be extended (0.15 m up to a maximum of 1.5 m from the meter box) the entire vent pipe will require to be increased in size to 12 mm or 15 mm copper.

20.8.6 Meter box

The meter box (enclosure) shall be undamaged, having no openings into the property it serves and comply with the minimum clearances stated in fig 20.30 from any re-entry points into the property.

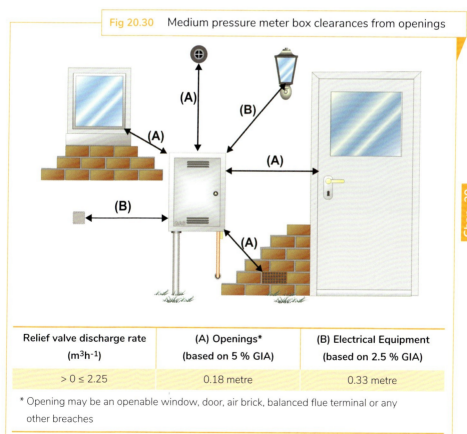

Fig 20.30 Medium pressure meter box clearances from openings

Relief valve discharge rate (m^3h^{-1})	(A) Openings* (based on 5 % GIA)	(B) Electrical Equipment (based on 2.5 % GIA)
$> 0 \leq 2.25$	0.18 metre	0.33 metre

* Opening may be an openable window, door, air brick, balanced flue terminal or any other breaches

20.8.7 Relocation of medium pressure fed meters

Before relocating (or installing, replacing or removing) a MP fed meter installation an appropriate risk assessment shall be conducted of the proposed installation, with any appropriate mitigation action taken/procedures put in place to deal with the risks identified (see sub-clause 20.8.7.1 in this Chapter).

As indicated previously no pipework or fittings exposed to medium pressure shall be located within a premises and as such additional criteria shall be met when relocating this type of installation.

A medium pressure fed meter or meter installation shall be relocated by:

- Alteration of the gas service to a different position external from the building.
- With reference to the type of installation as shown in fig's 20.26 & 20.27, where a LP regulator is installed as part of the meter installation. Leave the existing MP regulator assembly (including MIV) in place and relocate the meter and LP regulator assembly to a different position. An AECV shall be installed upstream of the meter.
- With reference to the type of installation as shown in fig's 20.24 & 20.25, where a MP regulator only is installed. Replacement of the existing MP regulator assembly (including MIV) with a new MP regulator assembly with the meter relocated to a different position. An AECV and new LP regulator shall be installed upstream of the meter.

An additional pressure test point shall be installed immediately after the MIV on the MP regulator assembly to facilitate pressure and tightness testing.

20.8.7.1 Risk assessment

The generalities of a risk assessment are discussed in more detail within Chapter 5 (section 5.6) of part 1 of this Guide, but as a minimum and in relation to MP fed meter installations shall include:

- Identifying any hazards;
- Confirmation that there is no smell of gas;
- Ensuring exposed metallic surfaces are checked for the presence of voltage – at its most basic level, the use of a single-pole voltage indicator (see **Warning**) will quickly highlight the presence of a voltage before physically handling the installation;

- For existing installations – any evidence of tampering (theft of gas) in which case inform the gas supplier;
- Consideration as to who may be affected by the work activity – are existing measures adequate or if additional measures are required to reduce the risk;
- Safety of the work area – safe access to and egress from the meter installation, sufficient ventilation for the work activity, etc.;
- Confirmation that the meter and electrical equipment are suitable for the hazardous area classification of the installation; and
- Periodically reviewing the risk assessment(s) in place and updating them as necessary, to ensure they remain fit for purpose.

Warning: Single-pole voltage indicators are just that 'indicators' and will only illuminate where a voltage is present. They do not measure current or voltage, or the absence of either and therefore, shall not be relied upon to confirm safe isolation of electrical equipment or ancillary components

20.8.8 Medium pressure metering labels

Due to the nature of MP installations a variety of labels are used to ensure clear identification of the medium pressure system and provide information to ensure the safe installation and reinstatement of the medium pressure fed installation.

Figure 20.31 shows the arrangement of labels as installed in a medium pressure fed meter box (refer to Chapter 13 of this Guide for further detail).

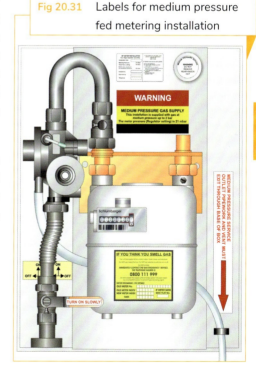

Fig 20.31 Labels for medium pressure fed metering installation

20.8.9 Routine inspection and maintenance of the MP meter installation

The gas supplier, as the owner of the meter assets, should conduct periodic inspections and maintenance of the MP meter installation – this is to ensure that no external factors such as building alterations, extensions, landscaping, etc. has encroached onto the meter installation making it noncompliant with minimum requirements of BS 6440-2. Similarly, gas engineers who in theory could come into contact with the meter installation on a more frequent basis should be mindful of works that could affect the MP meter installation.

BS 6400-2 now specifies minimum time periods that both inspections and functional checks of the components of the MP meter installation shall be conducted:

- Routine inspections shall be conducted at a period not exceeding 5 years; and
- Functional checks/test shall be conducted at a period not exceeding 10 years.

Routine inspections and functional checks shall be recorded on appropriate documentation and retained by the business for subsequent review, as required.

The 5-yearly inspection shall consist of:

- a risk assessment (see sub-section 20.8.7.1);
- a check of the minimum clearances required from possible ignition sources/openings into the property for –
    - the pressure relief vent tip (see section 20.8.5), and
    - the meter box (see section 20.8.6).
- a check of the physical condition of the meter enclosure, ensuring no damage/alteration is evident that could result in the passage of gas directly into the property;
- a check to confirm that the pressure relief vent pipe remains connected to the regulator, is secured and terminates outside the meter box (section 20.8.5);
- a check of the meter installation for water ingress or signs of corrosion;
- a check of the pressures (OP and lock-up at the outlet of the meter (see section 20.8.3));
- a check of the required labelling within the meter enclosure (see section 20.8.8).

A 10-yearly inspection shall consist of the checks outlined for the 5-yearly check and in addition, include functional checks of the pressure control and protection systems of the MP meter installation; in effect the checks are the same as those used when commissioning a new meter installation.

To avoid repetition, see Chapter 23, section 23.5.2 for commissioning procedures of both single and two-stage pressure regulators.

20.9 Meter Removal

Meters may only be removed where there has been a request by the customer to do so or under authority of the meter owner or gas supplier.

When this request has been authorised the full meter installation (regulator and any associated fittings) shall be removed with the ECV and installation pipework appropriately sealed. If the primary meter is being permanently removed and not replaced, any "live" gas pipes, i.e. service pipe must be clearly marked as containing gas.

The sealed outlet of the ECV shall be tested for tightness by opening the valve and spraying the sealing cap with leak detection fluid. Any escape must be repaired with the joint retested. It is normal practice for the locking screw to be screwed in to prevent operation of the ECV with an appropriate tamper seal (similar to that of the regulator) to be fitted through the screw and sealing cap to prevent unauthorised operation or connection.

If a gas meter is being permanently disconnected and the service pipe and the installation pipe could be simultaneously touched, they shall be permanently bonded. If the ends are in excess of 2 m apart there is no need to bond. Bonding is not necessary if the meter inlet and outlet connections remain attached to a meter bracket or if one side of the disconnection is short and not earthed i.e. a PE service or short length of outlet.

20.10 Secondary Meters

Secondary meters must not be supplied by a prepayment primary meter. The meter shall be installed on the low pressure side of the installation within the installation pipework in accordance with BS 6400-1. There is normally no requirement to install a regulator on a secondary meter.

A label shall be installed at the primary meter indicating the location and number of secondary meters supplied through it (see Chapter 13, section 13.3).

As per the GS(I&U)R a line diagram in permanent form must also be prominently displayed on or near the primary meter and all emergency controls showing the configuration of all meters, installation pipework and emergency controls (including AECV's).The secondary meter itself shall also be labelled "secondary meter".

Chapter 21
Tumble Dryers

		Page No.
21.1	Introduction	21.1
21.2	Scope	21.1
21.3	Design Considerations	21.1
21.4	Appliance Types	21.2
21.5	Room Types	21.2
21.6	Location	21.3
21.7	Ventilation	21.3
21.8	Exhaust	21.4
21.9	Gas Supply	21.6
21.10	Electrical Supply	21.7
21.11	Construction and Operation	21.8
	21.11.1 Principle of operation	21.8
	21.11.2 Typical sequence of operation	21.10
	21.11.3 Burner type	21.10
21.12	Controls	21.11
21.13	Commissioning	21.16
	21.13.1 Commissioning procedure for domestic dryers	21.16
21.14	Maintenance	21.17
	21.14.1 Servicing procedure for domestic dryers	21.17

Chapter 21
Tumble Dryers

References in this Chapter

[1] BS 7624: 2004 Installation and maintenance of domestic direct gas-fired tumble dryers of up to 6 kW heat input (2nd and 3rd family gases). Specification.

21.1 Introduction

- These notes have been prepared in relation to domestic, natural gas and LPG tumble dryers.
- The installation will be in accordance with British Standard 7624[1] and the GS(I&U)R.

21.2 Scope

Work activities will include installation, commissioning, repair and maintenance.

Normally, work will be performed in domestic premises including permanently sited leisure accommodation vehicles (LAV), residential park homes (RPH) and permanently moored boats (B).

BS 7624 also applies to domestic type installations in commercial or industrial premises. There may be additional requirements in these situations; engineers shall be appropriately qualified for the scope of work that they perform. Examples include staff kitchens, small scale hotel and bed & breakfast facilities, etc.

BS 7624 specifies a maximum net heat input limit of 6 kW.

21.3 Design Considerations

It is essential that designers and installers are aware of the clearances specified by appliance manufacturers' prior to the installation of kitchen units. How the vent will be arranged will impact on the appliance location, e.g. if a wall venting kit is to be used, are there any external down pipes close to the termination?

Other considerations will include:

- Gas and electrical supply requirements.
- Room type and size.
- Ventilation requirements including windows and/or extraction system.

21.4 Appliance Types

New appliances shall be CE marked and "second hand" appliances must have the manufacturer's installation and commissioning instructions supplied.

The appliance must be suitable for the gas type supplied. If a conversion is required this shall be performed in accordance with the manufacturer's instructions and using their conversion kit; **ad hoc conversion is not permitted**.

All appliances must have a readable data plate which provides important information in relation to:

- Gas type:
    - G20 is nat. gas @ 20 mbar.
    - G30 is butane @ 29 mbar.
    - G31 is propane @ 37 mbar.
- Intended country of use (GB).
- Supply pressure.

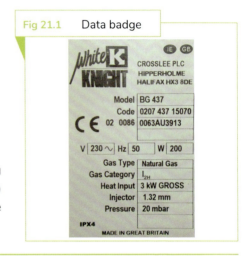

Fig 21.1   Data badge

The appliance serial number (along with the make, model and colour) is essential if any spare parts have to be ordered.

21.5 Room Types

- Tumble dryers shall not be installed in rooms containing a bath or shower.
- Consideration shall be given to any hazards which may be present due to flammable vapours e.g. hairdressing salons or workshops.
- LPG dryers shall not be installed in basements or cellars.
- Tumble dryers shall not be installed in bedrooms or bedsitting rooms unless:
    a). The manufacturer's permit such a location, and
    b). There is at least 7 m^3 of room volume for every 1 kW net of appliance rated input.

21.6 Location

The dryer shall be located in accordance with the appliance manufacturer's instructions. Consideration should also be given to associated use of other kitchen equipment such as sinks, washing machines, etc.

The installation of any decorative door front shall be in accordance with the appliance manufacturer's instructions. Insulation panels, if permitted by the manufacturer may reduce any clearances required.

The base upon which the dryer is standing shall be firm and stable and there shall be sufficient space in front to allow for withdrawal and disconnection.

Stacking one dryer upon another shall only be done where the manufacturers permit; this will require a stacking kit as recommended by the manufacturer. If it is intended to stack the dryer on top of a washing machine or other appliance, the base appliance shall be confirmed as being stable when operating.

Fig 21.2   Air inlet

Blockage of the air grill at the front of the heater (fig 21.2) needs to be avoided; this is easily done by allowing wet items to lie on the floor at the front of the dryer.

21.7 Ventilation

There shall be an openable window or equivalent within the room or internal space in which the dryer is installed. Louvres, hinged panels or mechanical extraction systems may be an acceptable alternative to a window.

Additional purpose provided ventilation is not required where the room volume is greater than 3.7 m^3 for every 1 kW net of appliance rated input. Where the room volume is less than this, purpose provided ventilation with a minimum effective free area of 100 cm^2 is required.

Example: If a kitchen measures 3 m x 2 m x 2.4 m and the dryer is rated at 4.23 kW net, the ventilation free area would be –

= 3 x 2 x 2.4

= 14.4 m³

= $\dfrac{14.4}{4.23}$

= 3.4 m³/kW

Therefore, a minimum of 100 cm² free area of ventilation would be required.

Any ventilation required by the dryer is additional to the ventilation requirements of any other appliance(s) in the same room. When installing the dryer there shall be no restriction to the air inlet point with any clearances to adjacent surfaces maintained as per the manufacturer's instruction.

The air supply is not only required for combustion purposes, but also provides sufficient air for the drying process. The air supplied is often referred to as "make up air".

21.8 Exhaust

The products of combustion are highly diluted by the warm, moist exhaust air; consequently the contaminated air is terminated via the flexible exhaust venting hose and not a flue. The terminal however, should not be located in covered passageways due to the possibility of carbon monoxide production and entry into properties.

The flexible exhaust venting hose options are:

- Permanent (or temporary) connection to a wall vent.
- Temporary (or permanent) connection to a window vent.
- Hanging the hose out of an open window (not an option if the heat input exceeds 3 kW net).

Installation of the wall tube through the wall of a timber frame property is specified in document IGE/UP/7.

The practice of venting directly into the room with a window opened is no longer permitted.

The manufacturer's instructions shall be followed when siting the terminal. Where a terminal is located at low level, a minimum clearance of 300 mm shall be maintained between the underside of the terminal and the ground so as to prevent the likelihood of a blockage caused by flooding, snow or leaves.

The design of the outlet terminal shall be such that any exhaust openings will not be smaller than 6 mm or larger than 16 mm. Alternatively, a guard complying with this specification may be fitted over the terminal or the terminal may be of a type which is closed when not in use.

The security risks posed by window vent terminals should be taken into consideration before using this type of exhaust method (fig 21.3a). If the terminal is a fixed wall vent (fig 21.3b) the sleeve or wall tube should incline downwards to allow any water or moisture to run freely to outside.

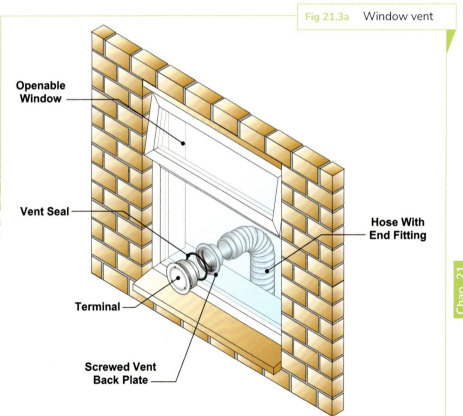

Fig 21.3a   Window vent

Fig 21.3b Wall vent

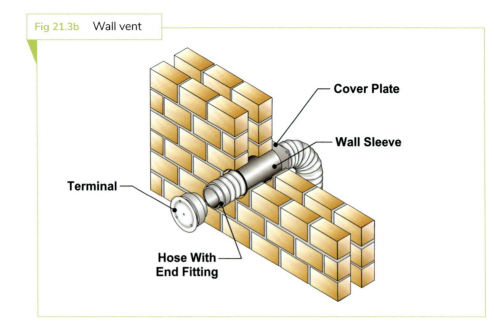

21.9 Gas Supply

Internal pipework shall be in accordance with BS 6891. The supply pressure shall be measured with the appliance operating where the manufacturer will specify any pressure tolerance that may be permitted. Most appliances are provided with an Rc½ connection (½ inch BSP female).

Dryers shall be connected by means of a flexible pipe and self-sealing bayonet type connector conforming to BS 669 -1. The manufacturer's instructions shall be followed in this regard so as to avoid the flexible pipe coming into contact with hot appliance parts. If no guidance is given, the bayonet should be positioned so that the connection is accessible when the dryer is moved. LPG flexible connections have their specification indicated by a red stripe along the length of the pipe. Natural gas flexible connections may not be suitable for use with LPG.

See the guidance within Chapter 16 of this Guide with regards to the flexible pipe requirements.

If the dryer is to be stacked or moved regularly it shall be fitted with a restraining device fixed securely to the dryer and the building fabric (fig 21.4). This is required in order to prevent damage to the gas supply pipe or flexible connector. It is also advisable to fit a restraining device if the dryer has a drop down door.

Fig 21.4   Restraining kit

21.10 Electrical Supply

All wiring shall be installed in accordance with BS 7671.

The cable size and fuse rating shall be in accordance with the manufacturer's instructions; dryers are normally protected by a fuse rated at 13 amperes.

The means of isolation may be by:

- a three pin plug and an unswitched socket (in order to encourage physical disconnection when work is performed), or
- a fused, double pole, switched connection unit (spur box).

See also Chapter 14; section 14.9.2 for detailed guidance on safe isolation of gas appliances.

21.11 Construction and Operation

A domestic gas-fired tumble dryer is an appliance designed to be used in a domestic environment for the purpose of drying fabrics (clothes, bedding, linen, etc.). It is directly fired by natural gas or LPG and is typically rated at 3 kW gross input, although high-speed versions are available rated at 4.7 kW gross. They are equipped with a timer (up to two hours, fig 21.5) and are thermostatically controlled (fig 21.6).

Fig 21.5   Time control

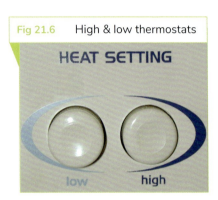

Fig 21.6   High & low thermostats

Accessories available include:

- Wall/window venting kit.
- Stacking kit.
- Restraining kit.
- Vent hose assembly.

21.11.1   Principle of operation

Referring to fig 21.7 air enters through a grille at the front of the appliance. This air is mixed with the products of combustion (PoC) from the fully automatic induced draught burner. The mixture of dry, hot air and PoC travel into the rear banjo and from there through the drum which contains the damp fabric. The dry air and PoC mixture becomes cooler and more humid as it dries the fabric in the drum. This warm, humid air and PoC mixture passes through the lint filter, the front banjo, the fan and finally the exhaust duct.

The drive belt may have a spring assisted tensioning mechanism, see fig 21.8.

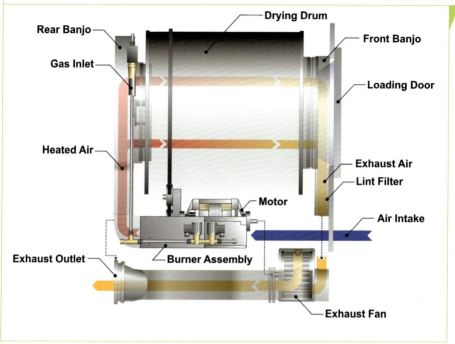

Fig 21.7 Cross section of tumble dryer showing air movement through the dryer

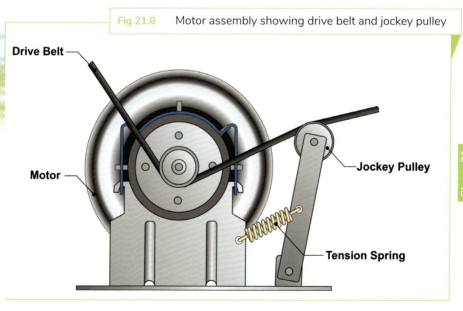

Fig 21.8 Motor assembly showing drive belt and jockey pulley

21.11.2 Typical sequence of operation

Initially when the timer is switched on, this sends power to the motor which turns the drum – power will also now be supplied to the electronic control unit.

After a delay of about 8 seconds (this is to purge the dryer with fresh air), the ignition electrode will start sparking and the double solenoids will open, admitting gas to the burner assembly. Once lit, the flame sensing electrode should now pick up a flame signal (if this does not happen within approximately 7 seconds the unit will go to lockout).

The flame signal will be constantly monitored throughout the firing cycle. When the thermostat reaches the required temperature the solenoids will close. Should the unit lockout this can be reset by turning the power supply off then back on.

21.11.3 Burner type

The burner is pre-aerated, induced draught (fig 21.9 & 21.10), i.e. the draught is generated by an impeller which is driven by the drum motor. The PoC and the cold, dry air are sucked through the burner duct and into the rear banjo.

Fig 21.9 Burner assembly

Fig 21.10 Burner injector

21.12 Controls

Safety features include:

- Rectification type flame supervision.
- Full sequential automatic ignition.
- Inlet and exhaust temperature thermostats.
- Vitiation thermocouple.
- Door switch.
- Timer with built-in cool down period.

Additional controls and features will or can include:

- Anti-crease feature.
- Electronic humidity sensing.
- High speed models.
- Reversing motor.
- Exhaust lint filter.
- Isolation valve (self-sealing bayonet). See Chapter 16 on gas cookers.

The pressure test point is normally located at the bottom, right hand corner (fig 21.11 viewed from the rear). The appliance connection is normally at the top right hand corner (fig 21.12 viewed from the rear).

Fig 21.11 Pressure test point

Fig 21.12 Gas inlet

The ignition and flame supervision (fig's 21.13 & 21.14) is fully automatic and is controlled by an electronic sequence control box (fig 21.15).

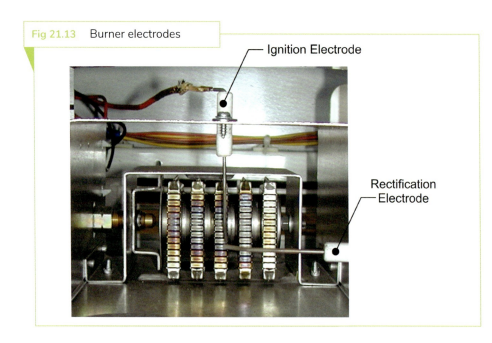

Fig 21.13   Burner electrodes

Fig 21.14   Sensing electrode

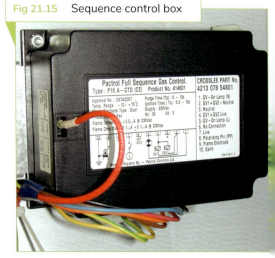

Fig 21.15   Sequence control box

Temperature control is achieved by disc type stats (fig's 21.16 & 21.17), which limit the inlet and exhaust temperatures and are located at the rear banjo and front banjo respectively.

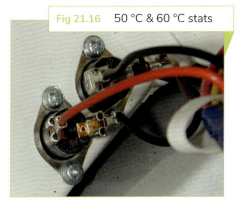

Fig 21.16   50 °C & 60 °C stats

Fig 21.17   130 °C & 143 °C stats

The exhaust filter should be regularly removed and cleaned by the user (fig 21.18 & 21.19).

Fig 21.18   Filter location

Fig 21.19   Filter

The motor services two purposes:

a). it drives the drum (belt driven), fig 21.20, and
b). it drives the impeller (fig 21.21), which generates the air flow.

Fig 21.20   Motor & belt

Fig 21.21   Motor & impeller

Twin solenoid valves are used to automatically control the gas flow (fig 21.22).

The timer (fig 21.23) is unlike that engineers might associate with heating systems.

Fig 21.22   Solenoids

Fig 21.23   Timer

Figure 21.24 shows a typical wiring diagram

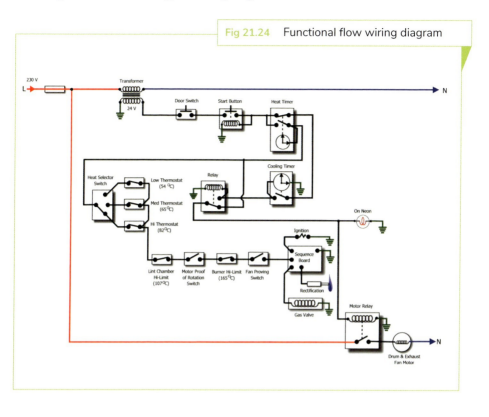

Fig 21.24 Functional flow wiring diagram

21.13 Commissioning

In all cases the manufacturer's commissioning procedure shall be complied with.

A generic procedure is detailed below:

21.13.1 Commissioning procedure for domestic dryers

1. Check site –
    1.1 Suitability of location (BS 7624).
    1.2 Clearances from obstacles/combustibles.
    1.3 Suitability of room (size, type and openable window required).
    1.4 Ventilation requirements.
    1.5 Assembly and fixing (level and stable, filter, etc.).
    1.6 Packaging removal.
    1.7 Stability (stacked appliances).
    1.8 Exhaust method (temporary or permanent).
    1.9 Adequate supplies:
        1.9.1 gas (flexible and restraining cable).
        1.9.2 electricity.
2. Tightness test and purge gas installation.
3. Test operation and performance –
    3.1 Control devices:
        3.1.1 bayonet/flexible connection,
        3.1.2 timer(s),
        3.1.3 ignition systems (spark),
        3.1.4 inlet and exhaust thermostats,
        3.1.5 drum rotation.
    3.2 Safety devices:
        3.2.1 flame supervision device (rectification),
        3.2.2 thermocouple,
        3.2.3 gas escapes,
        3.2.4 door interlock.
    3.3 Set burner pressure and/or check heat input.
    3.4 Check flame pictures:
        3.4.1 stability, colour.
    3.5 Ensure that the dryer does not adversely affect the operation of any open flue type appliances.

4. Electrical checks –
   4.1 Check for correct cable (type, insulation resistance and fuse size).
   4.2 Check for correct earth and polarity.
   4.3 Check for correct provision of isolation of supply.
5. Instruct customer –
   5.1 Correct usage (leave all instructions with customer).
   5.2 Advise the user and landlord of the maintenance requirements.
   5.3 Gas emergency procedure.

21.14 Maintenance

In all cases the manufacturer's maintenance and servicing procedures shall be complied with.

A generic procedure is detailed below:

21.14.1 Servicing procedure for domestic dryers

1. Check site –
   1.1 Ask the customer if they have any problems or concerns regarding the dryer.
   1.2 Test the operation and visually inspect for obvious damage.
   1.3 Suitability of location (BS 7624).
   1.4 Clearances from obstacles/combustibles.
   1.5 Ventilation requirements.
   1.6 Assembly and fixing (level and stable, filter, etc.).
   1.7 Condition and arrangement of exhaust method.
   1.8 Adequate supplies:
       1.8.1 gas (flexible and restraining cable),
       1.8.2 electricity.
2. Tightness test gas installation.
3. Dismantle and clean –
   3.1 Remove panels, ducts and fittings as necessary.
   3.2 Remove and clean filter.
   3.3 Remove burner assembly, clean burner and injector.
   3.4 Inspect/clean/check spark electrode (gap, ceramic, corrosion) and thermocouple.
   3.5 Remove drum drive belt, motor and fan impeller; inspect and clean.

- 3.6 Inspect drum mounting and rotation.
- 3.7 Reassemble.
4. Test operation and performance –
    - 4.1 Control devices:
        - 4.1.1 bayonet/flexible connection,
        - 4.1.2 timers,
        - 4.1.3 ignition systems (spark),
        - 4.1.4 inlet and exhaust thermostats,
        - 4.1.5 drum rotation.
    - 4.2 Safety devices:
        - 4.2.1 flame supervision device (rectification),
        - 4.2.2 thermocouple (vitiation),
        - 4.2.3 gas escapes,
        - 4.2.4 door interlock.
    - 4.3 Set burner pressure and/or check heat input.
    - 4.4 Check flame pictures:
        - 4.4.1 stability, colour.
    - 4.5 Ensure that the dryer does not adversely affect the operation of any open flue type appliances.
5. Electrical checks –
    - 5.1 Check for correct cable (type, insulation resistance and fuse size).
    - 5.2 Check for correct earth and polarity.
    - 5.3 Check for correct provision of isolation of supply.
6. Instruct customer –
    - 6.1 Advise the user of your findings and any remedial or advisory work required.

Chapter 22
Leisure Appliances

		Page No.
22.1	Introduction	22.1
22.2	Scope	22.1
22.3	Design Considerations	22.2
22.4	Pokers	22.2
	22.4.1 Portable gas pokers	22.2
	22.4.2 Fixed gas pokers	22.4
	22.4.3 Commissioning	22.5
	22.4.4 Servicing	22.5
	22.4.5 Common faults	22.6
22.5	Lighting	22.7
	22.5.1 Construction	22.7
	22.5.2 Location	22.7
	22.5.3 Operation	22.8
	22.5.4 Gas supply	22.9
	22.5.5 Installation	22.9
	22.5.6 Automatic control	22.10
	22.5.7 Commissioning	22.10
	22.5.8 Servicing	22.11

Chapter 22
Leisure Appliances

			Page No.
22.6	Barbecues		**22.12**
	22.6.1	Construction	**22.13**
	22.6.2	Location	**22.13**
	22.6.3	Operation	**22.14**
	22.6.4	Gas supply	**22.14**
	22.6.5	Commissioning	**22.15**
	22.6.6	Servicing	**22.16**
22.7	Patio Heaters		**22.17**
	22.7.1	Construction	**22.18**
	22.7.2	Location	**22.18**
	22.7.3	Operation	**22.18**
	22.7.4	Gas supply	**22.19**
	22.7.5	Installation	**22.19**
	22.7.6	Commissioning	**22.19**
	22.7.7	Servicing	**22.20**

Chapter 22
Leisure Appliances

			Page No.
22.8	Greenhouse Heaters		**22.21**
	22.8.1	Construction	**22.21**
	22.8.2	Location	**22.22**
	22.8.3	Ventilation	**22.22**
		22.8.3.1 Stand alone greenhouses	**22.22**
		22.8.3.2 Greenhouses accessed from the property	**22.22**
	22.8.4	Gas supply	**22.22**
	22.8.5	Installation	**22.23**
	22.8.6	Controls	**22.23**
	22.8.7	Commissioning	**22.23**
	22.8.8	Servicing	**22.24**
22.9	Flambeaux (Torch)		**22.25**
	22.9.1	Construction	**22.25**
	22.9.2	Location	**22.26**
	22.9.3	Gas Supply	**22.26**
	22.9.4	Installation	**22.26**
	22.9.5	Controls	**22.26**
	22.9.6	Commissioning	**22.27**
	22.9.7	Servicing	**22.28**

Chapter 22
Leisure Appliances

References in this Chapter

None

22.1 Introduction

The focus of this Chapter is the leisure market, primarily the garden recreational activities surrounding a barbecue on domestic premises, with additional information regarding greenhouse heaters and ornamental flambeaux.

This area of gas installation can be somewhat specialised and as such as much information about the appliance should be gathered from the appliance manufacturer as possible. Further guidance should be sought from the manufacturer's technical help line for specific and unusual installation requirements.

It needs to be said from the outset that the manufacture of the appliances listed in the scope is limited and one may have to search further afield to locate them. However, some of the appliances can be obtained fairly easily when shopping for LPG models. As well as the scarcity of appliance manufacturer's, the information on these appliances is very limited, which only increases the need to pay particular attention to manufacturer's installation and servicing instructions for guidance on all aspects.

22.2 Scope

Work activities will include installation, commissioning, repair and maintenance of leisure appliances, which include the following;

- Pokers.
- Lights.
- Barbecues.
- Patio heaters.
- Greenhouse heaters.
- Flambeaux.

All of which are supplied by natural gas or LPG.

22.3 Design Considerations

The installation of the appliance should be located in a position most desirable to the customer however, guidance in support of manufacturer's requirements should be given to the customer in order to achieve the safest installation.

The installation of the gas pipework to the appliances should be carried out in accordance with the current edition of BS 6891. That is to say that the pipework should be as short as possible, be sited so as to provide protection against physical damage and corrosion.

It is important that an isolation valve, located immediately outside the property be accessible at all times and with security in mind, it is advisable to have an internal isolation valve to prevent unauthorised access to the customers gas or the unauthorised use of the customers appliances. The external valve and for that matter the internal valve, if fitted, should comply to the requirements of an ECV as dictated by the current GS(I&U)R.

As the leisure appliances are generally low consumers of gas it is accepted that the size of the pipework may be smaller than that feeding internal appliances.

22.4 Pokers

There are two types of gas poker; the portable gas poker and the fixed gas poker. The main purpose of this appliance is to ignite solid fuel appliances. They are very simple in design and normally consist of a single control: a valve in the form of a gas tap or bayonet.

22.4.1 Portable gas pokers

The construction consists of a bayonet connection attached to 8 mm armoured hose, which is approximately 900 mm long. However, dependent on the manufacturer the length varies, some as much as 2 m long.

The location of the floor or wall bayonet should be selected so that whilst the appliance is in operation the hose is not subjected to excessive heat. The main component is located at the other end of the hose. The poker is constructed of a handle, an injector, primary air ports and finally the burner itself (fig 22.1).

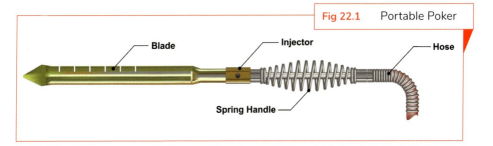

Fig 22.1 Portable Poker

The handle is made from a spiral wound 3 mm wire. This allows the air to act as an insulator, keeping it cool and helps to prevent conduction of the heat travelling up the handle.

The injector and primary air ports facilitate complete combustion at the burner producing a hotter flame which in turn makes the appliance more effective in lighting the solid fuel. The injector will be sized to permit 0.2 m^3/hr of gas to pass (3 kW approximately) at the installations inlet pressure. As there is no pressure regulation on this appliance the burner pressure will be the same as the inlet pressure.

The burner is manufactured from heavy gauge brass or copper which looks similar to a flattened section of pipe, sealed at the end and formed to a point to enable ease of insertion into the solid fuel. The burner ports are precisely cut slots along the flattened edge of the poker allowing the gas to be distributed evenly along its length.

The portable gas poker can be used by connecting the end of the hose to the gas supply via a floor or wall mounted bayonet connection (fig 22.2). At this point the gas will flow to the burner unrestricted. The poker is then lit and put into operation.

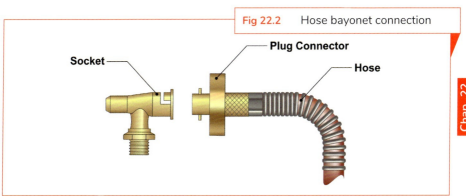

Fig 22.2 Hose bayonet connection

As soon as the solid fuel has ignited, the poker can be disconnected from the gas supply. It needs to be noted at this point that the poker is very hot and should be carefully placed so that it is allowed to cool without causing a danger to person of property.

22.4.2   Fixed gas pokers

The construction of the fixed gas poker is very similar to that of the portable variety, in that the only control is a gas tap. The installation is piped with rigid pipework. The appliance is permanently located to the front of a fire place, just below the grate or coal bed (fig 22.3). The burner will run the entire length of the front of the fire grate where the flames are distributed evenly across the underside of the fire where they will ignite the solid fuel coals. Again, once the coals have been lit the gas to the appliance can be turned off.

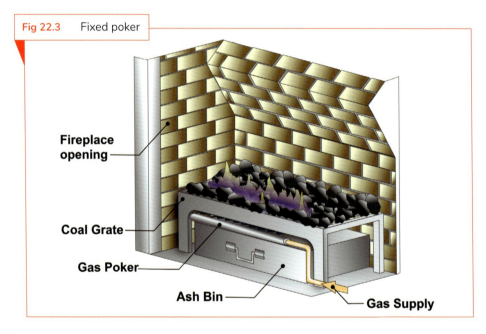

Fig 22.3   Fixed poker

The main problem associated with this type of poker is the danger of ash from the fire blocking the burner ports. However, the problem of cooling the poker in a safe place is not required as the appliance is permanently fixed.

22.4.3 Commissioning

As the appliance is simple in construction, operation and function the commissioning of the appliance is also simple.

1. After installing the appliance, the installation should be tested to the current tightness test requirements.
2. Visually inspect the condition of the hose or supply pipework to ensure no damage has occurred during the installation.
3. The appliance should then be lit and the flame observed to ensure a stable flame picture.
4. Using leak detection fluid (LDF), test all joints with the appliance in operation.
5. Gas rate the appliance to ensure conformity with the manufacturer's instructions.
6. Test the operation of the bayonet or gas tap to ensure smooth operation.
7. Explain the operation of the appliance to the user. Advise them of the safety precautions that are required when the appliance is in operation and any general care that is required by the manufacturer that can be conducted by the customer.
8. Complete any documentation that is required and leave all manufacturer's instructions with the customer.

22.4.4 Servicing

1. Gather information from the customer regarding any problems with the appliance since the last service.
2. The installation should be tested to the current tightness test requirements.
3. Visually inspect the condition of the hose or supply pipework and the burner to ensure no damage has occurred since the last service.
4. The appliance should then be lit and the flame observed to ensure a stable flame picture.
5. Using LDF test all joints with the appliance in operation.
6. Gas rate the appliance to ensure conformity with the manufacturer's instructions.
7. Test the operation of the bayonet or gas tap to ensure smooth operation (ease and grease as required).

8. Reiterate to the gas user of the safety precautions that are required when the appliance is in operation and any general care that is required by the manufacturer that can be conducted by the customer.

9. Complete any documentation that is required and leave all manufacturer's instructions with the customer

22.4.5 Common faults

The most common faults that occur with this type of simple appliance are listed in table 22.1.

Table 22.1 Common faults for gas pokers

Component	Fault	Remedy
Isolation valve	Stiff to operate	Ease and grease
	Let-by	Ease and grease or replace
Hose	Damaged/scorched/frayed	Replace
Primary air ports	Blocked by debris	Clear and ensure injector is undamaged
Burner	Burned out due to prolonged exposure to the fire	Replace

22.5 Lighting

22.5.1 Construction

Gas lights, lanterns or lamps as they have been called in the past, are often used to light a driveway and patio areas. They usually consist of a four sided glass shade, topped with a tent which incorporates the flueing system. The tent and the structure for the glass shade are manufactured from cast iron or copper. The copper lamps require strengthened pillars to resist distortion and possible damage from the wind. One side of the shade is hinged to allow access for lighting and maintenance (fig 22.4).

Fig 22.4   Street style lamp

The tent of the lamp includes the flueing arrangement which allows air to flow into the shade and the products to be expelled to the atmosphere. This arrangement has the same effect as a balanced flue. The advantage of this flueing arrangement is that the lamp is more resistant to being extinguished in high winds.

22.5.2 Location

The lamp is mounted on a bracket (known as a 'frog'), which allows the lamp to be fixed onto either a lamp post, column or a wall.

In either case the location of the lamp should be carefully selected to prevent damage to property.

It is generally accepted that the clearance distance to combustible materials and foliage should be a minimum of 300 mm (reference should be made to the manufacturer's literature for precise dimensions for the model being installed).

If the required distance cannot be achieved, then a non-combustible shield should be fitted to protect any part of the property at risk from the effects of the products of combustion. It should be noted that when selecting the location, consideration should be taken regarding access to the appliance by children in order to reduce the risk of injury to them. Consultation and agreement with the customer will determine the final location.

22.5.3   Operation

The internal components (fig 22.5) consist of a permanent pilot located at high level within the shade, a supply to the burner head(s), injector(s) dependent on the number of burners and gas mantle(s). The gas mantle operates on the same principle as a solar grill in cooker whereby the gas passes through a fine mesh and burns on the surface of the mesh. The mantle is very delicate and needs to be handled with care.

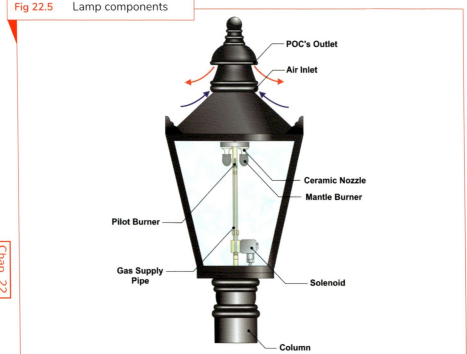

Fig 22.5   Lamp components

The low density material which is used in the manufacture of the mantle creates a warm incandescent white light. This luminaire has the approximate intensity of a 40 watt electric light bulb. Larger models of lamp can have as many as 6 mantles within the same shade.

The daily on/off control of the lamp is mainly conducted from a remote location via a solenoid valve. The remote devices range from a simple timing device to a combination of controls, which include light sensitive cells that automatically operate the appliance when the natural daylight fades.

An isolation valve on the gas supply is required for maintenance and servicing. Where the installation includes a lamp post, the isolation valve is located in the lower section of the post.

22.5.4　Gas supply

The gas supply to the appliance will be installed in accordance with BS 6891 for external pipework (see also Part 1; Chapter 5 for further guidance).

22.5.5　Installation

As with any other appliance the manufacturer's installation instruction shall be followed. However, there are some points to consider when installing a lamp post.

As a gas supply is being used to power this appliance the installing engineer shall ensure that a firm and solid fixture is achieved. This is normally achieved by driving a 750 mm fixing spike into the ground. The location of underground pipes and cables should be ascertained prior to the commencement of any work.

Attach an adaptor supplied by the lamp manufacturer from the spike to the finished ground level. Concrete to a minimum depth of 200 mm encasing the spike and adaptor. Provide sleeves for the gas and electrical supplies and include these in the concrete cast so that they enter the lamp post from below ground level. Once the concrete has set, the lamp post can be mounted and bolted to the ground fixing, then the final assemblies can take place. If the lamp post is to be erected on to an existing slab of concrete and there is the facility to supply gas and electricity to the appliance, then the lamp post may be bolted directly to the concrete slab.

22.5.6 Automatic control

Essentially there are two common methods of control used to automatically operate the lamp;

- a timing switch, similar to that of a central heating timer. This should be located where it is convenient for the customer to access it for alterations, or
- a photo electric cell (this device will energise the solenoid when the daylight fades). It is important that its location is selected carefully away from garden foliage where the sensor may not pick up the daylight.

Be aware of extraneous sources of light that could fool the sensor that there is daylight and switch the lamp off. Examples of these extraneous sources are lights from the windows of the house. Flood lighting from properties surrounding that installation and car head lamps.

22.5.7 Commissioning

As always the engineer shall comply with the manufacturer's instructions. However, the following procedure is designed to give supplementary guidance where the commissioning instructions are insufficient.

1. Conduct a visual inspection of the whole installation rectifying any nonconformity before proceeding.
2. Turn the isolation valve to the appliance on and check for escapes with LDF at each joint within the appliance as they may have worked loose during transit.
3. Following the instruction given by the manufacturer of the mantle, "burn off" the mantle.
4. Light the pilot, making any necessary adjustments required. It is important that the pilot flame does not impinge onto the mantles as this could have a detrimental effect on not only the combustion but the mantle itself.
5. When the pilot has been lit, operate the appliance to ensure ease of use and that the mantle(s) will light smoothly. If the pilots position has been altered and is too far from the mantle there is the possibility of explosive ignition.
6. Check the safe operation of any flame supervision device.
7. Using LDF, check for escapes from the operating control to the burner heads.

8. Check the user controls for correct operation and setting;
   a). Timer switches should be set and tested for automatic control. Usually setting the timer to an "on" period of 5 minutes will be sufficient to test.
   b). If light sensitive devices are to be used then covering the device will operate the solenoid and bring the lamp on.
9. Explain the operation of the appliance to the user, advise them of the safety precautions that are required when the appliance is in operation and any general care that is required by the manufacturer that can be conducted by the customer.
10. Complete any documentation that is required and leave all manufacturer's instructions with the customer.

22.5.8 Servicing

1. Gather information from the customer regarding any problems with the appliance since the last service.
2. The installation should be tested to the current gas tightness test requirements.
3. Visually inspect the condition of the appliance, the supply pipework and the burner to ensure no damage has occurred since the last service.
4. Remove the mantle carefully and store in a secure position.
5. Remove, inspect the injector, clean if necessary then replace the mantle.
6. The appliance should then be lit and the flame observed to ensure a stable flame picture.
7. Check the safe operation of any flame supervision device.
8. Using LDF, test all joints with the appliance in operation.
9. Gas rate the appliance to ensure conformity with the manufacturer's instructions.
10. Test the operation of the appliance isolation valve to ensure smooth operation (ease and grease, as required).
11. Reiterate to the customer of the safety precautions that are required when the appliance is in operation and any general care that is required by the manufacturer that can be conducted by the customer.
12. Complete any documentation that is required and leave all manufacturer's instructions with the customer.

22.6 Barbecues

The barbecue is probably the most common type of leisure appliance used in the UK and can be purchased by the user at D.I.Y retail outlets (fig 22.6). It needs to be noted that the vast majority of these units are manufactured to be supplied by LPG.

The appliance will normally be supplied as "flat pack" or partially assembled, requiring the user or engineer to assemble the appliance on site. In either case the manufacturer's instructions shall be adhered to and deviation from the instructions is not permitted.

The barbecue **shall only be used outside** and shall not be operated in external structures, whether permanent or temporary, such as garages, sheds, etc.

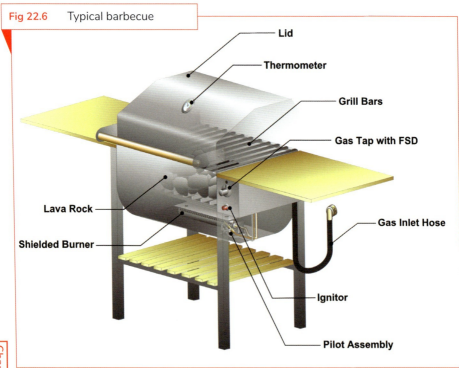

Fig 22.6 Typical barbecue

22.6.1 Construction

The construction of the gas barbecue is relatively simple in design and is typically mounted on a mobile base to facilitate positioning the unit in a secure location after use, i.e. garage or garden shed once it has cooled down. The appliance can also be permanently fixed in a purpose built housing. When the barbecue is to be fixed in a permanent mounting, care shall be taken to ensure that the combustion air path to the burner is not impeded in any way.

The appliance consists of a base container, which has three levels of construction; the first being the burner located in the base of the container. Secondly, a grate may be suspended above the burner, which supports small egg sized pebbles or lumps of volcanic rock and finally the grilling surface. The container is then topped by a lid.

This appliance is normally a fixed rated appliance and as such there is no adjustment to burner pressure. However, some models do have a regulator fitted and as such it is important that the burner pressure is taken to confirm that it complies with the manufacturer's instructions.

The user controls are relatively simple and consist of a gas tap and an ignition device. Newer and more modern models of barbecue have different cooking options for the user in that a flat or ribbed griddle can be provided, which may cover as much a half the grilling surface with some having a hot plate facility attached to the side of the barbecue.

Although not essential many appliances now come with small working surfaces at either side of the grill. Newer models have dispensed with the need for volcanic rock and have a designed distribution heat plate instead. These sit above the burner and offer the same function and protection to the burner.

22.6.2 Location

Again it is important that the location of the barbecue should be carefully selected to prevent damage to property or foliage. A stable and level base is required for both methods to be mounted on. Consultation and agreement with the customer will determine the final location.

Note that barbecues fired by LPG may attract additional requirements such as minimum clearances from drains - refer to NICEIC Certification's Liquefied Petroleum Gas Safety On Site Guide for further guidance, as relevant.

22.6.3 Operation

With the gas supply connected, the gas tap, which is conveniently mounted on the front of the unit, is turned on, gas then flows to the burner. There is normally no flame supervision device fitted to this type of appliance. The ignition device is then operated, lighting the gas at the burner. Most appliances will have a Piezo ignition system fitted for convenience. Where there is more than one burner a cross-lighting bar or ribbon is used to ignite all burners. The flames then heat the volcanic rock which will provide an even heating surface across the grill and afford some protection to the burner from the fallout of the food in the form of fats. The fats are burned off the volcanic rock during the cooking process adding to the flavour of the food.

The lid is an important feature of the unit as it allows the user to increase the heat within the unit and allow the food to be infused by different flavours. (cinnamon and oak are often grilled to create the more traditional taste of barbecued food). The lid can also contain a thermometer giving the user an indication of the cooking temperature however, the lid needs to be in the closed position for it to register correctly.

22.6.4 Gas supply

The gas supply to the appliance will be installed in accordance with BS 6891 for external pipework. The mobile appliance is connected to the gas supply by means of a flexible hose and can be plugged in to the gas supply via a leisure point kit suitably located.

Permanently mounted units can be supplied with gas by the hose method previously described or be piped using rigid pipework. In either case the appliance shall have a means of isolation.

22.6.5 Commissioning

As always, the engineer shall comply with the manufacturer's instructions. However, the following procedure is designed to give supplementary guidance where the commissioning instructions are insufficient.

1. Conduct a visual inspection of the whole installation rectifying any nonconformity before proceeding.
2. Conduct a tightness test on the whole installation.
3. Turn the isolation valve to the appliance on and check for escapes with LDF at each joint within the appliance.
4. Ensure that the volcanic rock is evenly distributed on the grate.
5. Light the burner, checking that the ignition probe is correctly located.
6. Check the burner for flame picture ensuring that the flames are burning evenly across the whole burner.
7. Check the safe operation of any flame supervision device.
8. Measure and record the burner pressure ensuring it conforms to that of the manufacturer.
9. Using LDF, check for escapes from the operating control to the burner heads with the burner on.
10. Check the user controls for correct operation.
11. The appliance may require burning off (check the manufacturers' instructions).
12. Explain the operation of the appliance to the user, advise them of the safety precautions that are required when the appliance is in operation and any general care that is required by the manufacturer that can be conducted by the customer.
13. Complete any documentation that is required and leave all manufacturer's instructions with the customer.

22.6.6 Servicing

1. Gather information from the customer regarding any problems with the appliance since the last service.
2. The installation should be tested to the current gas tightness test requirements.
3. Visually inspect the condition of the appliance, the supply pipework or hose and the burner to ensure no damage has occurred since the last service.
4. Remove the grill, volcanic rock and grate and clean if necessary.
5. Remove, inspect the burner(s), primary air port(s), injector(s) and clean if necessary.
6. The appliance should then be reassembled, lit and the flame observed to ensure a stable flame picture. Check the safe operation of any flame supervision device.
7. Test the user controls for ease of operation.
8. Using LDF test all joints with the appliance in operation.
9. Measure burner pressure and gas rate the appliance to ensure conformity with the manufacturer's instructions.
10. Test the operation of the appliance isolation valve to ensure smooth operation (ease and grease as required).
11. Reiterate to the customer of the safety precautions that are required when the appliance is in operation and any general care that is required by the manufacturer that can be conducted by the user.
12. Complete any documentation that is required and leave all manufacturer's instructions with the customer.

22.7 Patio Heaters

Patio heaters (fig 22.7), like the humble barbecue, can be purchased by the user at D.I.Y retail outlets and like the barbecue, the vast majority are manufactured to be supplied by LPG.

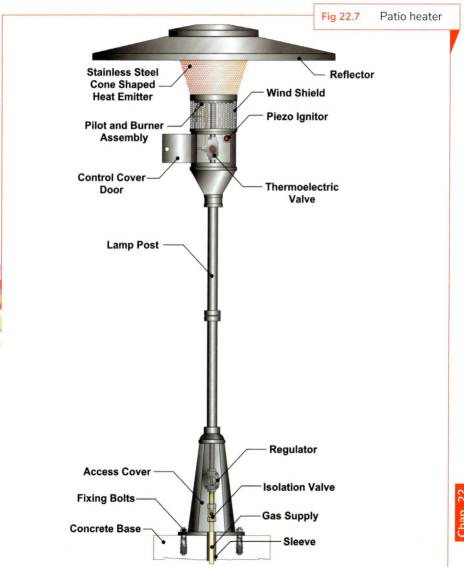

Fig 22.7 Patio heater

The appliance will normally be supplied as "flat pack" or partially assembled, requiring the user or engineer to assemble the appliance on site. In either case the manufacture's instructions shall be adhered to and deviation from the instructions is not permitted. This appliance shall only be used outside and should not be operated in garages, sheds, etc.

The main purpose of the heater is to provide heat to the user whilst enjoying the cooler evenings in the garden. The typical rating for these appliances is 13 kW.

22.7.1 Construction

The appliance is normally designed to be mounted on a post as part of its construction however, there are tabletop versions available. Like the gas light the appliance should be securely fixed (see Lighting in this Chapter) to ensure that they remain safe during times of high winds.

In the base of the post an access panel is provided to gain access to the appliance isolation valve. At the top of the post, there is also a sliding panel or door to gain access to the user controls.

The heating element is fitted directly on top of the control housing which is topped by a reflector. This assembly is often referred to as the cone.

The heating element is constructed of a ceramic fibre lined or mesh lined cone. The reflector includes a combustion gas vent to allow the products of combustion to be expelled to atmosphere without affecting the combustion of the gas on the face of the heater.

22.7.2 Location

The location requirements are similar to that of gas lights, in that, care should be taken when siting this appliance to ensure that there is no damage to property or surrounding foliage. In the absence of guidance from the manufacturer a distance of 1.5 m should be maintained from combustible materials or parts of buildings which could be damaged by the heater. Consultation and agreement with the customer will determine the final location.

22.7.3 Operation

The internal pipework to the appliance is controlled by an appliance isolation valve situated in the base of the column or post. The internal pipework rises within the appliance to the control housing where the users gas tap is located. A Piezo ignite will be located in the control housing. The gas then passes through to the burner.

The burner is preceded by the primary air ports and the appliance injector. The gas/air mixture then passes through the mesh of the burner and is ignited on the outside of the burner.

The appliance should be allowed to burn until the heater has warmed up before assessing the flame picture as the initial heat up period may display an unstable flame.

22.7.4   Gas supply

The gas supply to the appliance will be installed in accordance with BS 6891 for external pipework.

22.7.5   Installation

As with any other appliance the manufacturer's installation instructions shall be followed (see Installation for Lights in section 22.5).

22.7.6   Commissioning

As always the engineer shall comply with the manufacturer's instructions. However, the following procedure is designed to the give supplementary guidance where the commissioning instructions are insufficient.

1. Conduct a visual inspection of the whole installation rectifying any nonconformity before proceeding.
2. Conduct a tightness test on the whole installation.
3. Turn the isolation valve to the appliance on and check for escapes with LDF at each joint within the appliance.
4. Light the burner, checking that the ignition probe is correctly located.
5. Check the burner for flame picture after a heat up period has passed ensuring that the flames are burning evenly across the whole burner. Check the safe operation of any flame supervision device.
6. Measure and record the burner pressure ensuring it conforms to that of the manufacturer.
7. Using LDF, check for escapes from the operating control to the burner heads with the burner on.
8. Check the user controls for correct operation.
9. The appliance may require burning off (check the manufacturer's instructions) to remove any protective oils that have been applied.

10. Explain the operation of the appliance to the user, advise them of the safety precautions that are required when the appliance is in operation and any general care that is required by the manufacturer that can be conducted by the customer.
11. Complete any documentation that is required and leave all manufacturer's instructions with the customer.

22.7.7   Servicing

1. Gather information from the customer regarding any problems with the appliance since the last service.
2. The installation should be tested to the current gas tightness test requirements.
3. Visually inspect the condition of the appliance, the supply pipework and the burner to ensure no damage has occurred since the last service or installation.
4. Remove the reflector and the burner and clean as required.
5. Remove, inspect the primary air ports, injector(s) and clean if necessary.
6. The appliance should then be reassembled, lit and the flame observed to ensure a stable flame picture.
7. Test the user controls for ease of operation.
8. Using LDF test all joints with the appliance in operation.
9. Check the safe operation of any flame supervision device.
10. Measure burner pressure and gas rate the appliance to ensure conformity with the manufacturer's instructions.
11. Test the operation of the appliance isolation valve to ensure smooth operation (ease and grease, as required).
12. Reiterate to the user of the safety precautions that are required when the appliance is in operation and any general care that is required by the manufacturer that can be conducted by the customer.
13. Complete any documentation that is required and leave all manufacturer's instructions with the customer.

22.8 Greenhouse Heaters

As its name implies the purpose of the green house heater is to maintain heat in a greenhouse (fig 22.8). This appliance is not necessarily a leisure appliance however, it is considered to play a role in a leisure activity i.e. gardening. As the appliance may be installed in an enclosed space and coupled with the fact that it is a flueless appliance, ventilation is a major consideration. It is also one of the few leisure appliances which incorporate a temperature control.

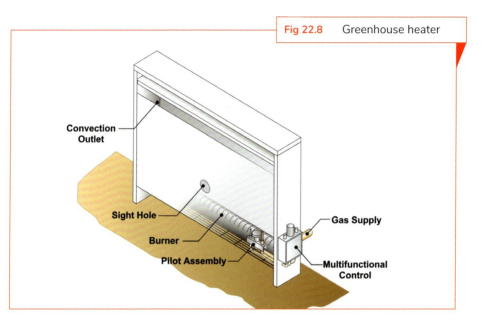

Fig 22.8   Greenhouse heater

The fact that the appliance is flueless encourages a carbon dioxide rich atmosphere which is beneficial for most plant life. Typical heat inputs are generally found to be less than 3 kW.

22.8.1 Construction

Like a flueless space heater that would be installed in a domestic property, the appliance is very simple in design. It consists of a metal case which has the burner and controls located within. The appliance has an air inlet grille at the bottom and a heat outlet grille at the top. There is no heat exchanger in this appliance as the products of combustion are directed through the appliance and out into the space being heated.

22.8.2 Location

The clearance around the appliance are specified by the manufacturer. However, consideration shall be taken as to the location of doors, air vent(s), etc., within the greenhouse. Additionally, consideration shall be given to the location of the plants and their eventual growth size to prevent obstruction of the heaters inlet and outlet grilles.

22.8.3 Ventilation

As this appliance is located inside a heated space ventilation may be required. For specific ventilation requirements refer to the manufacturer's instructions.

22.8.3.1 Stand alone greenhouses

If the heater(s) total heat input does not exceed 2.7 kW there is no requirement for ventilation however, where the heat input does exceed 2.7 kW (net) then 39 cm^2 of ventilation is required for every kW above 2.7 kW or part kW thereof.

22.8.3.2 Greenhouses accessed from the property

As the greenhouse is essentially part of the property then there is a risk, that an unacceptable level of CO_2 may be produced and may enter the main living areas.

Therefore, the following method for calculating the required ventilation should be adopted. The size of the heater is restricted to 90 W/m^3, and the ventilation is based on the actual heat input of the heater whereby 100 cm^2 is required for an appliance up to 5.4 kW and an additional 27.5 cm^2 for every kW above 5.4 kW or part thereof. There is also a requirement for an openable window in addition to the vent, in the greenhouse.

22.8.4 Gas supply

The gas supply to the appliance will be installed in accordance with BS 6891 for external pipework. The appliance can be connected to the gas supply by means of a flexible hose, itself connected to a leisure point kit suitably located or can be piped using rigid pipework. In either case the appliance shall have a means of isolation.

22.8.5 Installation

As with any other appliance the manufacturer's installation instructions shall be followed. The appliance should be securely fixed to a concrete base or concrete slab using the method of fixing detailed in the manufacturer's instructions. Any rigid pipework supplying gas to the appliance shall be fixed to the structure of the greenhouse for support. If the appliance has a thermostatic control then a suitable location is required for the sensing device. This should be located where it will not be affected by direct sunlight and be able to monitor the heat within the space.

22.8.6 Controls

The appliance controls will normally consist of a multifunctional device which will incorporate a gas tap for on/off selection, a remote temperature sensing device (usually a liquid expansion thermostatic valve), a thermoelectric flame supervision device and a Piezo igniter.

22.8.7 Commissioning

As always the engineer shall comply with the manufacturer's instructions. However, the following procedure is designed to give supplementary guidance where the commissioning instructions are insufficient.

1. Conduct a visual inspection of the whole installation rectifying any nonconformity before proceeding.
2. Conduct a tightness test on the whole installation.
3. Turn the isolation valve to the appliance on and check for escapes with LDF at each joint within the appliance.
4. Light the burner, checking that the ignition probe is correctly located.
5. Check the burner flame picture ensuring that the flames are burning evenly across the whole burner.
6. Measure and record the burner pressure ensuring it conforms to that of the manufacturer.
7. Using LDF, check for escapes from the operating control to the burner heads with the burner on.
8. Check the user controls for correct operation, including if applicable the sensing probe for the temperature is securely fixed and sited correctly.
9. Check the safe operation of any flame supervision device.

10. The appliance may require burning off (check the manufacturer's instructions) to remove any protective oils that have been applied.
11. Explain the operation of the appliance to the user, advise them of the safety precautions that are required when the appliance is in operation and any general care that is required by the manufacturer that can be conducted by the customer.
12. Complete any documentation that is required and leave all manufacturer's instructions with the customer.

22.8.8   Servicing

1. Gather information from the customer regarding any problems with the appliance since the last service.
2. The installation should be tested to the current gas tightness test requirements.
3. Visually inspect the condition of the appliance, the supply pipework and the appliance components to ensure no damage has occurred since the last service.
4. Remove front case panel and the burner and clean as required.
5. Remove inspect the primary air ports, injector(s) and clean if necessary.
6. The appliance should then be reassembled, lit and the flame observed to ensure a stable flame picture.
7. Test the user controls for ease of operation.
8. Using LDF test all joints with the appliance in operation.
9. Check the safe operation of any flame supervision device.
10. Measure burner pressure and gas rate the appliance to ensure conformity with the manufacturer's instructions.
11. Test the operation of the appliance isolation valve to ensure smooth operation (ease and grease, as required).
12. Reiterate to the user of the safety precautions that are required when the appliance is in operation and any general care that is required by the manufacturer that can be conducted by the customer.
13. Complete any documentation that is required and leave all manufacturer's instructions with the customer.

22.9 Flambeaux (Torch)

This appliance is designed with decoration in mind and is thought to create an atmosphere of days of old. Often referred to as a torch, it would have been and is, used to create illumination along pathways and areas for evening or night time events. There are many different designs but the principle of construction has a basic format (fig 22.9). The torch is designed to be installed either on a post or wall mounted. This appliance should never be installed inside a property.

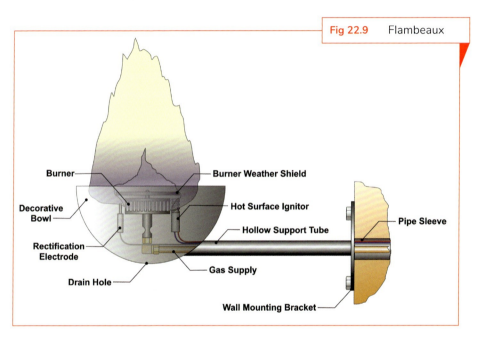

Fig 22.9   Flambeaux

22.9.1   Construction

An open burner is located inside the body of the appliance. The body is often referred to as the bowl regardless of its actual shape. In order to create a yellow flame, the burner has no aeration ports. The injector is located within the sealed burner. As the appliance is constantly subjected to the effects of the wind and is at risk of being blown out, a re-ignition system is employed. This also ensures that unburned gases are not released to the atmosphere as well as having unlit areas. In line with the regulations the appliance requires an isolation valve on the gas supply to the appliance and a method of disconnection.

22.9.2 Location

The clearances around the appliance are specified by the manufacturer. The main consideration that shall be taken into account when siting that appliance is the effects of the wind on the flame. The flame can be distorted to such an extent that combustible materials within the flames proximity may ignite or may even cause injury to people passing.

As the flames can be blown in all directions it is important to ensure that the required clearances are maintained in every direction around the appliance. The model and heat input of the appliance will dictate the actual dimensions, but typically this ranges from 600 mm to 900 mm. To prevent products of combustion from entering the building the appliance should not be located under or near openings like windows or doors. Consideration should also be given to access for maintenance and servicing when deciding the final location.

22.9.3 Gas Supply

The gas supply to the appliance will be installed in accordance with BS 6891 for external pipework. The appliance can only be connected to the gas supply by means of rigid pipework.

22.9.4 Installation

As with any other appliance the manufacturer's installation instruction shall be followed. Provision needs to be provided for the supply of electricity to operate the re-ignition system. This may be a 230 volt supply or battery powered.

22.9.5 Controls

The appliance controls will normally consist of an isolation valve and the re-ignition system. However, some models do have remote operation where the control is achieved by using an internal electrical switch linked to a solenoid on the pipework to the appliance. This in turn will also activate the re-ignition system.

22.9.6 Commissioning

As always the engineer shall comply with the manufacturer's instructions. However, the following procedure is designed to the give supplementary guidance where the commissioning instructions are insufficient.

1. Conduct a visual inspection of the whole installation rectifying any nonconformities before proceeding.
2. Conduct a tightness test on the whole installation.
3. Light the burner, checking that the ignition probe is correctly located (extra care should be taken when working around this appliance when it is lit).
4. Check the burner for flame picture ensuring that the flames are burning evenly across the whole burner and that the correct effect is achieved.
5. Using LDF, check for escapes from the operating control to the burner heads with the burner on.
6. Check the user controls for correct operation.
7. Check the safe operation of any flame supervision device. The appliance may require burning off (check the manufacturer's instructions) to remove any protective oils that have been applied.
8. Explain the operation of the appliance to the user, advise them of the safety precautions that are required when the appliance is in operation and any general care that is required by the manufacturer that can be conducted by the customer.
9. Complete any documentation that is required and leave all manufacturer's instructions with the customer.

22.9.7 Servicing

1. Gather information from the customer regarding any problems with the appliance since the last service.
2. The installation should be tested to the current gas tightness test requirements.
3. Visually inspect the condition of the appliance, the supply pipework and the appliance to ensure no damage has occurred since the last service or installation.
4. Remove the burner and clean as required close inspection for corrosion is required as this burner is exposed to all the elements of the weather.
5. Remove inspect the injector(s) and clean if necessary.
6. The appliance should then be reassembled, lit and the flame observed to ensure the desired flame picture is achieved.
7. Test the user controls for ease of operation.
8. Check the safe operation of any flame supervision device.
9. Using LDF, test all joints with the appliance in operation (extra care should be taken when working around this appliance when it is lit).
10. Test the operation of the of the appliance isolation valve to ensure smooth operation and ignition.
11. Reiterate to the user of the safety precautions that are required when the appliance is in operation and any general care that is required by the manufacturer that can be conducted by the customer.
12. Complete any documentation that is required and leave all manufacturer's instructions with the customer.

Chapter 23
Emergency Service Provider Engineer & Meter Installer

		Page No.
23.1	Introduction	23.1
23.2	Non-domestic Ventilation	23.2
	23.2.1 General	23.2
	23.2.2 Heating appliance ventilation	23.4
	23.2.2.1 Natural ventilation	23.6
	23.2.2.2 Mechanical ventilation	23.6
	23.2.2.3 Ducted ventilation	23.7
	23.2.2.4 Ventilation methods	23.8
	23.2.2.5 Ambient air temperatures	23.11
	23.2.2.6 Construction and location of ventilation grilles and vents	23.12
	23.2.2.7 Ventilation provision For hot water boilers	23.12
	23.2.2.8 Forced convection air heaters	23.15
	23.2.2.9 Radiant heaters	23.16
	23.2.3 Ventilation in commercial catering establishments	23.16
	23.2.3.1 Make-up air	23.17
	23.2.3.2 Kitchen extract	23.18
	23.2.3.3 Interlocking of gas supply	23.20
	23.2.4 Ventilation for commercial laundry equipment	23.22

Chapter 23
Emergency Service Provider Engineer & Meter Installer

			Page No.
23.3	Non-domestic Chimney/Flue, Extract & Exhaust Systems		**23.25**
	23.3.1 Heating appliance chimney/flue systems		**23.25**
		23.3.1.1 Materials	**23.26**
		23.3.1.2 Insulation	**23.27**
		23.3.1.3 Termination	**23.28**
		23.3.1.4 Flue dampers and stabilisers	**23.34**
		23.3.1.5 Common flues and chimneys	**23.34**
		23.3.1.6 Balanced compartments	**23.36**
		23.3.1.7 Modular flue systems	**23.36**
		23.3.1.8 Fan dilution flue systems	**23.38**
	23.3.2 Commercial laundry equipment exhaust system		**23.40**
	23.3.3 Commercial catering extract discharge		**23.42**
23.4	Non-domestic Pipework Installation		**23.42**
	23.4.1 Materials and jointing methods		**23.43**
		23.4.1.1 Steel	**23.44**
		23.4.1.2 Polyethylene (PE)	**23.46**
		23.4.1.3 Copper	**23.47**

Chapter 23
Emergency Service Provider Engineer & Meter Installer

			Page No.
	23.4.2	Installation	23.48
		23.4.2.1 Corrosion protection	23.49
		23.4.2.2 Pipework identification	23.49
		23.4.2.3 Pipework in ducts	23.50
		23.4.2.4 Pipework In multi-storey and multiple dwelling buildings	23.52
		23.4.2.5 Buried pipework	23.52
		23.4.2.6 Entry and exit from buildings	23.53
		23.4.2.7 Emergency control valves	23.55
23.5	Medium Pressure Fed Meter Installations		23.58
	23.5.1	Metering installation pressure control and protection system	23.58
		Operating pressure limits	23.58
	23.5.2	Commissioning medium pressure regulators	23.60
		23.5.2.1 Commissioning SINGLE STAGE regulator	23.61
		23.5.2.2 Commissioning TWO STAGE regulator	23.63
		23.5.2.3 Commissioning PRS/28 & PRS/29 regulators with additional LP regulator	23.65

Chapter 23
Emergency Service Provider Engineer & Meter Installer

References in this Chapter

[1] BS EN 1749: 2020 Classification of gas appliances according to the method of supplying combustion air and of evacuation of the combustion products (types).

Note: BS EN 1749 replaces the previous standard BS EN 1749: 2014.

[2] IGEM/UP/11 Edition 3 Gas installations for educational establishments.

[3] IGEM/UP/6 Edition 2 Application of positive displacement compressors to natural gas fuel systems.

[4] IGEM/UP/16 Design for natural gas installations on industrial and commercial premises with respect to hazardous are classification and preparation of risk assessments.

[5] IGEM/SR/25 Edition 2 Hazardous are classification of natural gas.

[6] IGEM/GM/6 Edition 2 Non-domestic meter installations. Standard.

[7] IGE/GM/8 Edition 2 (Parts 1 to 5) Non-domestic meter installations.

23.1 Introduction

This Chapter has been compiled to provide the Emergency Service Provider (ESP) engineer and meter installer with the additional information required to allow them to perform their duties within domestic and non-domestic premises, where it is used to supplement previous Chapters within this Guide. In addition, any work which is specifically related to ESP engineers and meter installers duties such as commissioning medium pressure regulators, is also covered.

Strength testing, tightness testing and purging of non-domestic installations and large meter installations are not covered due to their complexity and specialist subject matter.

As mentioned in previous Chapters of this Guide, the ESP engineer and meter installer have specific training and qualifications which limits their competence to meter related work, attending gas emergencies and re-establishing gas supplies and as such, they are not deemed competent to carry out "work" as defined in the GS(I&U)R on gas appliances. This does not detract from the fact that **they are responsible** to ensure that any appliance(s) which they may encounter while carrying out their duties do not constitute a danger.

To meet this obligation they must carry out a basic visual risk assessment of the appliance installation, which must cover the following points:

- Appliance location.
- Flue/chimney installation.
- Ventilation provision.
- Signs of distress.
- Evidence that the appliance is stable and secure.
- Flame picture (only following an interruption of supply when this has occurred).

These bullet points are covered and expanded upon within Chapter 12 of this Guide.

In order to make the correct judgement on safety, the ESP engineer and meter installer shall have an understanding of regulations, standards and other relevant industry documents pertaining to both domestic and non-domestic gas installations.

23.2 Non-domestic Ventilation

Non-domestic installations can be split into three distinct categories, each with their own specific ventilation requirements, these being:

- heating,
- catering, and
- laundry.

The ventilation provision for these different types of installation can be quite complex and as such is a specialist subject. The ESP engineer and meter installer do not require to be "subject matter experts" however, they are required to have a basic understanding of any requirements.

23.2.1   General

One of the main factors in building design is the provision of adequate ventilation for all internal spaces, this includes not only habitable areas but also unhabitable areas such as below floor voids, ceiling voids and roof spaces. Ventilation is used to change the air within these spaces in order to remove moisture, heat, odours, smoke and any other airborne contaminants; it's one of the prime factors for maintaining a healthy environment within a building.

Ventilation includes both the entrainment and evacuation of air to outside including circulation of air within the building. This can be achieved by natural ventilation through fixed openings or the use of air moving devices, or a mixture of both. To increase the operational efficiency of some heating and ventilation systems a level of re-circulation may be included where all or part of the internal air is passed through a filtration system before being discharged back into the building. It should be noted that we do not re-circulate the air from toilets, bathrooms, shower rooms, etc., due to odours, contaminants and moisture levels.

The time taken to completely change the air volume of a room is classed as the ventilation rate (sometimes called the air change rate) and is normally expressed in air changes per hour.

When a gas-fired appliance is installed, additional ventilation may be required over and above the buildings normal ventilation requirement.

This additional ventilation is used to:

- Provide air for the complete combustion of the fuel.
- Where applicable, limit the temperatures within an area due to the additional heat emitted by the appliance.
- Ensure the safe operation of open flue chimneys.
- Provide replacement (make-up) air for appliances and/or processes which extract large volumes of air from the area in which they are installed during their normal operation, for example tumble dryers and catering establishments.
- Reduce the concentrations of combustion products in atmosphere in areas where type A appliances are installed.
- Ensure the safe and effective operation of the appliance and any ancillary plant.

To ensure the additional ventilation provision is sufficient for gas-fired appliance(s), guidance can be found within the following industry documents:

- **BS 5440 Part 2** – Flueing and ventilation for gas appliances of rated input not exceeding 70 kW net (1st, 2nd and 3rd family gases). Specification for the Installation and maintenance of ventilation provision for gas appliances.
- **BS 6173** – Specification for installation and maintenance of gas-fired catering appliances for use in all types of catering establishments (2nd and 3rd family gases).
- **BS 6230** – Specification for the installation of gas-fired forced convection air heaters for commercial and industrial space heating (2nd and 3rd family gases).
- **BS 6644** – Specification for the installation and maintenance of gas-fired hot water boilers of rated inputs between 70 kW and 1.8 MW (net) (2nd and 3rd family gases).
- **BS 6896** – Specification for the installation and maintenance of gas-fired overhead radiant heaters for industrial and commercial heating (2nd and 3rd family gases).
- **BS 8446** – Specification for the installation and maintenance of open-flue, non-domestic gas-fired laundry appliances.

- **BS EN 13410** – Gas-fired overhead radiant heaters. Ventilation requirements for non-domestic premises.
- **BESA DW/172** – Specification for Kitchen Ventilation Systems.
- **IGEM/UP/10 Edition 4 +A: 2016** – Installation of flued gas appliances in industrial and commercial premises.
- **IGEM/UP/11 Edition 3** – Gas installations for educational establishments
- **IGEM/UP/19 +A: 2015** – Design and application of interlock devices and associated systems used with gas appliance installations in commercial and catering establishments.

NOTE: Where an appliance is installed in the same room or space as other fuel fired plant or processes which consume air from that area, a risk assessment shall be carried out to ensure that they can all operate safely and do not have an adverse affect on each other.

Where specific manufacturer's instructions are not available, the ventilation provision for bio-fuelled appliances (gaseous, liquid or solid fuel) installed in the same room or space as a gas-fired appliance shall be considered as part of the overall ventilation provision.

23.2.2 Heating appliance ventilation

There is a large diversity of appliances used to heat non-domestic premises, however they can be segregated into three different groups namely:

- **Hot water boiler** – as the name implies these appliances are used to heat water. The heated water may then be distributed around a heating system, used for domestic hot water (bulk storage water heaters) or used for process. These appliance can range from small domestic sized appliances up to very large units which can be a few storeys high (fig 23.1).

Fig 23.1 Large boiler

- **Forced convection air heater** – these heat the premises by circulating heated air by means of a fan unit. They may be direct-fired (the products of combustion are mixed with the air used to heat the building and do not have a flue system) or indirect-fired (the products of combustion are separated from the air used to heat the building by way of a heat exchanger, fig 23.2).

- **Radiant heater** – these appliances are normally suspended or fixed at high level where they heat the premises by means of radiated heat. They come in two forms - radiant plaques (fig 23.3) or radiant tubes (fig 23.4) and may be flued or unflued/flueless. They shall be installed at a height as specified by the manufacturer due to the intensity of the heat produced.

Fig 23.2   Floor standing cabinet heater

Fig 23.3   Radiant plaque heater

Fig 23.4   Radiant tube heater

23.2.2.1 Natural ventilation

Natural ventilation can be defined as the exchange of air within a building, typically between an indoor space and outside air, without the use of a fan or other mechanical system.

To ensure the effective ventilation within the space in which a gas-fired appliance(s) is installed, grilles or ventilators shall be located as high and as low as reasonably practicable. Any natural air inlet grille shall be positioned within 1 m of the finished floor level (250 mm for LPG) with the high level relief located within 15 % of the room height from the ceiling (It should be noted that the use of louvre doors alone may not meet this requirement). In relation to the appliance, ventilation grilles shall be installed in such a manner as to ensure an effective circulation of air over the appliance without causing an adverse affect on its safe operation.

For exposed free-standing boiler houses, any openings used to provide natural ventilation shall be located on at least two sides of the structure (preferably four, where practicable). This will ensure sufficient circulation of air through the boiler house under extreme weather conditions.

23.2.2.2 Mechanical ventilation

Mechanical ventilation can be provided by installing a fan unit directly on to an external wall, or by an in-line fan installed as part of a duct system. This type of ventilation system is usually installed where the provision of natural ventilation may be impracticable, intrusive or insufficient to meet the needs of the installation.

All mechanical ventilation must have an automatic control that will immediately cause either safety shut down or lockout of the appliances in the event of fan failure. This is a mandatory requirement. Where a safety interlock is not installed or when installed, fails to shut down the appliances in the event of fan failure, the installation is deemed AT RISK in accordance with IGEM/G/11 (the Gas Industry Unsafe Situations Procedure (GIUSP)).

23.2.2.3 Ducted ventilation

Appliances installed in basements, underground or similarly sited boiler houses/plant rooms, or where no direct means of ventilation to outside is practical, ventilation shall be provided by means of a duct. Individual ducting shall be used for both high and low level ventilation (Option 2 in fig 23.5). A single duct or grille shall not be used for both inlet and extract unless it is subdivided throughout its complete length. For semi-submerged plant rooms we may only require to duct the inlet vent to low level (Option 1 in fig 23.5), the high level vent can be installed as for an above ground installation.

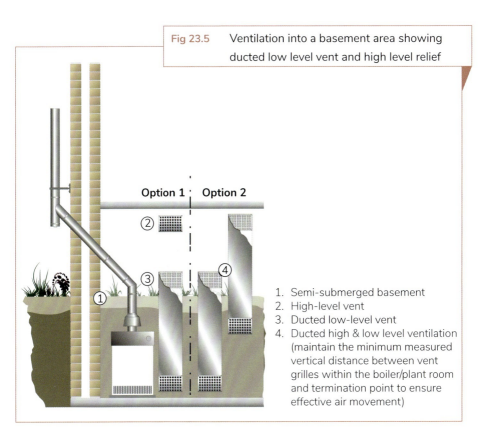

Fig 23.5 Ventilation into a basement area showing ducted low level vent and high level relief

1. Semi-submerged basement
2. High-level vent
3. Ducted low-level vent
4. Ducted high & low level ventilation (maintain the minimum measured vertical distance between vent grilles within the boiler/plant room and termination point to ensure effective air movement)

23.2.2.4 Ventilation methods

Ventilation can be supplied into a building by one of the following methods:

1. One or more natural low level openings with discharge via one or more natural high level openings (fig 23.6).

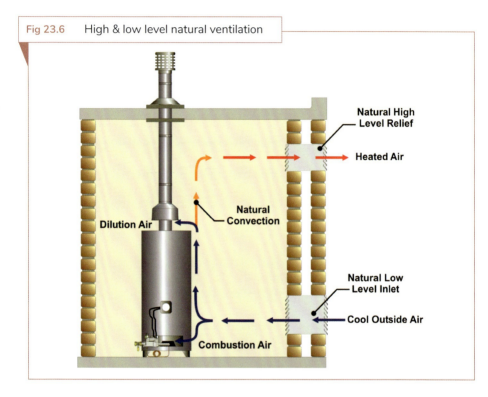

Fig 23.6 High & low level natural ventilation

2. Natural high and low level ventilation provided by louvre door (fig 23.7).
3. Purpose designed high level supply and discharge (balanced compartment, mono-draught), fig 23.8.

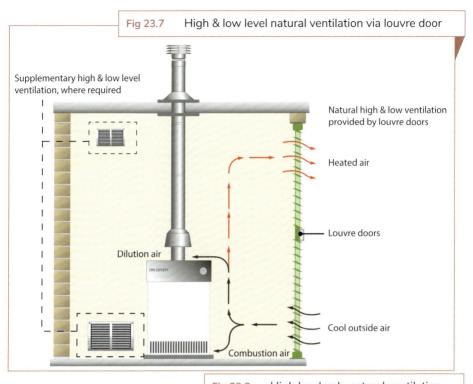

Fig 23.7 High & low level natural ventilation via louvre door

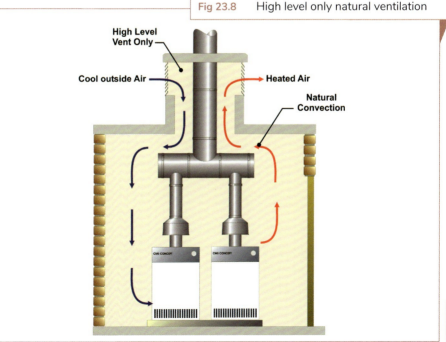

Fig 23.8 High level only natural ventilation

4. Low level supply fan and natural discharge through one or more high level openings (fig 23.9).

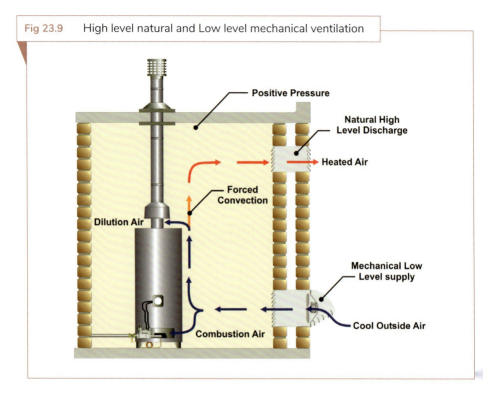

Fig 23.9 High level natural and Low level mechanical ventilation

5. High and low level fan assisted ventilation (fig 23.10).

Extract only and natural draught low level with fan assisted high level (extract) is not allowed due to the possibility of a negative pressure being created within the plant room, which may lead to flue reversal.

Within the non-domestic environment and due to fire safety issues any ventilation shall be direct to outside air and not communicate with any other internal space unless it is suitably ducted through that space. Only in extreme circumstances will ventilation be allowed to communicate with any internal space and even then it will be subject to local government building control approval.

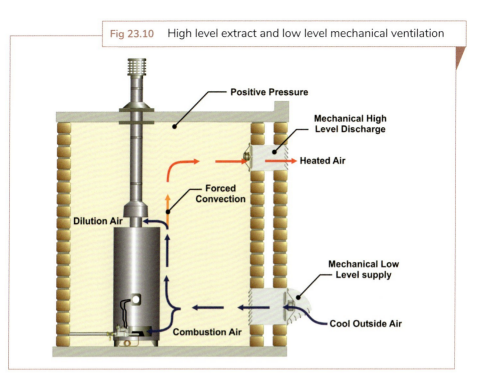

Fig 23.10 High level extract and low level mechanical ventilation

23.2.2.5 Ambient air temperatures

Ventilation shall be designed to ensure ambient air temperatures within any plant room, compartment or enclosure does not increase to a level which may affect the safe operation of the installation.

Ambient temperatures shall not exceed:

- 25 °C within 100 mm of the floor,
- 32 °C mid height, and
- 40 °C within 100 mm of the ceiling height.

These temperatures are used as one of the primary indicators as to the effectiveness of the ventilation.

23.2.2.6 Construction and location of ventilation grilles and vents

Ventilation grilles and vents for non-domestic applications fundamentally have the same installation restrictions as domestic vents, for example shall be non-closeable or have no fly screens or gauzes, etc.

However, unlike the domestic air vent the non-domestic grille or vent has a minimum opening size of 5 mm but no maximum (10 mm for domestic) due to their construction and application (fig 23.11). To prevent the entry of vermin and debris these vents may have a vermin mesh located behind them normally with an aperture dimension of approximately 10 mm x 10 mm.

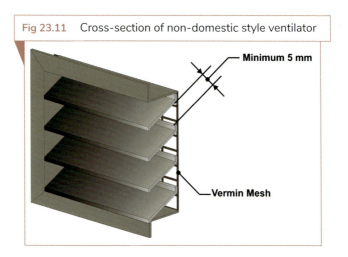

Fig 23.11 Cross-section of non-domestic style ventilator

23.2.2.7 Ventilation provision For hot water boilers

For hot water boiler where the heat input is less than 70 kW (net) the domestic ventilation criteria given in Part 1; Chapter 4 should be applied. For single or groups of appliances where the maximum rated input is 70 kW (net) and above the following calculation methods apply unless specific ventilation requirements are provided by the appliance manufacturer.

NOTE: These are the minimum ventilation requirement direct to outside (unless stated otherwise) and may require to be increased accordingly depending on the outcome of any operational tests. These tests are outside the scope of the ESP engineer and meter installer and will not be detailed in this section.

Room sealed hot water boilers

As with domestic sized room sealed boilers additional ventilation is normally not required when the appliance is installed within a heated space. For plant rooms, boiler rooms or enclosures the ventilation provision is for cooling purposes only.

NOTE: The manufacturer's instructions shall be consulted for room sealed appliances. Most modern appliances are high efficiency and as such generate a minimum amount of heat. Additional ventilation may not be required.

Table 23.1 Ventilation for room sealed boilers with a maximum rated heat Input 70 kW and above

Appliance Location	Minimum Natural Ventilation Provision (cm^2/kW net)	
	Low Level	High Level
Plant/boiler room or compartment	2	2
Enclosed ventilated direct to outside	5	5
Enclosed ventilated to internal space	10	10

Open flue hot water boilers

Depending on the size of the appliance(s), building restrictions and location, ventilation may be supplied either through natural or mechanical means. For a hot water boiler(s) installed in a heated space the configuration and calculation methods for sizing the vents are dictated by the room volume and air change rate.

For buildings with a room volume less than 1500 m^3 and an air change rate less than 0.5 per hour, we require both high and low level ventilation. The additional natural ventilation is calculated using the following formula:

Effective free area of vent (cm^2) = Maximum rated input (kW) x 2 cm^2

For buildings with a room volume greater than 1500 m^3 and an air change rate greater than 0.5 per hour, we only require a single vent, sized as above, at low level.

NOTE: For very large spaces & greater than 0.5 air changes, additional ventilation may not be required but this would be subject to further tests.

For a plant room, boiler room or enclosure we require both high and low level ventilation as specified in table 23.2.

Table 23.2 Natural ventilation for open flue boilers with a maximum rated heat input 70 kW and above

Appliance Location	Minimum Natural Ventilation Provision (cm²/kW net)	
	Low Level	High Level
Plat/boiler room or compartment	4	2
Enclosure	10	5

For installations up to 1.8 MW ventilation is supplied in a ratio of 1 high level to 2 low level distributed evenly around the plant room, boiler room, compartment or enclosure depending on the number of external walls.

For an appliance(s) with a maximum rated input in excess of 1.8 MW burning lighter than air gases, where it is not practicable to install high and low level ventilation, if the volume of the space in which the appliance is installed is equal to or greater than 1 m³ for every 2 kW net heat input of the installation, it is permitted to install high level ventilation only. The total free area of the ventilation is 6 cm² per kW and shall be provided via two or more ventilators. This is not permissible for heavier than air gases.

Where the plant room volume is less than 1 m³ per 2 kW total rated input, ducting the ventilation to low level using natural means is not recommended; it is preferable to have mechanical assisted low level ventilation. High and low level vents shall be configured on a ratio of 1 at high level and 2 at low level on any one wall. If more than one wall is used for ventilation purposes then the easiest method is to divide the total ventilation requirement by the number of walls such that the ventilation is spread evenly around the plant room maintaining the required 1:2 ratio.

Mechanical ventilation is calculated on a minimum flow rate generated by a fan Since this involves the use of specialised measuring equipment it is not within the scope of the ESP engineer or meter installer to measure and confirm its adequacy and as such will not be covered in any detail within this section. However mechanical ventilation is calculated as given in table 23.3.

Table 23.3 Mechanical ventilation of open flue appliances of net heat input in excess of 70 kW installed within a plant/boiler room, compartment or enclosure.

Appliance Type	Inlet Fan Flow Rate (m³/h)	Difference Between Inlet & Extract (m³/h)
With draught diverter(s) (Type B_1)	Total Net Heat Input x 2.8	2.07 ± 0.18
Without a draught diverter(s) (Type B_2) with or without draught stabilisers.	Total Net Heat Input x 2.6	1.35 ± 0.18

Where doubt exists the appliance should be turned off until its safe operation has been confirmed by an appropriately competent Gas Safe registered engineer.

For balanced compartments the ventilation provision is at high level only. The compartment criteria mirrors that of the domestic as given in Part 1; Chapter 11. The ventilation criteria is calculated as given in table 23.4.

Table 23.4 Natural ventilation for open flue hot water boilers in balanced compartments

Maximum Rated Input (kW)	Minimum Natural Ventilation Provision (cm²/kW net)
	High Level
Up to 500	10
500 and above	8

23.2.2.8 Forced convection air heaters

The natural ventilation requirement for indirect-fired forced convection air heaters is calculated using the same formula as that for hot water boilers when installed in a plant room, compartment or enclosure. Where the heater is installed within the heated space, irrespective of room volume, if the air change rate is less than 0.5 per hour the ventilation provision will be 2 cm² per kW maximum rated input at low level only. The mechanical ventilation however, is different from that of a hot water boiler and as indicated previously will not be covered in this section.

For direct-fired air heaters confirmation of their safe operation is subject to an atmospheric test of the heated space which again is a specialist activity outside the scope of the ESP engineer and meter installer.

23.2.2.9 Radiant heaters

Radiant heaters due to their method of heating are always installed within an occupied internal space. For flued heaters they only require a low level vent located below the heater. The 1 m specification does not apply in this respect due to the installation height of the appliance. The calculation method is as that for the hot water boiler and air heater (2 cm^2 per kW).

For flueless/unflued radiant heaters, further information can be found in BS EN 13410 and again is subject to an atmospheric test for confirmation of safe operation.

23.2.3 Ventilation in commercial catering establishments

Commercial catering can cover a broad range of appliances installed in varying types of catering establishments, each one with different catering needs. The layout and cooking appliance types are all dictated by the volume of meals and cooking needs of the kitchen, this can include burger vans, small takeaway premise, cafes, education establishments, public houses, hotels through to large restaurants. In addition, the type of menu and preparation requirements influence the type of appliances required by the caterer. Food can be freshly prepared, from snacks to full "a la carte" menus or precooked where it can be chilled or frozen.

Commercial catering is quite a specialised subject which holds may different challenges for the gas engineer. Catering establishments being wide and varied as they are, promote a more objective look at gas safety.

Some appliances and systems can be many decades old, even though the appliances do not meet the safety standards of today, the user awareness and condition of the appliance and installation dictate safety.

During the cooking process a considerable amount of contamination is produced in the form of convective and radiated heat, odours, grease vapours, products of combustion, starch and water vapour. The effective removal, filtration and discharge of this contamination together with a supply of cool fresh clean replacement air (commonly known as make-up air) are imperative for a safe and comfortable working environment. In all accounts specific extract rates and make-up air requirements detailed by the appliance manufacturer shall be adhered to. Where no specific information is available the installation shall meet the requirements as specified in BESA DW/172 (formally the HVCA).

23.2.3.1 Make-up air

Ventilation supplied into a commercial kitchen does not only take into account the combustion air but also the air extracted via the extract hood/canopy. This air is called make-up air. Combustion ventilation is only 2 to 6 % of the total ventilation required for a kitchen. It is advisable that due to the volume of air being entrained into the kitchen area that make-up air is taken direct from outside and not through eating areas; fast moving air can cause discomfort to customers and also quickly chills cooked foods.

To ensure that no contamination generated through the cooking process can spread into other areas, commercial kitchens are maintained at a negative pressure. To achieve this make-up air direct from outside represents only 85 % of the total ventilation needs of the kitchen, the other 15 % comes from adjacent internal areas with the exception of contaminated areas such as toilets, smoking areas, etc.

To calculate the make-up air we should firstly find out the extract flow rates as they represent the total air being removed from the room. Make-up air will be 85 % of this extract rate.

To comply with health and hygiene requirements, any make-up air provided into the kitchen area shall be filtered to remove any dusts, insects or airborne contaminants prior to the air entering the kitchen area. Remember this is make-up air and not combustion air, therefore filtration is allowed. Where the filtration causes a significant restriction, the make-up air should be increased to make allowances for this restriction.

Where make-up air is provided by mechanical means a safety interlock must be installed to shut down the gas supply if the fan(s) were to fail or the flow rate decreases below safe working levels (this may be due to a blocked air filter, etc).

23.2.3.2 Kitchen extract

Catering appliances are normally installed below an extract canopy which is designed to collect the cooking fumes and safely disperse them to outside. The dimensions of a canopy is specific to the layout of the catering suite however, unless restricted by walls, the plan dimensions shall always exceed that of the catering equipment on all free sides. Any overhang dimensions relate to the collection area of the hood and do not take into account the condensation or stiffening channel around the canopy.

Figure 23.12 shows the standard overhang and clearance dimensions for a canopy.

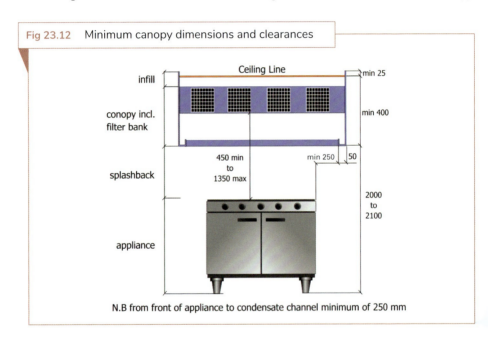

Fig 23.12 Minimum canopy dimensions and clearances

N.B from front of appliance to condensate channel minimum of 250 mm

There are a number of different canopy designs such as overhead wall mounted, island, passover, eyebrow, etc., the design of which is given in DW/172. Any new canopy shall be constructed of stainless steel however, older canopies may be of other materials such as aluminium, fibre glass, etc.

In some instances due to building restrictions, ventilated ceilings may be used instead of a canopy. These ceilings have the extract, make-up air and lighting fully integrated into the ceiling structure. An example of the construction of a ventilated ceiling is shown in fig 23.13.

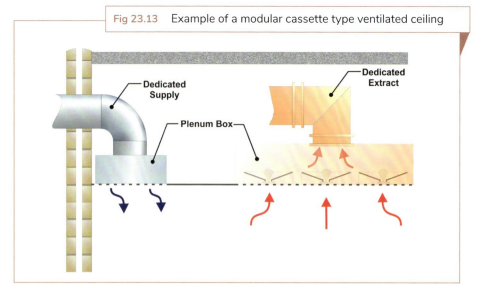

Fig 23.13 Example of a modular cassette type ventilated ceiling

NOTE: Appliances such as expansion hot water boilers do not require to be placed under a canopy due to their intermittent use. However, they must still be taken into account when calculating the total extract requirement.

Filters are used within the canopy area to extract and remove grease, water and other forms of contamination from the cooking fumes prior to entry into the extract plenum and ductwork (fig's 23.14 & 23.15). Filters shall limit any fire penetration into the canopy plenum, have no sharp edges or protrusions and be designed as such for easy removal and cleaning. Disposable panel type filters **SHALL NOT** be used. Filters shall be cleaned by the caterer at regular intervals; failure to clean the filters will result in poor canopy performance.

Fig 23.14 Mesh impingement filter

Fig 23.15 Baffle filter

23.2.3.3   Interlocking of gas supply

In all accounts for new installations, whether extraction canopy, mechanical ventilation system or complete kitchen, the extract must be interlocked to the gas supply such that the appliances cannot be operated if the fan(s) were to fail; this requirement also prohibits any means of overriding any interlock provisions.

However, in older, existing installations this may not be the case. In this account we refer to advice contained within IGEM/UP/19 (this replaces previous advice in Gas Safe Register Technical Bulletin TB 140 which has been withdrawn).

IGEM/UP/19 provides guidance to the catering engineer in correctly determine the safety of the installation. This is includes a new/replacement type A appliance installed under an existing mechanical ventilation system.

Regulation 27(4) of the GS(I&U)R specifies that where a fan is used to evacuate the products from a chimney system it must be interlocked to the gas supply in such a manner that the appliances cannot be operated if the fan were to fail. In most gas installations this would indicate that if the fan is not interlocked we can exercise the GIUSP and categorise the installation as AT RISK. However, in commercial catering establishments this is not as clean cut and further risk assessments shall be carried out to determine the safety of the installation.

In the first instance it is the interpretation of what is and what is not a chimney system.

Any extract in a kitchen does not extract pure combustion products. The contaminated air extracted is a combination of cooking fumes such as water vapour, starches and oil vapours, etc., vast amounts of dilution air from the kitchen area and PoC. So can we classify this as a chimney? To answer this we need to look at the types of appliances located under the canopy.

Most catering appliances are classed under BS EN 1749[1] as type A (flueless) appliances, which are not designed to be connected to a chimney system or any other means of evacuating the products of combustion (fig 23.16). However, there are some appliances such as ovens and fryers which are designed as type B (open flued) appliances (fig 23.17). The manufacturers' of this type of appliance allow them to be installed below an extract hood without the use of a flue.

Fig 23.16 Type A – cooking range

Fig 23.17 Type B - pizza oven

Given this, where a type B appliance is installed below the canopy the extract system is acting as the chimney system for the appliance and therefore, must be interlocked to the gas supply and if not, is deemed as At Risk.

In the case of type A appliances, where the extract system is not interlocked we shall carry out a risk assessment as described in IGEM/UP/19 before making a decision on the safety of the installation. This also includes installations where a safety interlock has been installed with an override mechanism (switch) that allows the system to be used for a preset period of time if the mechanical extract and/or associated controls were to fail.

Where maintenance and/or repair of existing appliance(s) is performed and the appliances are installed under an existing mechanical ventilation system which has no interlock provision, the following shall be in place as part of the assessment process:

- the existing extract system shall operate effectively, removing any fumes from the catering area,
- adequate provision for make-up air and air changes shall exist,
- suitable 'systems of work' and written procedures should be made available and are in place and being applied,
- suitably worded signs shall be provided in a prominent position to warn catering staff that the extract shall be on when any cooking is being performed,
- the system shall be in good working order and well maintained.

The assessment will include a degree of atmospheric sampling to ascertain if the existing installation is operating within safe limits when in use. Where it is proven not to be the case, the caterer should be informed and the GIUSP applied.

NOTE: The assessment process, including atmosphere sampling are outside the scope of the ESP engineer and meter installer and will not be detailed in this section.

For installations within education establishments, which includes food technology areas, further guidance can be found in IGEM/UP/11[2].

23.2.4   Ventilation for commercial laundry equipment

Tumble dryers work on the principle of inducing large volumes of fresh outside air into the machine and heating it by means of steam tubes, electric elements or gas burners. This heated air passes through a rotating drum, which "tumbles" the clothing in the warm air stream – effectively removing moisture from the fabric. The moisture laden air is then drawn through a lint filter, which removes any airborne fibres and contaminants, prior to discharge through a fan unit into an exhaust duct. Contaminated air is then evacuated direct to outside.

Due to the large volume of contaminated air, all commercial sized tumble dryers shall be fitted with an exhaust duct. Given that we classify the appliances as type B_2 to BS EN 1749, the exhaust duct shall hold the same precedence as an appliance chimney system and as such cannot evacuate any contaminated air into an internal space as this would result in unacceptable levels of condensation, contamination and vitiation of the atmosphere.

Commercial tumble dryers are normally sized dependent on the dry weight capacity of clothing that the machine can handle; this can be measured in poundage, litres or kilogram's dependent on the origin of the machine.

Common smaller sizes are 15 lb (6.8 kg), 25 lb (11.3 kg), 30 lb (13.6 kg) and 50 lb (22.6 kg) with heat inputs ranging from 5 kW for light commercial dryers to above 170 kW for heavy commercial.

Common manufacturer's include the American Dryer Corporation (ADC), Miele, Maytag Corporation, Elecrtolux, Alliance Laundry Systems, Warner Howard and Jensen to name but a few. Although the principle of operation is common throughout all makes and models, each manufacturer applies different methods of operation and control normally through an electronic user interface (UI).

Most laundries install a bank of smaller dryers to allow a level of flexibility and efficiency due to the varying demands during operation. In most accounts the dryers are free standing single cabinets (fig 23.18) however, in some instances to make the best use of space, we can have double units commonly known as "stackers" (fig 23.19). Each unit in a stacked dryer is called a "pocket" or "pod".

Fig 23.18　Single freestanding tumble dryer

Fig 23.19　Double (stacker unit) tumble dryer

Due to the method of operation of a tumble dryer large volumes of air are consumed during the drying process. As with commercial catering the ventilation for a commercial laundry installation is not only air for combustion but also "make-up" air for that being extracted through the machine.

The make-up air inlet shall be positioned at least 300 mm but preferably 2 m away from any exhaust outlet; this will ensure no re-circulation of contaminated exhaust air into the laundry room. Any vent shall be non-closable and offer minimum resistance to the flow of air – insect and vermin meshes are not allowed. The ventilation grilles shall be installed as to prevent blockages from lint, etc., from the drying process.

The overall size of the grille shall be adequate to supply the ventilation needs of all the equipment installed within the laundry room. Consideration shall be given to other equipment within the same room as the laundry equipment. To ensure the exhaust system does not adversely affect the operation of the system, additional ventilation may be required to ensure a negative pressure is not present which may cause flue reversal on any open flued gas appliance.

Where additional extract is provided allowance shall be made over and above the total make-up air requirements of the installation; this will ensure the fan does not adversely affect the air flow within the laundry.

Where make-up air is provided by mechanical means, the fan must be interlocked to the gas supply such that the appliances will not operate if the fan were to fail. In all cases the manufacturer should be consulted as to the minimum air requirements.

Tables 23.5 & 23.6 are used to calculate the make-up air requirement for both tumble dryers and rotary ironers based on the requirements detailed in BS 8446. The table specifies the make-up air requirement for each individual unit depending on dry load capacity. Where stacker units are used each individual stacker pocket shall be treated as an individual dryer to ensure adequate ventilation and exhaust provisions are met.

Table 23.5 Effective free air ventilation requirement for tumble dryers

Dry Load Capacity		Air Flow m³/min	Make-up Air cm²
kg	lb		
13	30	9.9 - 19.8	1,000
23	50	19.9 - 22.7	1,500
34	75	22.8 - 32.6	2,250

To convert kg to lb, multiply by 2.205 or to convert lb to kg, divide by value stated

Table 23.6 Effective free air ventilation requirement for rotary ironers

Ironer Bed Length (m)	Air Flow m³/min	Make-up Air cm²
0.8 - 2.1	4.17 - 16.7	1,000
2.2 - 3.6	5 - 20	1,500

23.3 Non-domestic Chimney/Flue, Extract & Exhaust Systems

23.3.1 Heating appliance chimney/flue systems

The design of an appropriate non-domestic chimney system can be a complex procedure due to the large volume of flue gases involved. If designed incorrectly this could lead to a highly dangerous condition. Although similar in construction to domestic chimney/flue systems many different parameters have to be taken into consideration, for example:

- Location of appliance.
- Type of appliance.
- Number of appliances.
- Total rated heat input of appliance(s).
- Chimney height.
- Chimney route.
- Chimney termination.
- Associated heat losses.
- Carbon Dioxide content.

IGEM/UP/10 details the design of non-domestic chimney and ventilation systems. Other additional information can be obtained from the relevant appliance/chimney manufacturer's instructions, Building Regulations, Industry Standards and the 1956 Clean Air Act "Chimney Heights".

The types of chimney system used for non-domestic applications can be wide and varied depending on building restrictions and application. However, they can be grouped into specific categories:

- Natural draught - individual appliances.
- Common natural draught- multiple appliances.
- Modular natural draught- multiple appliances.
- Mechanically (fan) assisted - all of above individual or multiple appliances.
- Fan dilution low level discharge - individual or multiple appliances.

23.3.1.1 Materials

All materials used in chimney systems shall have the ability to withstand the high operating temperatures of the products of combustion and also be resistant to corrosion from the condensate.

Materials shall be selected to ensure the safe operation of all appliances connected to the chimney/flue system and be fit for purpose. In some occasions the appliance burners may be dual fuel (oil and gas) and as such the material selected shall be compatible with the constituents of all the fuels being used.

Points/tapping shall be provided in a suitable location to allow a flue gas analysis of the combustion products to be performed. The sample point/tapping shall be sealable.

Stainless steel and aluminium chimney/flue components shall meet the relevant standards as specified in IGEM/UP/10. Aluminium chimney/flue components may not be suitable for some applications due to its low temperature threshold not meeting the required fire resistance levels which the installation may demand.

Chimney systems shall not pass through or penetrate any fire resistant fire compartment wall, floor or ceiling. Nonmetallic flues shall not pass through any internal walls, floors or ceiling and shall go straight to outside air.

Where a single wall chimney pipe passes through a roof, ceiling, floor, wall or partition constructed of combustible material, an air gap of not less than 50 mm should be maintained between the chimney pipe and the combustible materials (fig 23.20). However, if the chimney is encased in a non-combustible sleeve, the air gap can be reduced to 25 mm. This applies to twin wall prefabricated chimney piping with an air gap between the inner and external walls, the 25 mm is measured from the inner wall (fig 23.21).

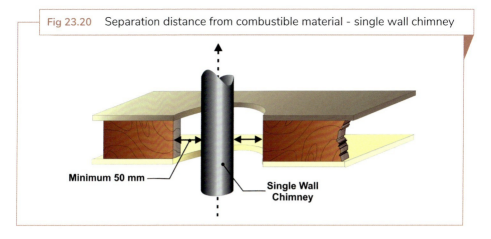

Fig 23.20 Separation distance from combustible material - single wall chimney

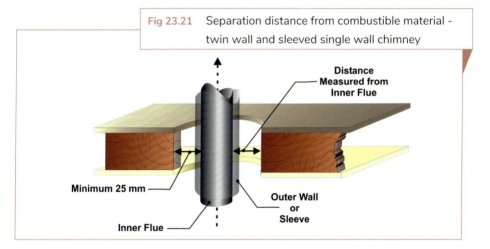

Fig 23.21 Separation distance from combustible material - twin wall and sleeved single wall chimney

23.3.1.2   Insulation

Where insulation is used on a non-domestic chimney system, under normal operating temperatures the material shall:

- show no evidence of softening or melting,
- show no change in its physical structure,
- retain sufficient physical strength to remain in the intended position,
- not increase in thermal conductivity.

If the material is not sufficiently strong to support itself, it should be secured to solid surfaces to prevent sagging and a consequent loss of its insulating properties. Any adhesive or cement used to attach the insulation to the chimney should retain its adhesive properties at the operating temperature of the chimney. Water absorbing material should be protected from condensation and rain with a suitable weather proof cladding.

23.3.1.3 Termination

As with other aspects of a gas installation, the correct termination of a chimney/flue system can be involved; dependent on appliance size, type and flueing method used. IGEM/UP/10 provides information on chimney/flue terminations for appliances above 70 kW up to 20 MW net which sees a move away from stated values to one of providing formulas and plotted graphs.

The gas engineer, using this information, would then calculate the required dimensions – this is generally outside the scope of an ESP engineer or meter installer.

However and in general, chimneys should be terminated so as to allow a free flow of air over the top of the chimney. If this air flow is restricted in any way it can create turbulence and high pressure zones which can have an adverse affect on chimney performance. For open flue appliances, they should terminate at least 3 m above any adjacent area where there is access, for example adjacent openable windows, flat roof areas or open ground areas.

For open flue appliances below 70 kW net BS 5440 shall be consulted. Above 70 kW net BS 6644 and IGEM/UP/10 apply. Termination positions for pitched roofs needs to be greater than 1.5 m when measured horizontally to the roof pitch and at least distance 'X' when measured vertically from the roof to the underside of the terminal (see fig's 23.22, 23.23, 23.24 & 23.25).

The point of termination needs to take account of re-entry points (doors, window, vents, etc.) in to premises. Figure 23.26 provides the minimum clearances required depending on appliance net heat input.

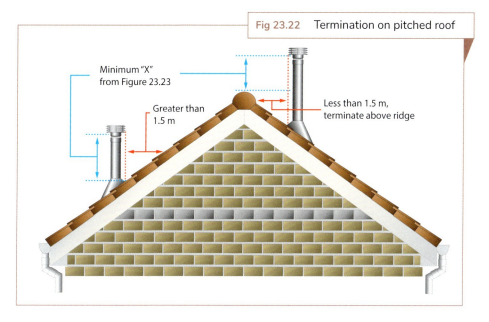

Fig 23.22　Termination on pitched roof

As with domestic systems a terminal is not required where the chimney/flue has a dimension of 170 mm or greater across any axis. However, the height and termination point of any non-domestic chimney/flue system (horizontal or vertical) must in all accounts meet the requirements of the 1956 Clean Air Act when the maximum rated input exceeds 333 kW net; above 135 kW net the termination shall be above roof level unless otherwise agreed by the local Environmental Health Officer (EHO).

Figure 22.27 provides the minimum clearance for room sealed terminals facing another terminal or flat surface (see Note), again this distance is dependent on appliance net heat input.

NOTE: Where the termination is in close proximity to an adjacent wall or obstruction, the minimum clearance (measured from the side of the terminal) as stated for 'G' in fig 23.27 should be ensured. Where the vertical adjacent surfaces comprises of two walls, i.e. a recess without incorporating a roof or other form of covering, distance 'Y' of fig 23.26 should be ensured. The recess depth (the length of enclosing walls) shall not impair the safe dispersal of combustion products under all foreseeable weather conditions – where doubt exists or the required distances cannot be achieved, the termination shall be vertical above the roof line.

Fig 23.23 Height "X" of the flue terminal on a roof for appliances upto a net heat input of 333 kW

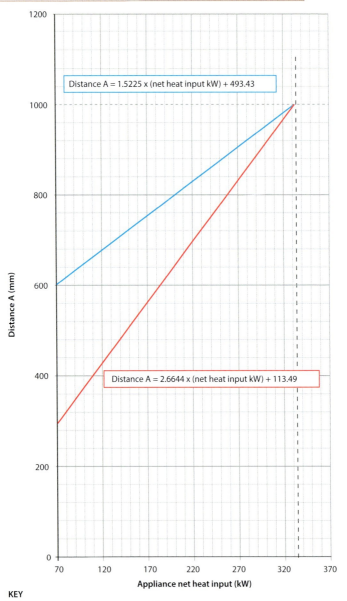

KEY
- - - Clean Air Act lower limit of 333 kW
— Natural draught flues
— Fanned draught flues

Note 1: The type of flue does not necessarily reflect the type of connected appliance.
Note 2: The equations on the graph are represented by the appropriate plotted line.

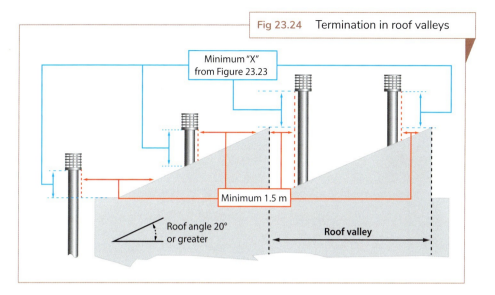

Fig 23.24 Termination in roof valleys

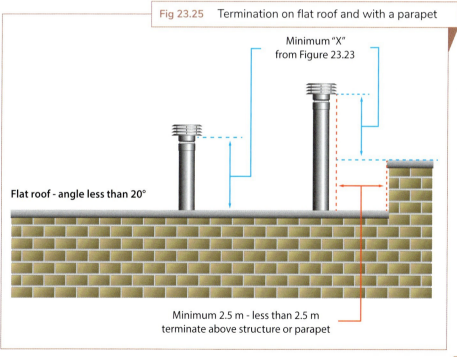

Fig 23.25 Termination on flat roof and with a parapet

Fig 23.26 Minimum distance of flue terminal(s) from any opening into a building

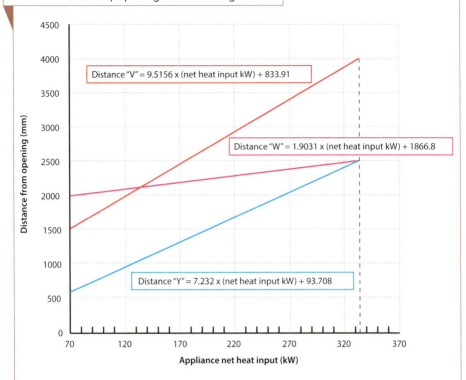

KEY

- - - Clean Air Act lower limit of 333 kW

— "V" - Open flued and fan draught appliances

— "W" - Balanced or room sealed natural draught appliances

— "Y" - Room sealed fanned draught appliances

Minimum distances of flue terminals from any opening into a building

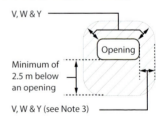

"opening" - air bricks, windows, doorways, ventilation grilles, etc.

Note 1: All vertical flues will terminate above roof level and not be nearer any opening than distance "V" for open flued, "V/Y" for fanned draught or "W" for natural draught appliances.

Note 2: The equations on the graph are represented by the appropriate plotted line.

Note 3: Where the termination is both below and diagonally to an opening, the minimum clearances of either V, W or Y are to be applied horizontally with a minimum of 2.5 m vertically below an opening (i.e. a diagonal measurement does not apply in this regard).

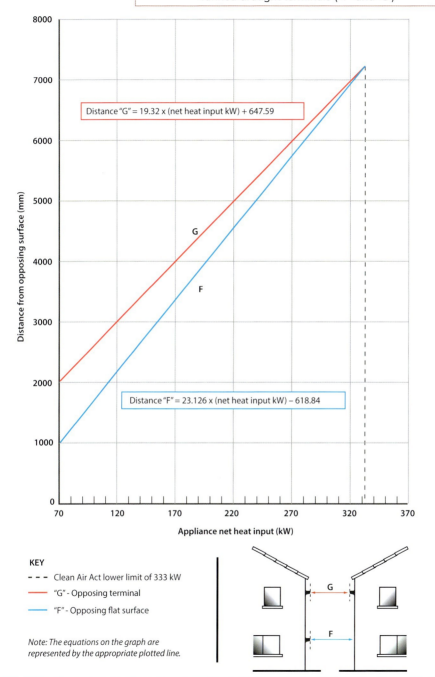

Fig 23.27 Minimum spacing of room sealed appliance fanned draught terminals ('F' and 'G')

23.3.1.4 Flue dampers and stabilisers

Manual flue dampers shall only be installed in the secondary flues of common and fan dilution flue systems. They shall be lockable and only be 75 % of the cross-sectional area of the chimney. Where automatic flue dampers are installed they shall:

- Be selected on their applicability to the specific appliance(s) make and model concerned (consult the manufacturer as necessary).
- Not be installed in to any structural chimney.
- Not adversely affect the operation of the appliance.
- Only be installed in the secondary flue of appliances where the net heat input is less than 70 kW unless the burner is forced draught and no flue break. Appliances 70 kW and above may have the damper in either the primary or secondary flue.
- Only be installed if the appliance has a flame safeguard protecting both the pilot and main flame.
- Not be installed into a common chimney of multiple or combined appliances. Only manual dampers to be used.
- Operate in conjunction with its associated burner(s).
- Be proved in the correct, open position prior to appliance start up. Failure to do so shall cause the appliance to go to lockup.
- Be accessible for removal, inspection, maintenance and repair.
- Be protected against undue strain from the weight of the chimney/flue system.

23.3.1.5 Common flues and chimneys

Common flue and chimney systems shall be designed so that all connected appliances can operate safely under varying load conditions. Any fault on one appliance shall not adversely affect any of the other appliances connected to the same common flue or chimney system such that an unsafe condition may occur. This shall be verified at both the design and commissioning of the system.

Although industry standards allow the connection of dissimilar fuel burning appliances to a common flue, all appliances shall have similar burners, i.e. all forced or all natural draught. In some occasions the installation of appliances with different burner types may be permissible where their safe operation has been confirmed at both the design and commissioning stages of the system.

Gas-fired appliances are not permitted to be connected to a chimney or flue system used for either a solid fuel or bio-mass fired appliance.

Natural draught appliances shall be installed in the same room space as any other appliances installed to the same flue or chimney unless the rooms are appropriately cross-ventilated.

Any appliance connected to a common flue should be as near as practical to the main flue (fig 23.28). Any branch shall not enter the main flue within 250 mm of its base, nor protrude beyond the inner face. The connection to the main flue shall be a smooth bend or a sloping 135° fitting with at least 500 mm length of secondary flue from the draught diverter to the main flue connection.

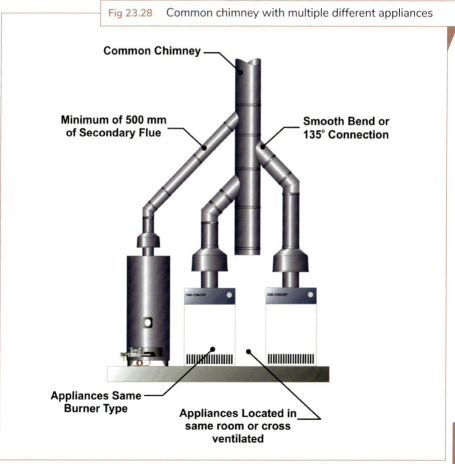

Fig 23.28   Common chimney with multiple different appliances

It is possible to deviate from the requirements but ONLY when supported by suitable design studies, in which case a System Design Verification Notice would be issued - the notice being affixed near to the chimney/flue installation providing further details.

Where condensing and non-condensing appliances are installed into the same common chimney system, the condensing appliance should be located nearest to the main chimney exit. It is also advisable that where an appliance operates for a longer period than the rest of the appliances, that appliance should be nearest to the main chimney.

23.3.1.6   Balanced compartments

The design of a non-domestic balanced compartment is similar to that as described in Part 1; Chapter 11 of this Guide. However, the height and termination of appliance(s) with a total net heat input in excess of 135 kW shall meet the same criteria as for other non-domestic chimney/flue systems (i.e. terminate above roof level) and by meeting the requirements of the 1956 Clean Air Act Memorandum.

With the termination point being part of or adjacent to the high level air inlet grille, care shall be taken on their location to ensure that their installation and subsequent operation does not affect the fire integrity of the roof and also that of the building.

23.3.1.7   Modular flue systems

A modular flue system is specially designed to accommodate two or more similar hot water boilers which are used to share the same heating load. It consists of a uniform horizontal flue (common header) in which all appliances are connected. The cross-sectional area of the header shall be large enough to ensure the safe evacuation of all the products of combustion produced by the appliances. The main chimney which disperses the flue products to outside atmosphere is connected to either the centre or end of the common header as shown in fig 23.29.

Fig 23.29 Common chimney - modular systems with main chimney located in centre or end of header

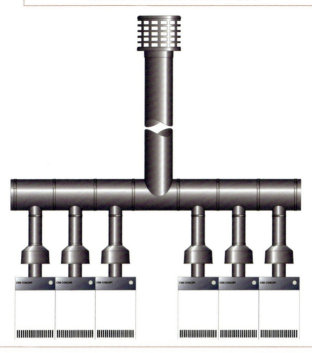

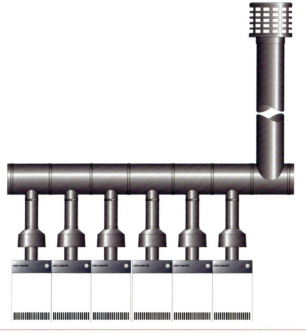

23.3.1.8 Fan dilution flue systems

The fan dilution flue was developed for situations where it was impractical to install a natural draught flue system, such as ground floor plant rooms in large office blocks. They are a widely used method of flueing small to medium range commercial plant; they should not be used for installations with a heat input above 5.4 MW (6 MW gross). For large installations the traditional natural draught flue is usually more practicable.

Fan dilution flues usually terminate at low level (see fig 12.30), therefore the design of the system allows for fresh air to be drawn directly from outside and mixed with the products of combustion. This process dilutes the products of combustion enough to allow safe discharge at lower levels without being a potential hazard at ground level. The maximum concentration of CO_2 in the discharge shall not exceed 1 %, with CO and NOx not exceeding 0.005 % and 0.0005 %, respectively.

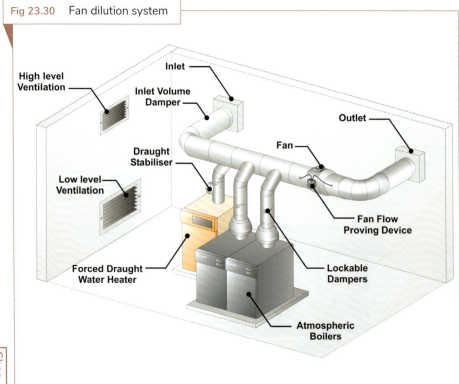

Fig 23.30   Fan dilution system

The discharge point shall be located at a point where air is allowed to flow freely over the grille to ensure safe disposal of the diluted products. Sheltered positions should be avoided. Again, calculating discharge and air intakes is outside the scope of the ESP engineer or meter installer however, fig 23.31 illustrates termination factors to be taken into consideration for fan dilution systems. The position of the bottom edge of the discharge point (as can be seen in fig 23.31) should be a minimum of:

- 2 m above ground level for boilers with total net heat input not exceeding 0.9 MW.
- 3 m above ground level for boilers with total net heat input above 0.9 MW up to 2 MW.

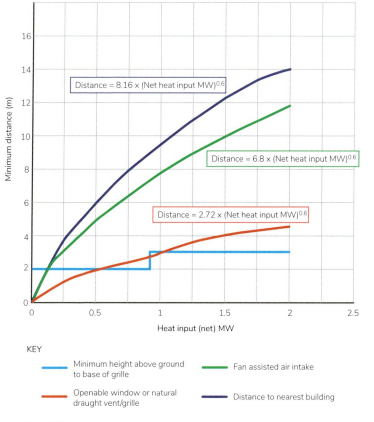

Fig 23.31 Minimum distance of fan diluted flue discharge for appliances up to 2 MW

Equations shown on graph:
- Distance = $8.16 \times$ (Net heat input MW)$^{0.6}$
- Distance = $6.8 \times$ (Net heat input MW)$^{0.6}$
- Distance = $2.72 \times$ (Net heat input MW)$^{0.6}$

KEY
- Minimum height above ground to base of grille
- Openable window or natural draught vent/grille
- Fan assisted air intake
- Distance to nearest building

Note 1: The equations on the graph are represented by the appropriate plotted line.
Note 2: The distance needs to be rounded up to the nearest metre.

23.3.2 Commercial laundry equipment exhaust system

A commercial laundry exhaust system shall be constructed such that it allows the free removal of the products of combustion, dilutent air, water vapour and contaminants from the drying process (efflux). The ventilation provision shall be capable of providing not only sufficient air for combustion, but also additional air for the dilution. Similarly the exhaust system shall be designed to cope with this increased volume of efflux and be capable of safely dispersing them to outside atmosphere without affecting the performance of the machine.

Exhaust systems may accommodate either a single appliance or multiple appliance installations. Any common exhaust ductwork shall have a cross-sectional area large enough to accommodate and safely disperse the total volume of efflux from the appliances it serves. Common exhaust headers normally step up in size as the number of appliances increase (figure 23.32).

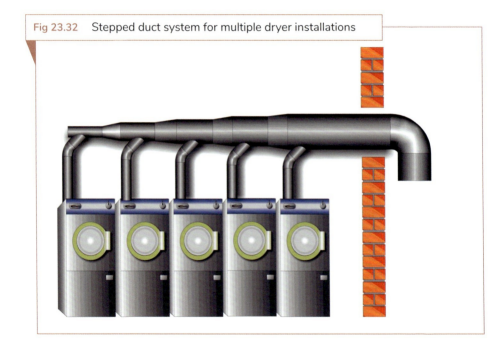

Fig 23.32   Stepped duct system for multiple dryer installations

All exhaust systems shall meet the following criteria:

- It shall terminate to outside atmosphere in a safe and satisfactory position.
- It shall present minimal resistance to the airflow.
- It shall be of smooth metal construction, as short as possible with the minimum amount of bends and changes in direction.
- It shall be able to withstand the operational temperatures, up to 80 °C for dryers & 110 °C for ironers.
- It shall provide access for cleaning and maintenance.

A length of flexible ducting may be used as the final connection to the appliance if specified by the manufacturer. Any flexible ducting used shall:

- be as short as possible,
- not exceed 2 m in length,
- be of a material constructed to withstand the operating temperatures,
- be installed such that the hose does not become kinked or deformed when the machine is in place,
- not have any changes in direction other than formed pre-fabricated bend.

Any termination point shall be installed to prevent the ingress of weather and protect the air flow from prevailing wind conditions. In addition, it should not allow the build up of lint or impair the operation of any appliance. We normally achieve this by terminating with a 45° or 90° down facing elbow or plenum box. Termination above the roof line should be via a 180° return bend or 'chinaman's hat'. **No restrictions shall be placed at the termination point such as grilles or mesh**.

The termination point shall be at least 300 mm from ground level or 2 x diameter, whichever is the greater. A minimum separation distance of 300 mm shall be maintained between the exhaust outlet and any air inlet or opening into a building. It is recommended that a minimum distance of 2 m is applied. In all accounts the termination point shall exhaust the gases in a safe and satisfactory manner without causing a nuisance or hazard. Reference shall be made to manufacturer's Instruction.

23.3.3 Commercial catering extract discharge

The design and construction of a commercial catering extract system is given in section 23.2.3 of this Chapter, as it is a critical part of the total ventilation provision for the kitchen area.

The discharge point of a commercial kitchen extract system is generally dictated by the surrounding area for example buildings etc. Its location shall ensure any efflux being discharged does not re-enter into the building through other openings such as fan inlets or through the ventilation system.

The discharge point shall be at least 1 m above any openable window. The termination point shall be free from obstruction such as a mesh.

'Chinaman's Hat' style terminals shall not be used due to the increased likelihood of down draught occurring.

23.4 Non-domestic Pipework Installation

As with all non-domestic gas installations, the scale and diversity of industrial and commercial environments warrants any person working on installation pipework to be familiar with current legislation, standards and procedures. IGEM/UP/2 – 'Installation pipework on Industrial and Commercial premises', which is now in its third edition, is the normative document used by the non-domestic engineer to ensure safe working practices.

IGEM/UP/2 specifies requirements for the design, installation, commissioning, operation, maintenance and decommissioning of gas installation pipework carrying lighter than air 2nd family gases (for example Natural gas) and heavier than air 3rd family gases in their gaseous state (LPG; Propane or Butane) within large domestic, industrial and commercial premises.

The scope of this standard also includes the following:

- Installation pipework with a maximum operating pressure (MOP) not exceeding 60 bar.
- Pressure-raising and pre-mix machines with a discharge pressure not exceeding 500 mbar. For pressures above this refer to IGEM/UP/6[3].
- Pipework integrity systems (formally known as weep by-pass pressure proving systems).

- Pipework downstream of a plant isolation valve except preinstalled pipework which forms part of the appliance. This section of pipework is normally installed by the gas engineer and is known as the 'appliance connector'.
- Installation pipework within domestic premises with a nominal bore (NB) in excess of 35 mm. For natural gas and LPG installation pipework with a NB of 35 mm or less, installed within domestic premises, we refer to BS 6891.

Any gas system which operates above 500 mbar may be subject to the Pressure Systems Safety Regulations (PSSR). Non-domestic installations must meet the requirements of the Dangerous Substances and Explosive Atmosphere Regulations (DSEAR) with reference being made to IGEM/UP/16[4] or IGEM/SR/25[5], as appropriate for hazardous area risk assessments. Where primary and/or secondary meters are installed as part of the installation we need to refer to IGEM/GM/6[6] or IGE/GM/8[7], as appropriate depending on operating pressure, meter type and maximum flow rate (Q_{max}).

23.4.1 Materials and jointing methods

Materials used for installation pipework, including any fittings, valves and components, shall be suitable for the environment and duty for which its intended to be used. Location, operating temperature and pressure, stresses, corrosion and operating parameters shall be taken into consideration during the design and installation of any gas system.

Due to the nature of non-domestic premises, steel piping is generally used due to its resilience to damage. Copper piping is less robust and may not be suitable for the majority of installations. Cast iron and ductile iron is not suitable for use with gas due to its susceptibility to catastrophic failure under stress. Ductile iron, although more robust than cast, may fail due to localised corrosion. When installed, pipework shall be suitably protected against mechanical damage and corrosion.

Due regard shall also be given to the electrolytic action between two dissimilar metals particularly steel and copper/copper based alloys. Depending on the installation environment, electrolytic action can cause accelerated corrosion of the metal, leading to catastrophic failure of the pipe and/or fittings.

23.4.1.1 Steel

Specification of steel pipe and fittings shall be selected and installed in accordance with relevant industry standards or specification. They must also be "fit for purpose" with the wall thickness suitable for its proposed duty. Pipe sizes are given in nominal inside diameter. Steel pipe and fittings shall meet the following standards as appropriate.

Carbon steel:

- Pipe - BS EN 10216; BS EN 10217-1; BS EN 10255; or API 5L, Grade B.
- Fittings - BS 1560-3; BS 1640; BS 3799; BS EN 1092-1; BS EN 1514; BS EN 1759-1; BS EN 10253; or BS EN 10255.

Stainless steel:

- Pipe - BS EN 10216; ASTM A269 (304L, 315, 316L or 321); or ASTM A313 (TP 304 or T316)
- Fittings - BS 1640 (WP304 or 316); BS 3799; BS EN 10222; ASTM A182 (F304 or F316); or ASTM A193 (B8T or 8).

Steel can be jointed using a variety of different methods as listed:

- Welding.
- Use of flanges (welded or screwed).
- Screwed.
- Semi-rigid couplings, flange adaptors or compression fittings.
- Pressed joints (stainless only).
- Unique flare fitting (pliable CSST only).

Within the gas industry the British Standard Pipe thread (BSP) is used which shall conform to BS EN 10226 (supersedes BS 21). External screwed threads shall be tapered whereas internal thread may be either taper or parallel. Normally it is preferable to use taper on both internal and external threads since it forms a better gas tight joint. Jointing compounds shall meet the specifications laid down in BS EN 751 parts 1 and 2. PTFE tape to BS EN 751 part 3 shall only be used on pipe threads up to 50 mm unless otherwise stated by the manufacturer.

The number of joints should be kept to a minimum. Consideration should be given when using welded joints to provide adequate facility for isolation, sectioning of pipework, addition of future extensions and the replacement of components.

Semi-rigid couplings, flange adaptors and compression joints may be used on natural gas steel pipework above ground as an alternative to welding or screwing. For stainless steel, compression couplings and joints shall meet the requirements of BS 4368 with metallic O-rings or seals. Their use is restricted to a maximum diameter of 54 mm and shall be accessible for maintenance. These fittings shall be end load resistant with consideration given to fire resistance (depending on location, for example internal applications). They shall not be installed under floors, in shafts, channels, ducts or voids. For 3rd family gases compression joints are not permitted.

NOTE: See Part 1; Chapter 5 for standards related to pipework and fittings.

Pressed joints for use with stainless steel shall be jointed using the manufacturer's approved methods with the following limitations:

- MOP not exceeding 5 bar.
- Nominal bore not exceeding 108 mm.

Table 23.7 specifies the appropriate jointing methods for steel pipework depending on the maximum operating pressure and nominal bore.

Table 23.7 Jointing for carbon and stainless steel pipework

Nominal Bore	Maximum Operating Pressure (MOP)	
	≤ 500 mbar	> 500 mbar
≤ 25 mm	Screw or Weld	Screw or Weld
> 25 mm but not exceeding 50 mm	Screw or Weld	Weld
> 50 mm	Weld	Weld

≤ Less than or equal to   > Greater than

23.4.1.2 Polyethylene (PE)

PE pipe shall meet the specifications laid down in BS EN 1555 and may be of medium or high density polyethylene (MDPE or HDPE) dependent on operating pressures. PE piping can be supplied in coils or straight lengths with pipe sizes given in nominal outside diameters. The pipe sizes can cause confusion with operatives unfamiliar with PE pipework. For example 63 mm PE is the same as 50 mm steel, 180 mm PE is 150 mm steel, etc., be aware of these differences.

Due to the composition of polyethylene, PE piping degrades with prolonged exposure to UV light. Care therefore, should be taken when storing or installing piping in direct sunlight. PE piping is only suitable for external installations below ground or within purpose provided enclosures. It shall not be installed within a service duct, with other services or within buildings, except for entries and exits from the building. Above ground entries or exits shall be encased in a gas tight, fire resistant sleeve. Above ground exposed PE is deemed At Risk as per the GIUSP (IGEM/G/11).

PE piping can be jointed using the following methods:

- fusion welding,
- electro fusion welding (fig's 23.33 & 23.34),
- compression fittings.

Fig 23.33 Electrofusion fitting ready to be made (minus fitting clamp)

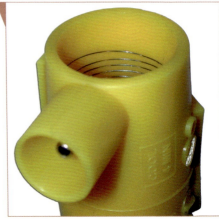

Fig 23.34 Fitting showing internal heating wire and lead connection

Fusion and electro-fusion welding shall only be carried out by engineers specialised and competent to do so. Solvent welding using chemicals is not permitted. All fittings shall comply with BS EN 1555-3.

Inspection of all joints shall be made after completion. The following should be observed:

- **Butt fusion joint** – the joint should be aligned correctly with the pipe wall with a smooth and symmetrical bead around the full circumference of the pipe. The bead width shall be correct against the size required for the nominal bore of the pipe. The bead depression shall not be below the surface of the pipe wall. All external beads shall be removed and inspected for contamination or lack of fusion, these are normally bagged and numbered.
- **Electro-fusion sockets** – as with the butt fusion joint they shall be aligned correctly with the pipe inserted full slip into the fitting. The fusion area shall be scraped sufficiently with no contamination from grease or dirt. When made no melted material should be visible outside the fitting (except at the fusion indication holes). No electrical wiring should be visible.
- **Electro-fusion saddles** – these should be inspected as the socket joints, however due to their location on the pipe wall they shall be checked to ensure the fitting has not risen off the pipe or collapsed into the pipe wall. No additional damage shall have occurred to the pipe due to ancillary tools such as saddle clamps, etc.

23.4.1.3   Copper

Copper pipe and fittings shall meet BS EN 1057. Pipe diameters are given in nominal outside diameter and shall not exceed 108 mm. All copper pipe and fittings installed within a commercial installation shall be adequately protected against mechanical damage.

Buried copper piping shall be factory sheathed. Connected to steel pipe or fittings is prohibited due to the electrolytic action set up between the two metals, which will cause accelerated corrosion of the steel.

Copper may be jointed by means of soldering, brazing, compression fittings and pressed joints.

Solder and brazed joints

Capillary joints shall meet BS EN 1254. Standard soft solder fittings which have a melting point of less than 600 °C shall only be used on low-pressure installations. Brazed joints with filler to BS EN ISO 17672 and Fluxes to BS EN 1045 can be used for pressures in excess of 75 mbar as long as the filler has a melting point above 600 °C.

Compression joints

If compression joints are used, they shall meet the standards laid down in BS EN 1254. They shall only be installed on above ground readily accessible pipework. Installation of these fittings is not allowed within ducts, under floors, within concrete floors, underground, etc. Compression joints are restricted to a maximum diameter of 54 mm.

Pressed joint fittings (copper and stainless steel)

Pressed joint fittings can only be used on copper and stainless steel up to a MOP of 5 bar and 108 mm nominal bore. Jointing shall be made as per the manufacturer's instruction using the approved jointing tool. The pipe wall thickness shall be a minimum as specified by the manufacturer of the fitting to ensure a mechanically strong joint is made. De-mountable fittings shall not be used. Fittings shall meet approved fire test requirements of Annex A, procedure A of BS EN 1775 and appropriate standards for high temperature tests such as DVGW VP614.

23.4.2 Installation

When installing pipework an element of engineering common sense should be applied. Pipework should take the shortest practicable route, with a minimum amount of fittings applied.

Consideration should not only be given to the aesthetic appearance of the installation but practicality for isolation, testing and purging, installation of future extension, and also maintenance and repair of the pipe and associated components. Pipework shall never be installed within an unvented duct or void, unless:

(i). It is encased in a gas tight sleeve continuous through the unventilated space, open at both ends ventilated to a safe area, or

(ii). The void is filled with a crushed inert infill. The infill should be a dry, chemically neutral fire resistant material.

Installation pipework must not be routed within a cavity wall except passing through the cavity by the shortest route (Regulation 19(3)). In addition, it shall not pass along or through a protected shaft (i.e. stairwell or lift) unless:

(i). It is a low-pressure installation (i.e. operating pressure does not exceed 75 mbar).
(ii). Pipework and fittings are of carbon or stainless steel.
(iii). Connections are welded or screwed.
(iv). Pliable CSST is of a continuous length and does not contain any joints.

23.4.2.1 Corrosion protection

If pipework is installed in a corrosive atmosphere internally, buried or installed above ground externally, the pipework should be protected either through the application of a corrosion resistant paint or by wrapping.

Wrapping normally consists of a petroleum-impregnated cloth such as Denso wrap applied with a 50 % overlap. It should be noted that after long exposure to the elements and chemicals within the soil, this type of wrap dries out losing its water repellent properties. Additional PVC tape should be applied to ensure the water resistant properties of the tape are retained.

Any coating to pipe joints shall only be applied after a satisfactory tightness test and purge of the installation.

23.4.2.2 Pipework identification

Regulation 23(1) of the GS(I&U)R specifies that any part of a non-domestic pipework installation which is accessible to inspection, must be permanently marked such that it is readily recognisable as conveying gas. It indicates that the installer is responsible for the initial identification of the pipe but it is up to the responsible person to maintain it as such.

The standard for pipework colour coding is given in BS 1710 'Specification for Identification of pipelines and services'. This standard applies a basic identification colour for fuel gas as yellow ochre to BS 4800 (reference number 08 C 35) or primrose yellow (reference number 10 E 53), fig 23.35.

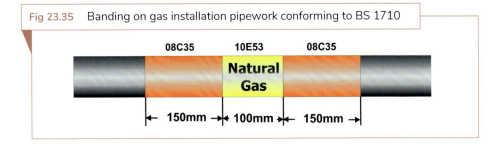

Fig 23.35 Banding on gas installation pipework conforming to BS 1710

Any banding should be applied 150 mm after any valve or control, points of entry and exit through walls, branches and other areas where recognition is necessary. For smaller pipe diameters, the application of self-adhesive "gas" tape may suffice (fig 23.36).

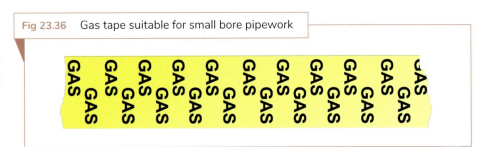

Fig 23.36 Gas tape suitable for small bore pipework

23.4.2.3 Pipework in ducts

A duct is generally a specifically designed and purpose made enclosure used to route any building services located either inside a building or externally underground. However, where pipework is installed above a false or suspended ceiling or below a suspended floor, these areas shall be treated as a duct.

Any duct shall meet the requirements laid down by the building and fire regulations, local authority directives and any other appropriate standards. Fire stopping, fire rating, valve access, access for maintenance, etc., should all be part of the initial duct design.

It is acceptable for gas pipework to run within the same duct as other services however, it cannot be run in the same duct as:

○ Ventilation ducts and vacuum pipes that operate below atmospheric pressure which are not of an all welded, solvent welded or brazed construction.

○ Services containing oxidizing or corrosive fluids.

Additionally, pipework shall not be installed within or through air distribution ducts e.g. warm air or ventilation ducting. Where the pipe runs within or through a ceiling void, which is used as an air distribution plenum for more than one room, then the pipe shall be enclosed in a fire-resistant, gas tight sleeve itself ventilated to a safe place.

Ventilation for ducts is designed such that any minor gas escapes within the duct do not build up to dangerous levels. It is preferable that ventilation is provided by natural means however, where this is not practical, mechanical ventilation may be used provided a risk assessment has been completed and robust safety measures are put in place.

Ventilation openings should be installed to promote the movement of air within the duct i.e. at the top and bottom of a vertical duct and at each end of a horizontal duct; each vent should terminate to a safe area, preferably to outside. Ventilation may be provided into a false ceiling from the room below however, if the ceiling is part of the fire protection of the room, ventilation shall only be taken from outside air.

Gas detectors may be used as an additional safety measure as required by a risk assessment although their general use should be promoted as a measure to increase gas safety. Their use shall not be regarded as a substitute for the provision of adequate ventilation into the duct.

In most accounts the ventilation of traditional ducts can be met with the provision of smoke ventilation openings each with an effective free area calculated as detailed in the table 23.8.

Table 23.8 Duct ventilation sizes

Cross Sectional Area of Duct (m^2)	Minimum free area of each vent (m^2)
Up to and including 0.05	Cross sectional area of duct
0.05 up to and including 7.5	0.05
Above 7.5	1/150th* of cross sectional area of duct

* To find a fraction of the whole number, multiply the numerator (1) by the whole number (size of duct) before dividing this number by the denominator (150) –
i.e. a duct measuring 8 m^2 = 8 x 1/150 = 8/150 = 0.053 m^2

23.4.2.4 Pipework In multi-storey and multiple dwelling buildings

When installing a riser we shall ensure adequate ventilation is provided in all areas to prevent gas accumulating within the building. Pipework passing through floors should be suitably sleeved and fire stopped unless the pipework is contained in its own purpose provided protected shaft ventilated at both high and low level. Any lateral off-take shall be suitably fire stopped as it enters each floor from this shaft.

Normally on high rise buildings a flexible connection is used on the lateral of the riser to protect the pipework against any strain imposed on it from the building movement. In this case, where it is enclosed in a duct, the whole section of the flexible connection shall be within the duct. Where the riser feeds more than one lateral, a means of isolation shall be installed at the start of the lateral, i.e. at the branch. This should be located outside all premises fed by the riser.

Where the riser is run external to the building, it shall not be within 500 mm of any lightning conductor.

All risers shall be supported to ensure their safe operation. Pliable CSST risers shall be supported using fire resistant methods; tie wrap is not suitable.

Where the pipework is in an exposed location running along a high roof of a building or in other similar locations it shall be protected by means of an appropriately sized and positioned lightning conductor(s).

23.4.2.5 Buried pipework

Consideration should be given when installing any gas pipework below ground that the route of the pipe does not affect the safety of the installation. The pipe route should be deep enough to guard against accidental damage to the pipe, fittings or any protective wrappings from future excavations, etc. Marker tape shall also be installed at approximately 250 mm above the pipe to minimise the risk of future mechanical damage.

Pipework shall also be suitably protected against the affects of any corrosive or chemically active soils and from physical damage from the likes of rocks, sharp objects and heavy traffic. Any underground pipework shall not pass under any load bearing walls, footings or building foundations due to the risk of damage to the pipe through natural structural movement unless it is suitably protected against damage. Any protection shall be either a load bearing structure, such as a service block, or sleeve which has been certified as fit for purpose by a structural engineer.

When planning the pipe route, care shall be given in avoiding the following:

- any unstable building or natural structures,
- congested underground service routes,
- areas, which may have heavy site traffic, especially on unsurfaced roads, etc.,
- installation in aggressive soils,
- installation near any unvented voids,
- any ground which may be liable to subsidence.

The minimum depth of cover above the crown of buried pipe which would require no additional protection is specified in table 23.9.

Table 23.9   Depth of cover for buried pipes

Pipe Diameter (mm)	Minimum Depth of Cover (mm)				
	Paved Footpath	Carriage Ways	Verges	Other Fields or Agricultural Land	Other Private Ground
Up to and Including 63 mm and MOP not exceeding 75 mbar	375	450	600	1,100	600
Greater than 63 mm or MOP above 75 mbar but not exceeding 7 bar	600	750	750	1,100	600

23.4.2.6   Entry and exit from buildings

Consideration should be given at all times when a gas supply enters a building to ensure ease of access for the operation of any emergency control valves (ECV) and also limit the amount of "live" pipework upstream from the ECV. High-level entry dropping down to low level is not recommended.

Pipework should enter and exit the building above ground level where practicable (fig 23.37). Installation bellow foundations, under the bases of walls or under floating foundations are not permitted unless measures have been put in place to ensure the safe use of the pipework with those measures confirmed as fit for purpose by a structural engineer.

Fig 23.37 Above ground entry into a building

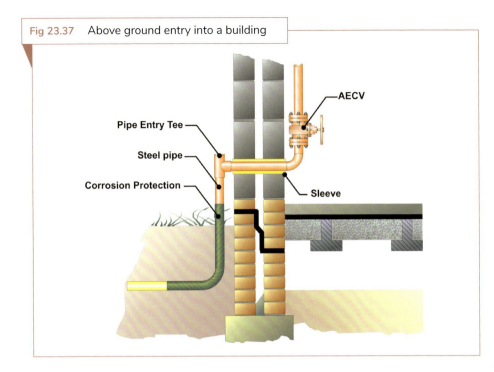

Steel pipe entries are preferred however, if PE is used, any part of the pipe shall be encased inside a metallic or GRP sheath so as to prevent damage to the pipe and to prevent gas entering the building in the event of an escape. Any transition from PE to steel should be as near as practical to the point of entry to the building.

If it is impractical for the pipe to enter or exit the building above ground, then below floor level installation may be acceptable (fig 23.38) however, the following criteria shall be observed:

- The pipe shall enter or exit the building through a continuous gas tight sleeve.
- The horizontal sleeve shall terminate in a square recess in the floor of minimum dimension of 300 mm.
    - for pipes in excess of 100 mm, the square recess should be at least three times the diameter of the pipe.
- The riser and bend shall be jointed to the incoming or outgoing pipework and wrapped from the external pipework to the recess.

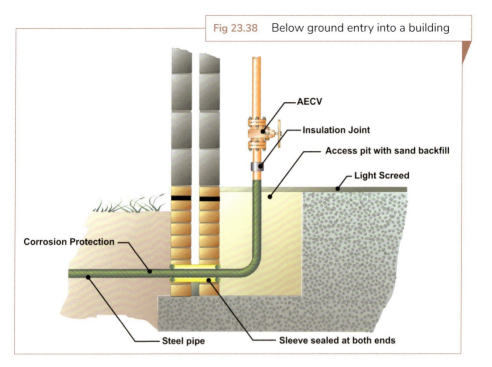

Fig 23.38 Below ground entry into a building

23.4.2.7 Emergency control valves

With non-domestic installations it's common for the metering installation to be within its own purpose built housing separate from the building(s) it supplies. Further to this the gas may be supplied to more than one building. With this in mind a non-domestic installation may have more than one additional emergency control valve (AECV) located as near as practical to the point of entry to each individual building (fig 23.39). A single gas supply should be provided per building.

Line diagrams are critical for the location of these valves and also indicating which sections of the installation they control. A line diagram must be installed on or near the primary meter and any AECV as specified in Regulation 24 of the GS(I&U)R.

Regulation 24 also specifies the requirement for additional isolation valves on the supply of gas to each floor of a building where that building has two or more floors and also where the building is only single storey, an isolation valve must be installed on the supply of gas entering each self-contained area such as a kitchen, plant room, laundry, etc. This requirement only applies where the supply of gas to the building and/or service pipe is 50 mm or greater.

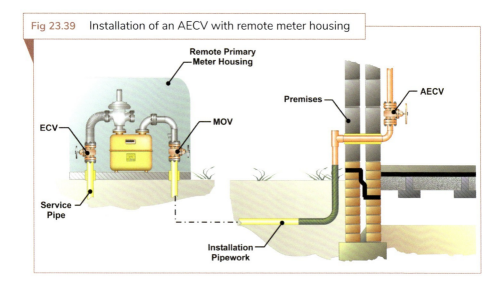

Fig 23.39   Installation of an AECV with remote meter housing

The type of emergency control is very important within the non-domestic environment. These valves can be very large and require to meet strict criteria to ensure ease of operation, meet the necessary fire resistance as required by the building and fire regulations and also provide positive closure over a varying range of operating pressures.

The main installation requirements are as defined in Regulation 9 of the GS(I&U)R (see also Chapter 5). Further requirements for these valves and their suitability of use is given in IGEM/UP/2. The following information is an overview of these additional requirements:

- **Non-lubricated plug valve** - a fast acting, two part valve which incorporates a rotating internal taper or parallel plug with a 90° movement between the on and off position. Lubrication is required usually with a graphite or similar type lubricant. The taper plug requires removal to lubricate. May be used as an ECV/AECV if fire resistant and the size does not exceed 50 mm (fig 23.40).
- **Lubricated plug valve** - similar to the non-lubricated plug valve but with the advantage of being able to be lubricated without the valve being taken out of service. May be used as an AECV if fire resistant and not fitted upstream of a safety shut off valve. The size should not exceed 100 mm due to high operational torque (fig 23.41).
- **Ball valve** - a common valve which has a 90° movement between on and off. Where it is used as an ECV or AECV it shall be fire resistant (normally the valve seating is stainless steel), fig 23.42.

○ **Gate valve** - these valves incorporate a sliding or rotating gate which moves into the gas way, normally by the rotation of a wheel handle. They are typically used on larger bore pipework. Again if used as an ECV or AECV they shall be proved fire resistant and also to ensure positive closure, they shall have valve position indication (fig 23.43). These valve are prone to let-by due to dusts being trapped in the valve seating. Filtration is advised.

Fig 23.40   Non-lubricated plug valve

Fig 23.41   Lubricated plug valve

Fig 23.42   Ball valve

Fig 23.43   Gate valve

○ **Butterfly valve** - this valve incorporates a disc which is rotated through its central axis in the gas stream. The valve handle has a 90° movement between the on and off position. Only lug-style butterfly valves (fig 23.44) are suitable for use in gas installations, and may be placed between two flanges or directly bolted onto the two flanges at either end (fig 23.45 shows a non-lugged, wafer-style butterfly valve). Due to its method of operation and lack of fire resistance, butterfly valves are not recommended for use as an ECV or AECV.

Fig 23.44 Lug-style butterfly valve

Fig 23.45 Wafer-style butterfly valve

- **Diaphragm valve** - as its name suggests the valve consists of a diaphragm which is compressed onto the valve seating by the rotation of a valve wheel. Again this is not suitable for use as an ECV or AECV.

23.5 Medium Pressure Fed Meter Installations

The following section is used in conjunction with Chapter 20 and will provide the additional information necessary for an ESP engineer and meter installer to commission and confirm the safe operation of medium pressure fed metering installations. The procedures highlighted can only be performed by suitably competent persons under the authority of the gas transporter.

23.5.1 Metering installation pressure control and protection system

Operating pressure limits

The following pressure limits refer to that at the outlet of the meter supplied by either a single stage regulator conforming to IGEM/GM/PRS/28 (see fig 20.25; Chapter 20) or two stage regulator conforming to IGEM/GM/PRS/29 (see fig 20.24; Chapter 20). No additional low pressure (LP) regulator conforming to IGEM/GM/PRS/3 is fitted upstream of the meter.

Single stage regulator (IGEM/GM/PRS/28) only

- Normal OP at outlet of meter - 21 ± 2 mbar.
- Regulator Lock-up Pressure (up to MOP) - 27.5 mbar.
- Regulator Lock-up Pressure (MOP up to DMIP) - 30 mbar.
- Relief Valve Opening Pressure - 35 ± 3.5 mbar.
- Slam-shut Closing Pressure - 47.5 ± 2.5 mbar.

Two stage regulator (IGEM/GM/PRS/29) only

- Normal OP at outlet of meter - 21 ± 2 mbar.
- Regulator Lock-up Pressure (up to MOP) - 27.5 mbar.
- Regulator Lock-up Pressure (MOP up to DMIP) - 30 mbar.
- Relief Valve Opening Pressure - 35 ± 3.5 mbar.
- Relief Valve Maximum Accumulation Pressure - 40 mbar.
- Excess Flow Valve - should close normally at a flow rate no greater than 7.2 m³/h.

Where an additional LP regulator is installed upstream of the primary meter as shown in figures 20.26 and 20.27 of Chapter 20, the permitted operating pressures change from that stated previously. This is due to the additional pressure control and downstream protection afforded by the LP regulator.

The following lists the pressure limits of these types of metering control systems.

Single stage regulator (IGEM/GM/PRS/28) with additional LP regulator

- Normal OP at outlet of regulator - 30 ± 2 mbar.
- Regulator Lock-up Pressure - 37 mbar.
- Regulator Lock-up Pressure (up to DMIP) - 40 mbar.
- Relief Valve Opening Pressure - 45 ± 3.5 mbar.
- Slam-shut Closing Pressure - 70 ± 5 mbar.

Two stage regulator (IGEM/GM/PRS/29) with additional LP regulator

- Normal OP at outlet of regulator - 30 ± 2 mbar.
- Regulator Lock-up Pressure - 37 mbar.
- Regulator Lock-up Pressure (up to DMIP) - 40 mbar.
- Relief Valve Opening Pressure - 45 ± 3.5 mbar.
- Relief Valve Maximum Accumulation Pressure - 75 mbar.
- Excess Flow Valve - should close normally at a flow rate no greater than 7.2 m³/h.

Additional LP regulator (IGEM/GM/PRS/3)

- Normal OP at outlet of regulator - 21 ± 2 mbar.
- Regulator Lock-up Pressure (up to MOP) - 27.5 mbar.
- Regulator Lock-up Pressure (MOP up to DMIP) - 30 mbar.

23.5.2 Commissioning medium pressure regulators

During the commissioning stage of a medium pressure fed metering system a tightness test and purge of the installation is performed. The main criteria to be met is that the installation is safe to use with operation of the pressure control and safety systems confirmed as correct.

Specific test equipment is used during these procedures ensuring reliability of the tests and safety during the purge procedure. Figure 23.46 shows a typical medium pressure test and purge kit.

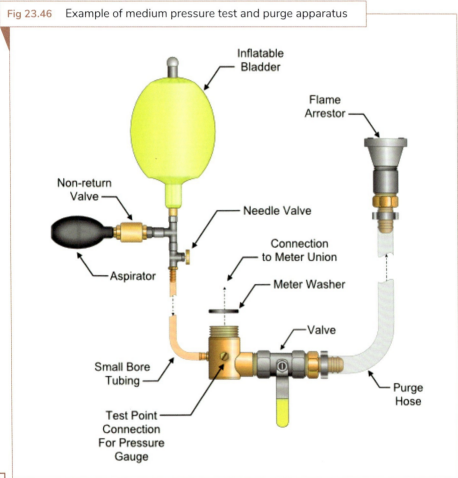

Fig 23.46 Example of medium pressure test and purge apparatus

23.5.2.1 Commissioning SINGLE STAGE regulator

To test and purge a single stage (IGEM/GM/PRS/28) regulator the following procedure is used:

1. Leave the meter disconnected, ensuring it's placed in an upright position with the inlet and outlet connection seals left in place.
2. Assemble the test apparatus and connect to the meter inlet connection. Connect a suitable pressure gauge to a test point on the test apparatus.
3. Position the purge hose and flame trap in a suitable safe position; avoiding any points of entry into the building such as doors, windows, vents, etc.
4. Ensure the MIV is in the OPEN position and purge valve is CLOSED.
5. Slowly open the ECV to allow the installation to pressurise, then close.
6. 'Crack open' the purge valve and reduce the pressure to between 7 mbar and 10 mbar. Close the purge valve when the desired pressure has been achieved.
7. Carryout a 1 minute let-by test on the ECV. A satisfactory test is where no perceptible rise is registered on the gauge (0.2 mbar for an electronic gauge and 0.25 mbar for a water gauge).
8. Following a successful let-by test slowly open the ECV.

    At this point the regulator can be confirmed as open by a pressure rise on the gauge. If there is no pressure rise, check the status of the slam-shut. Opening the valve to fast will cause a pressure surge which can trigger the valve to close. Release the pressure from the system by opening the purge valve, close and reset the slam-shut if necessary. If the slam-shut is found open the regulator may be deemed faulty, but only after it has been confirmed that gas is present at the ECV.

9. Open the purge valve slowly and purge the installation.

NOTE: Prior to the purge ensure the restricting orifice is in place. Fully opening the purge valve with no restriction may activate the service excess flow valve (if fitted) resulting in a cessation of supply during the purge.

10. During the purging process check the operating pressure at the outlet of the REGULATOR is 22 mbar ± 2 mbar.

11. Slowly close the purge valve and check the regulator lock-up pressure is not in excess of 27.5 mbar. With the ECV in the open position test all exposed joints (connections at the ECV, regulator and MIV) with LDF. Repair any escapes found. Wipe off excess LDF when complete.

12. Close the MIV. Slowly open the purge valve reducing the pressure to between 7 mbar and 10 mbar. Close the purge valve and carryout a 1 minute let-by test on the MIV. A satisfactory test is where no perceptible rise is registered on the gauge. If let-by is confirmed, the full regulator assembly shall be replaced (disassembly of the regulator is not permitted in order to replace the MIV only, due to the units being factory assembled and tested).

13. After a successful let-by test open the MIV.

14. With the ECV in the ON position and the regulator at lock-up pressure, insert the tip of the relief valve vent pipe into a container of water (submerge by no more than 5 mm). Monitoring for at least 15 seconds, no bubbles should be present, indicating the relief valve is not passing.

15. Close the ECV.

16. Ensure the needle valve on the test apparatus is closed. Using the hand pump, inflate the bladder. With the relief valve vent pipe tip still in the container of water, slowly open the needle valve to inject pressure into the system. Observe the pressure gauge. As the pressure begins to rise the operation of the relief valve will be indicated by a constant stream of bubbles at the vent pipe tip. Note this pressure which shall be between 31.5 mbar and 38.5 mbar. If the relief operates outside this range, the full regulator assembly shall be replaced.

17. To test the slam-shut, disconnect and remove the vent pipe from the regulator. Seal the vent pipe outlet using an appropriate fitting. Close the needle valve and inflate the test apparatus bladder.

18. Slowly open the needle valve to inject pressure into the system. Observe the pressure gauge. An audible click will be heard when the slam-shut has operated; note the pressure on the gauge at this time.

19. Depressurise the system by opening the purge valve. Re-set the slam-shut. Once closed shut the purge valve. Re-test the slam-shut for a further two times, noting the pressure in each occasion. The activation pressure shall be within the range of 45 mbar - 50 mbar. If it fails to operate within these parameters, replace the full regulator assembly.

20. Release the pressure and reset the slam-shut after the tests have been completed. Remove the fitting from the relief valve vent and install the relief vent pipe. Close the MIV and remove the test apparatus. The meter can be connected after all tests have been completed.

Complete documentation including a commissioning report, which details the meter serial number, manufacturer, year of manufacture, model, badged flow rate (Q_{max}), pressure and initial meter reading. Other relevant information may also be recorded, depending on the documentation used.

Once completed, the report shall be circulated to all relevant parties, i.e. MAM, gas supplier, consumer, etc.

23.5.2.2   Commissioning TWO STAGE regulator

To test and purge a two stage (IGEM/GM/PRS/29) regulator the following procedure is used:

1. Leave the meter disconnected, ensuring it is placed in an upright position with the inlet and outlet connection seals left in place.
2. Assemble the test apparatus and connect to the meter inlet connection. Connect a suitable pressure gauge to a test point on the test apparatus.
3. Position the purge hose and flame trap in a suitable safe position, avoiding any points of entry into the building such as doors, windows, vents, etc.
4. Ensure the MIV is in the OPEN position and purge valve is CLOSED.
5. Slowly open the ECV to allow the installation to pressurise. Close the ECV and hold open the reset lever to pressurise the downstream installation.
6. With the reset lever held open, 'crack open' the purge valve and reduce the pressure to between 7 mbar and 10 mbar. Close the purge valve.
7. Continue to hold open the reset lever and carryout a 1 minute let-by test on the ECV. A satisfactory test is where no perceptible rise is registered on the gauge (0.2 mbar for an electronic gauge and 0.25 mbar for a water gauge).
8. Following a successful let-by test slowly open the ECV. Operate the reset lever for a minimum period of 5 seconds to pressurise the test equipment then release the lever.
9. Open the purge valve slowly, purging the installation. Take care not to activate the excess flow valve which is incorporated within the regulator assembly.

10. During the purging process check the operating pressure at the outlet of the REGULATOR is 22 mbar ± 2 mbar.
11. Slowly close the purge valve and check the regulator lock-up pressure is not in excess of 27.5 mbar.

    With the ECV in the open position test all exposed joints (connections at the ECV, regulator and MIV) with LDF. Repair any escapes found. Wipe off excess LDF when complete.
12. Close the MIV. Slowly open the purge valve reducing the pressure to between 7 mbar and 10 mbar. Close the purge valve and carryout a 1 minute let-by test on the MIV. A satisfactory test is where no perceptible rise is registered on the gauge. If let-by is confirmed, the full regulator assembly shall be replaced (disassembly of the regulator is not permitted in order to replace the MIV only, due to the units being factory assembled and tested).
13. After a successful let-by test open the MIV.
14. With the ECV in the ON position and the regulator at lock-up pressure, insert the tip of the relief valve vent pipe into a container of water (submerge by no more than 5 mm). Monitoring for at least 15 seconds, no bubbles should be present indicating the relief valve is not passing.
15. Close the ECV.
16. Ensure the needle valve on the test apparatus is closed. Using the hand pump, inflate the bladder. With the relief valve vent pipe tip still in the container of water, slowly open the needle valve to inject pressure into the system. Observe the pressure gauge. As the pressure begins to rise the operation of the relief valve will be indicated by a constant stream of bubbles at the vent pipe tip. Note this pressure which shall be between 31.5 mbar and 38.5 mbar. If the relief operates outside this range the full regulator assembly shall be replaced.
17. To test the excess flow valve, remove any restricting orifice from the test apparatus. Ensure the ECV is open, then operate the regulator reset lever to rearm the regulator.
18. Fully open the purge valve. The flow of gas should cease indicating the excess flow valve has operated.
19. Close the purge valve and reset the regulator. Re-check the lock-up at this time. If the lock-up pressure is incorrect and/or the excess flow valve does not operate, the full regulator assembly shall be replaced.

20. Close the MIV and remove the test apparatus. The meter can be connected after all tests have been completed.

21. Complete documentation including a commissioning report, which details the meter serial number, manufacturer, year of manufacture, model, badged flow rate (Q_{max}), pressure and initial meter reading. Other relevant information may also be recorded, depending on the documentation used.

    Once completed, the report shall be circulated to all relevant parties, i.e. MAM, gas supplier, consumer, etc.

23.5.2.3 Commissioning PRS/28 & PRS/29 regulators with additional LP regulator

Where an additional LP regulator is fitted downstream of the MP regulator the procedures for testing and purging remain the same. However, the operational parameters of both the MP regulator and protection system differ.

To test and purge a MP regulator with an additional LP regulator the following procedure is used:

1. Leave the meter disconnected, ensuring it's placed in an upright position with the inlet and outlet connection seals left in place.
2. Assemble the test apparatus and connect to the meter inlet connection. Connect a suitable pressure gauge to a test point on the test apparatus.
3. Position the purge hose and flame trap in a suitable safe position; avoiding any points of entry into the building such as doors, windows, vents, etc.
4. Ensure the MIV is in the OPEN position and purge valve is CLOSED.
5. Slowly open the ECV to allow the installation to pressurise, then close.
6. 'Crack open' the purge valve and reduce the pressure to between 7 mbar and 10 mbar. Close the purge valve when the desired pressure has been achieved.
7. Carryout a 1 minute let-by test on the ECV. A satisfactory test is where no perceptible rise is registered on the gauge (0.2 mbar for an electronic gauge and 0.25 mbar for a water gauge).

8. Following a successful let-by test slowly open the ECV.

   At this point the regulator can be confirmed as open by a pressure rise on the gauge. If there is no pressure rise, check the status of the slam-shut. Opening the valve to fast will cause a pressure surge which can trigger the valve to close. Release the pressure from the system by opening the purge valve, close and reset the slam-shut if necessary. If the slam-shut is found open the regulator may be deemed faulty, only after it has been confirmed that gas is present at the ECV.

9. Open the purge valve slowly and purge the installation.

NOTE: Prior to the purge ensure the restricting orifice is in place. Fully opening the purge valve with no restriction may activate the service excess flow valve (if fitted) resulting in a cessation of supply during the purge.

10. During the purging process check the operating pressure at the outlet of the REGULATOR is 30 mbar ± 2 mbar.
11. Slowly close the purge valve and check the regulator lock-up pressure is not in excess of 37 mbar. With the ECV in the open position test all exposed joints (connections at the ECV, regulator and MIV) with LDF. Repair any escapes found. Wipe off excess LDF when complete.
12. Close the MIV. Slowly open the purge valve reducing the pressure to between 7 mbar and 10 mbar. Close the purge valve and carryout a 1 minute let-by test on the MIV. A satisfactory test is where no perceptible rise is registered on the gauge. If let-by is confirmed, the full regulator assembly shall be replaced (disassembly of the regulator is not permitted in order to replace the MIV only, due to the units being factory assembled and tested).
13. After a successful let-by test open the MIV.
14. With the ECV in the ON position and the regulator at lock-up pressure, insert the tip of the relief valve vent pipe into a container of water (submerge by no more than 5 mm). Monitoring for at least 15 seconds, no bubbles should be present, indicating the relief valve is not passing.
15. Close the ECV.

16. Ensure the needle valve on the test apparatus is closed. Using the hand pump, inflate the bladder. With the relief valve vent pipe tip still in the container of water, slowly open the needle valve to inject pressure into the system. Observe the pressure gauge. As the pressure begins to rise the operation of the relief valve will be indicated by a constant stream of bubbles at the vent pipe tip. Note this pressure which shall be between 41.5 mbar and 48.5 mbar. If the relief operates outside this range, the full regulator assembly shall be replaced.

17. To test the slam-shut, disconnect and remove the vent pipe from the regulator. Seal the vent pipe outlet using an appropriate fitting. Close the needle valve and inflate the test apparatus bladder.

    Slowly open the needle valve to inject pressure into the system. Observe the pressure gauge. An audible click will be heard when the slam-shut has operated; note the pressure on the gauge at this time.

18. Depressurise the system by opening the purge valve. Re-set the slam-shut. Once closed shut the purge valve. Re-test the slam-shut for a further two times, noting the pressure in each occasion. The activation pressure shall be within the range of 65 mbar - 75 mbar. If it fails to operate within these parameters, replace the full regulator assembly.

19. Release the pressure and reset the slam-shut after the tests have been completed. Remove the fitting from the relief valve vent and install the relief vent pipe. Close the MIV and remove the test apparatus. The meter can be connected after all tests have been completed.

20. Complete documentation including a commissioning report, which details the meter serial number, manufacturer, year of manufacture, model, badged flow rate (Q_{max}), pressure and initial meter reading. Other relevant information may also be recorded, depending on the documentation used.

    Once completed, the report shall be circulated to all relevant parties, i.e. MAM, gas supplier, consumer, etc.

Glossary & Appendices

	Page No.
Glossary	i
Appendix I	iv
SI Units	iv

References in this Chapter

None

Glossary & Appendices

Glossary

Appropriate fitting means a fitting which -

a). has been designed for the purpose of effecting a gas tight seal in a pipe or other gasway.

b). achieves that purpose when fitted; and

c). is secure, so far as is reasonably practicable, against unauthorised opening or removal.

The responsible person in relation to any premises, means the occupier of the premises or, where there is no occupier or the occupier is away, the owner of the premises or any person with authority for the time being to take appropriate action in relation to any gas fitting therein.

Distribution main means any main through which a transporter is for the time being distributing gas and which is not being used only for the purpose of conveying gas in bulk.

Cyclic volume - the volume of gas contained in each revolution of a diaphragm meter.

Emergency control means a valve for shutting off the supply of gas in an emergency, being a valve intended for use by a consumer of gas.

Fire stop - a non combustible seal which is designed to prevent the transmission of smoke or fire.

Flue means a passage for conveying the products of combustion from a gas appliance to the external air and includes any part of the passage in a gas appliance duct which serves the purpose of a flue.

Gas means any substance which is or (if it were in a gaseous state) would be gas within the meaning of the Gas Act 1986 except that it does not include gas consisting wholly or mainly of hydrogen when used in non-domestic premise.

Gas appliance means an appliance designed for use by a consumer of gas for heating, lighting, cooking.

Gas fittings means gas pipework, valves (other than emergency controls), regulators and meters, and fittings, apparatus and appliances designed for use by consumers of gas for heating, lighting, cooking or other purposes for which gas can be used.

Gas storage vessel means a storage container designed to be filled or re-filled with gas at the place where it is connected for use or a re-fillable cylinder designed to store gas.

Gas water heater - includes a gas fired central heating boiler.

Installation pipework - any pipework for conveying gas for a particular consumer and any associated valve or other gas fitting including any pipework used to connect a gas appliance to other installation pipework and any shut off device at the inlet to the appliance.

LPG - Liquefied Petroleum Gas.

Primary meter means the meter nearest to and downstream of a service pipe or service pipework for ascertaining the quantity of gas supplied through that pipe or pipework by a supplier.

Purge - the use of gas to displace air.

Operating pressure in relation to a gas appliance, means the gas pressure which it is designed to operate.

Room sealed appliance means an appliance whose combustion system is sealed from the room in which the appliance is located and which obtains air for combustion from a ventilated uninhabited space within the premises or directly from the open air outside the premises and which vents the products of combustion directly to open air outside the premises.

Service pipe means a pipe for distributing gas to premises from a distribution main, being any pipe between the distribution main and the outlet of the first emergency control, downstream from the distribution main.

Service pipework means a pipe for supplying gas to premises from a gas storage vessel, being any pipe between the gas storage vessel and the outlet of the emergency control.

Service valve means a valve (other than an emergency control) for controlling a supply of gas, being a valve -

a). incorporated in a service pipe; and

b). intended for use by a transporter of gas; and

c). not situated inside a building.

Supplier in relation to gas means -

a). a person who supplies gas to any premises through a primary meter; or

b). a person who provides a supply of gas to a consumer by means of the filling or re-filling of a storage container

c). a person who provides gas in re-fillable cylinders for use by a consumer.

Transporter in relation to gas means a person who conveys gas through a distribution main.

Work in relation to a gas fitting includes any of the following activities carried out by any person, whether an employee or not, that is to say -

a). installing or re-connecting the fitting;

b). maintaining, servicing, permanently adjusting, disconnecting, repairing, altering or renewing the fitting or purging it of air or gas;

c). where the fitting is not readily movable, changing its position; and

d). removing the fitting;

but the expression does not include the connection or disconnection of a bayonet fitting or other self-sealing connector.

Appendix I

SI Units

The SI metric system (Systems Internationals d'unites) is extensively used throughout most parts of the world and has widely replaced our more conventional British imperial system of measurement. However, within the gas industry we still use the imperial system in some of our measurements due to the age of equipment still in circulation such as meters reading in ft^3 and appliances with gross heat inputs in Btu's/hr.

SI system uses seven primary units (table 1.1), either on their own or in conjunction with one of twenty prefixes (table 1.2) to express a multiple or fraction of a unit.

Table 1.1 Primary SI units

Primary Units	Unit of Measurement	Symbol
Length	metre	m
Mass	gram	g
Temperature	Kelvin	K
Electrical current	ampere	A
Times	second	s
Quantity of substance	mole	mol
Luminous intensity	candela	cd

Table 1.3 expresses common conversion factors

Table 1.2 Prefixes to the seven primary SI units (smallest to largest units)

Prefix Name	Base 10*	Multiple or Fraction of a Unit of Measurement	Symbol
yocto	10^{-24}	septillionth	y
zepto	10^{-21}	sextillionth	z
atto	10^{-18}	quintillionth	a
femto	10^{-15}	quadrillionth	f
pico	10^{-12}	trillionth	p
nano	10^{-9}	billionth	n
micro	10^{-6}	millionth	µ
milli	10^{-3}	thousandth	m
centi	10^{-2}	hundreth	c
deci	10^{-1}	tenth	d
deca	10	ten	da
hecto	100	hundred	h
kilo	1000	thousand	K
mega	10^6	million	M
giga	10^9	billion	G
tera	10^{12}	trillion	T
peta	10^{15}	quadrillion	P
exa	10^{18}	quintillion	E
zetta	10^{21}	sextillion	Z
yotta	10^{24}	septillion	Y

* Base 10 is used to express the decimal placement, for example:
- 10^6 = 1.000 000
- 10^{-6} = 0.000 001

Table 1.3 Conversion factors

Unit	Imperial to Metric			Metric to Imperial		
Length	1 inch (in)	=	25.4 mm	1 mm	=	0.03937 in
	1 ft	=	304.8 mm	1 m	=	39.37 in
	1 yard (yd)	=	914.4 mm	1 m	=	3.281 ft
	1 mile	=	1.609 km	1 km	=	0.624 mile
Area	1 in^2	=	645.2 mm^2	1 mm^2	=	0.001550 in^2
	1 in^2	=	6.452 cm^2	1 cm^2	=	0.1550 in^2
	1 ft^2	=	929 cm^2	1 m^2	=	10.76 ft^2
	1 acre	=	4047 m^2	1 m^2	=	0.0247 acre
	1 acre	=	0.4047 ha	1 ha	=	2.471 acre
Volume (space)	1 in^3	=	16390 mm^3	1 mm^3	=	0.000061 in^3
	1 in^3	=	16.39 cm^3	1 dm^3	=	61.02 in^3
	1 ft^3	=	0.02832 m^3	1 dm^3	=	0.03531 ft^3
	1 ft^3	=	28.32 dm^3	1 m^3	=	35.31 ft^3
Volume (liquid/gas*)	1 pint	=	0.5683 litre	1 mm^3	=	0.000061 in^3
	1 gallon	=	4.564 litre	1 litre	=	61.02 in^3
	1 ft^3	=	28.32 litre	1 litre	=	0.03531 ft^3
	1 ft^3	=	0.02832 m^3	1 litre	=	0.22 gallon
				1 m^3	=	35.31 ft^3
Mass	1 oz	=	28.35 g	1 g	=	0.03527 oz
	1 lb	=	453.6 g	1 kg	=	2.205 lb
	1 lb	=	0.4536 kg	1 tonne	=	2205 lb
	1 ton	=	1016 kg	1 tonne	=	0.9842 ton
	1 ton	=	1.016 tonne			

* The volume conversion factor for gas changes dependant on temperature pressure and water vapour content. To ensure consistency we always refer to the volume of gas under standard reference conditions (st) which is 15 °C, 1013.25 mbar and dry

Table 1.3 Conversion factors

Unit	Imperial to Metric			Metric to Imperial		
Pressure	1 in wg	=	2.5 mbar	1 mbar	=	100 pa
	1 lbf/in²	=	68.95 mbar	1 mbar	=	0.4 in wg
	1 lbf/in²	=	0.06895 bar	1 bar	=	14.50 lbf/in²
	1 ft water	=	30.48 mbar	1 bar	=	100,000 pa
	1 ft water	=	0.3048 m water	1 m water	=	3.281 ft water
	1 atm	=	1013.25 mbar(st) 101325 Pa 1.01325 bar	1 m water	=	98.07 mbar
Heat energy	1 Btu	=	1055 J	1 kWh	=	3.6 MJ
	1000 Btu	=	1.055 MJ	1 cal	=	4.1868 J
	1 Therm	=	100,000 Btu	1 J	=	0.0009478 Btu
	1 Therm	=	105.5 MJ	1 MJ	=	0.009478 Therm
Heat rate	1000 Btu/h	=	0.2931 kW	1 kW	=	1 J/s
	1000 Btu/h	=	1.055 MJ/h	1 kW	=	3.6 MJ/h
	1 HP	=	0.7457 kW	1 kW	=	3412 Btu/h
	1 HP	=	2.685 MJ/h	1 kW	=	1.341 HP
				1 MJ/h	=	0.2778 kW
				1 MJ/h	=	947.8 Btu/h
Calorific value	1 Btu/ft³	=	0.03723 MJ/m³ (st)	1 MJ/m³	=	26.88 Btu/ft³ (st)
Flow rate	1 ft³/h	=	0.02832 m³/h	1 m³/h	=	35.31 ft³/h
	1 gallon/h	=	4.546 litre/h	1 litre/h	=	0.22 gallon/h